NATIONAL GEOGRAPHIC

ALMANAC

2020

Climbing the Athabasca Glacier in Alberta's Jasper National Park

NATIONAL
GEOGRAPHIC

ALMANAC
2020

TRENDING TOPICS

BIG IDEAS IN SCIENCE

PHOTOS, MAPS, FACTS & MORE

NATIONAL GEOGRAPHIC
WASHINGTON, D.C.

CONTENTS

Yellowstone's Grand Prismatic Spring

Honeybee emerging from brood cell

Hubble image of the Bubble Nebula

Prayers on Buddha Day in Bac Ninh Province, Vietnam

A pensive pause in the Sahara

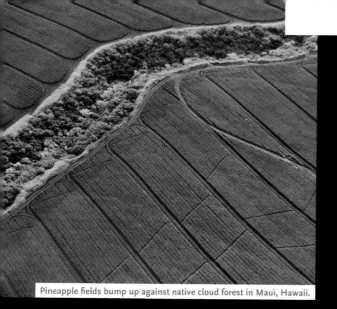

Pineapple fields bump up against native cloud forest in Maui, Hawaii.

Katydids at New Orleans' Insectarium

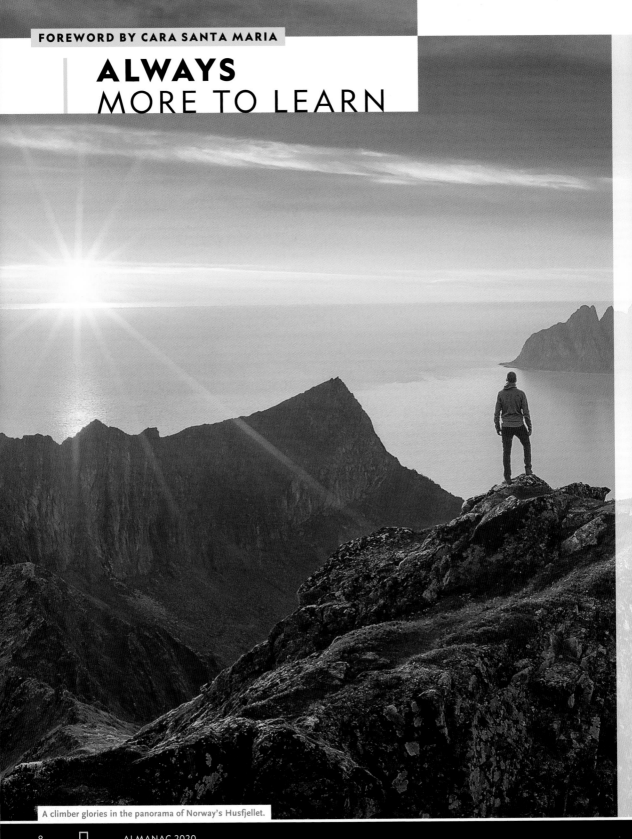

ALWAYS
MORE TO LEARN

A climber glories in the panorama of Norway's Husfjellet.

Cara Santa Maria sizes up a tiger shark jaw at London's Natural History Museum.

National Geographic has always had a special place in my heart. It's been a source of inspiration, excitement, and wonder ever since I was a young girl. As an adult, I've been lucky enough to join the NatGeo family, traveling the world in search of knowledge and adventure. I've investigated the global meteorite trade in Morocco, observed brain surgery in Boston, discovered the future of food in the Netherlands, and marveled at a total solar eclipse in the northwestern United States. During my travels for National Geographic's *Explorer* series and other projects, I've had the incredible opportunity to experience the stunning majesty of our planet's wildlife, people, and landscapes firsthand.

That's why I'm pleased to share the *National Geographic Almanac 2020* with you. From the comfort of your home (or wherever else you may find yourself), this book will transport you around the globe to places you could conjure only in your wildest imagination. Wherever you may be on your lifelong journey, this book was written for *you*. And it couldn't have happened without the tireless effort of an incredible team of writers, photographers, editors, and explorers who will stop at nothing to bring the awe and wonder of the natural world within reach for all of us.

The National Geographic Society's central mission is to promote "the power of exploration, science, and storytelling to change the world." With this in mind, the *Almanac 2020* is packed full of stunning scenery, cutting-edge experiments, and deeply personal tales of adventure. From hydrothermal vents at the bottom of the ocean to craters on the far side of the moon, we travel together to the ends of the Earth and beyond, unlocking their brilliant secrets. But as we learn about the awesome beauty of our home, we are also confronted with an unfortunate reality. Humankind's actions have taken a toll on Earth's interconnected systems currently hanging in the balance. Its landscape is forever changed due to our shortsightedness. Species are going extinct at an alarming rate, and once biodiversity is lost, it's gone forever. Ocean warming, acidification, and sea level rise affect us all, and the coming years will see climate refugees around the globe.

Yet I remain optimistic about the innovative technologies and problem-solving strategies humanity has to offer. With global connectivity at an all-time high, we have the capability to work together to heal the planet and restore balance to its varied inhabitants. Together, we can make a difference. But we have to act now.

Thank you for joining me on this colorful journey of exploration and adventure. In the following pages, we venture to the ends of the cosmos and dig deep into the mysteries of our own backyards. As your guide through the *Almanac 2020,* I open each section with Quizmaster pages full of fascinating trivia to whet your appetite for what lies ahead. Whether we are celebrating our primate family tree or the deep ripples in spacetime caused by gravitational waves, our eyes will be opened to nature's amazing power.

TRENDING 2020

PLANET IN BALANCE | FUTURE FOOD | CONNECTED WORLD

Massive photovoltaic arrays have been operational in southwestern Spain, a world leader in solar energy, for more than a decade.

PIONEERING WOMEN | INTO OUTER SPACE

QUIZ MASTER

The Journey Starts Here What are the most exciting things happening in science and discovery today? As we put this almanac together, we asked ourselves that question—and here are our answers: the perfect place to begin!

—**CARA SANTA MARIA,** *Our Favorite Nerd*

IN WHAT YEAR WAS NASA'S VOYAGER SPACE PROGRAM LAUNCHED?

p32

BY 2018, HOW MANY BLACK HOLE MERGERS HAD BEEN DETECTED?

p33

ABOUT HOW MUCH MEAT DOES THE AVERAGE AMERICAN CONSUME IN A YEAR?

p32

IN WHAT YEAR IS NASA'S NEW JAMES WEBB SPACE TELESCOPE DUE TO LAUNCH?

p32

ON WHICH ISLANDS DO MORE THAN 99% OF RESIDENTS USE THE INTERNET, HIGHEST PERCENTAGE IN THE WORLD?

p24

ABOUT HOW MUCH OF THE FOOD WE GROW GOES TO WASTE?

p18

WAX WORMS HAVE THE ABILITY TO BREAK DOWN WHICH NOTORIOUSLY RESILIENT SUBSTANCE?

p16

p20

ON WHICH ISLANDS IN THE ATLANTIC OCEAN CAN YOU FIND THE GRAN TELESCOPIO CANARIAS?

p33

WOMEN MADE UP WHAT FRACTION OF THE U.S. CONGRESS IN 2019?

p26

NAME THE COLLINS DICTIONARY 2018 WORD OF THE YEAR.

p16

ABOUT HOW MUCH OF THE EARTH'S SURFACE IS DEDICATED TO AGRICULTURE?

p18

WHAT FRUIT IS THE PREDOMINANT CROP OF UGANDA?

p21

HOW MANY TONS OF PLASTIC ARE CREATED EVERY YEAR?

p16

WHAT COUNTRY FIRST GRANTED FULL VOTING RIGHTS TO WOMEN?

p29

PLANET IN BALANCE

CONFRONTING CLIMATE CHANGE

In October 2018, one of the strongest hurricanes ever in the Pacific scraped an entire Hawaiian island off the map. The island, uninhabited by humans but home to monk seals, sea turtles, and shorebirds, disappeared beneath wind and wave. The next month, the town of Paradise, California, burned to the ground in the deadliest fire in the state's fiery history. Species are going extinct and biodiversity levels are crashing so severely that some call it a new mass extinction. The clock is ticking, but scientists are finding new ways to undo the harm and protect untouched places. The race for a sustainable planet is on.

Morning mist floats over the Danum Valley Conservation Area rainforest in Borneo.

OVER THE PAST CENTURY, THE GLOBAL AVERAGE SURFACE TEMPERATURE INCREASED BY MORE THAN 1.6°F (0.9°C) — AND SOME PREDICT IT WILL RISE ANOTHER 1.5°F BY 2032.

CREATIVE SOLUTIONS

FINDING WAYS TO REGAIN A PLANET IN BALANCE

Mounds of plastic accumulate worldwide.

JUST SAY NO

THE DISAPPEARING PLASTIC STRAW

When the *Collins English Dictionary* chose "single-use" as the 2018 word of the year, it presaged a massive international move away from plastic objects and containers designed to be used once and thrown away. Change has come swiftly. By 2019 many businesses, cities, and even countries had set regulations banning various single-use plastic items.

No longer will you be served a drink with a plastic straw at the Hilton Waikoloa Village Hotel on Hawaii's Big Island, at Disneyland or Disney World, anywhere in the cities of Seattle and Washington, D.C., on United Airlines flights, soon at Red Lobster restaurants—and the list keeps growing. The alternative? Paper or compostable straws, personally owned reusable straws, or no straw at all.

PLASTIC-EATERS

ANIMALS THAT CAN DIGEST PLASTIC

Our world is awash in plastic. Every year humans create more than 400 million tons of it, of which some eight million flow into our oceans. Even the most remote ocean trenches contain plastic debris, and each bit of plastic may take centuries to break down. One way to reverse this disaster might be found inside beehives.

Insect larvae known as wax worms, which naturally feed on wax and honey, have digestive systems that seem able to break down the long molecular chains known as polymers, whether those polymers are beeswax or plastic. Isolating the chemicals at work inside these natural recyclers could be one way to address our plastic problems.

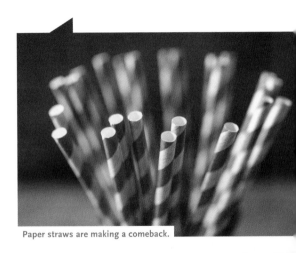

Paper straws are making a comeback.

A Sami herder leads his reindeer in Finland.

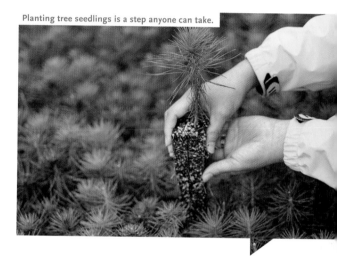

Planting tree seedlings is a step anyone can take.

INDIGENOUS PRACTICES

MASTERS OF SUSTAINABILITY

Indigenous peoples are masters of sustainable living—not only sources of wisdom but also activists fighting to protect natural habitats, preserve cultural traditions, and keep their parts of the planet in balance. The Sápara of Ecuador are organizing to resist oil extraction in their rainforest territory. The Karen of northern Thailand clear patches of forest for short-term cultivation and then allow wild greenery to return, a practice that supports pollinators better than continuous monoculture does. In Finland, efforts to develop wind and hydroelectric energy for populated regions interfere with the herding practices of the Sami, who depend on reindeer for survival. There, government and indigenous representatives are working to find common ground.

Many countries are establishing indigenous protected areas, where ancient tradition and modern conservation efforts can work side by side—a powerful team-up to protect both culture and nature.

GREEN WAYS OUT

REDUCING CARBON EMISSIONS BY PLANTING MORE TREES

When we burn fossil fuels—to drive cars, stoke factories, fly jumbo jets—we release massive amounts of carbon dioxide into the atmosphere—a key cause of climate change and global warming. A recent study suggests that one way to reduce carbon emissions is by using nature better.

Plants absorb carbon dioxide, so the more green things we can establish, the better: for example, by reforesting after timber harvesting, planting and plowing in field crops between growing seasons, and greening up cities with more tree-filled parks. Solutions can start in your own backyard, but changes must happen on a national and even global scale to make a real difference.

FUTURE FOOD

FARMING 2.0

More than a third of the planet's surface is dedicated to agriculture, but roughly a third of the food we grow goes to waste. If the world is going to feed an increasing population reliably, we need to do more, and with a smaller footprint. In the Netherlands, farmers have been able to more than double yields by working in massive greenhouses and controlling every part of the process, a technique known as precision farming. Each plant is individually monitored, and regular soil analysis gives information on temperature and water levels. Livestock too are getting an upgrade with humane housing for over 150,000 chickens in a single climate-controlled facility. These methods have helped the Netherlands, a small country with a cold climate, lead the world in tomato, potato, and onion exports.

Greenhouses light up at night in Westland, Netherlands, world renowned as an innovative hub of horticulture.

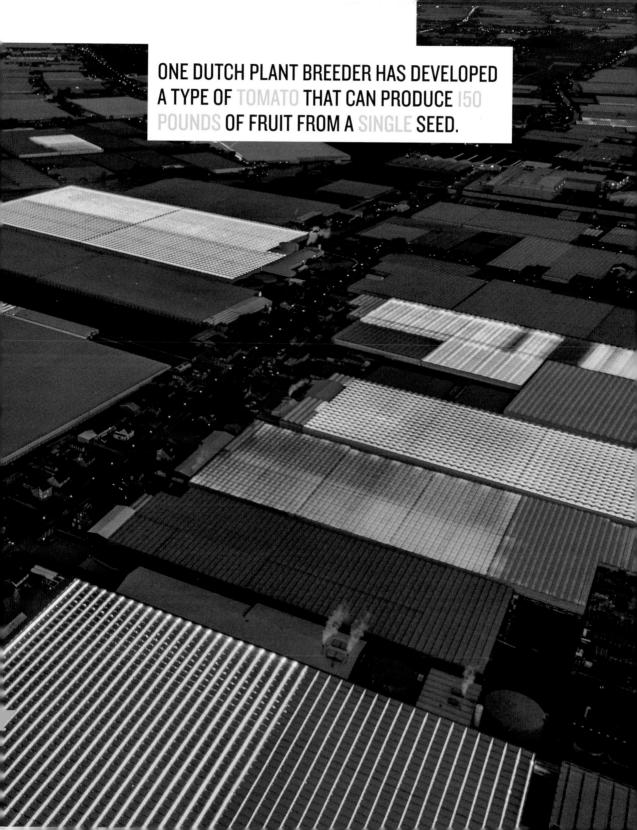

ONE DUTCH PLANT BREEDER HAS DEVELOPED A TYPE OF TOMATO THAT CAN PRODUCE 150 POUNDS OF FRUIT FROM A SINGLE SEED.

REVOLUTIONIZING THE WAY WE EAT

THE THINKING PERSON'S DIET

The Atlantic bluefin tuna, a sushi mainstay, is an endangered species.

SANE SEAFOOD

PROTECTING WILD FISH

Every year, we remove 170 billion pounds of fish from the ocean. Eating wild-caught fish depletes the marine food web, which can take generations to restore. Our preference for large, slow-growing fish like tuna and swordfish is like eating lions and gazelles rather than farmed cattle.

Thankfully, there are more sustainable approaches to fishing. This can mean eating only fish that grow rapidly and reproduce easily, or favoring farm-raised fish over wild-caught. In this way, the fishing industry can keep working and humanity can keep eating. Oceana, the Monterey Bay Aquarium, and other groups offer guides to environmentally friendly seafood choices.

LAB-GROWN MEAT

NOT YOUR ORDINARY VEGGIE BURGER

We're getting more carnivorous: Global consumption of meat has doubled in the past 50 years, and the average American now consumes over 220 pounds of red meat and poultry every year. Livestock accounts for some 15 percent of climate emissions and an increase in animal husbandry has been driving deforestation as trees are cleared to make room for pastureland.

To counter these effects, scientists and conservationists have been working to develop plant-based substitutes that can sizzle like steak, bleed like a burger, and look like ground beef. The Impossible Foods company creates proprietary recipes with protein-based plants and fats, while at Mosa Meat laboratory, chemists are growing beef from stem cells.

Meat lab-grown from stem cells may be on menus soon.

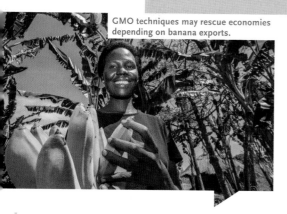
GMO techniques may rescue economies depending on banana exports.

IN AUSTIN, TEXAS, RESTAURANTS ARE REQUIRED BY CITY ORDINANCE TO DONATE OR COMPOST UNUSED FOOD. THEY MAY NO LONGER DISPOSE OF IT IN LANDFILLS.

GMOS

GENETIC MODIFICATION FOR GOOD

In Uganda, 75 percent of farmers grow bananas, a staple in a country where some eat two pounds of bananas a day. In recent years, a bacterial plague has devastated the crop. Scientists, however, have found a modification to a banana's base DNA that would prevent the disease and boost nutritional value. Uganda's bananas would become genetically modified organisms (GMOs).

For thousands of years, humans have deliberately bred plants and animals to shape them for our use. The discovery of DNA and the development of gene editing tools have led to new methods that can radically alter organisms in a single generation. As genetic modification becomes increasingly common, debates have arisen about how best to monitor and regulate these new organisms.

Misshapen vegetables, even if they are delicious, are considered waste.

FOOD WASTE

SAVING THE SCRAPS

Every year, more than 2.9 trillion pounds of food is thrown away, enough to feed the 800 million people suffering from hunger around the world. While some spoilage is inevitable, much of the food being tossed is edible. Markets and restaurants pride themselves on selecting the best produce — perfect peppers, the freshest fruit. So-called ugly food often never hits the market.

To fight this, new start-ups are promoting ugly produce, creating pathways to purchase it, donate it to food banks, or recycle leftovers into animal feed. Food waste will always be with us, but making even a small dent in the problem could lead to more food for the masses.

A WORD FROM

Do Your Part Food waste can be seen as a massive and daunting problem but within it lie great opportunities. Everyone can get up today and make a difference—volunteer your local gleaning effort, investigate recipes that use up that odd onion in the fridge, or donate to food waste fighting charities like Feedback [feedbackglobal.org]. The solutions are simple and positive, from farm to the fork.

—**TRISTRAM STUART,** *food waste activist*

CONNECTED
WORLD

AN EXPANDING NETWORK

Our world has never been more connected, both literally and figuratively. A vast web of communication satellites allows us to make phone calls from the top of Mount Everest to the Australian outback. Business supply chains flow around the world almost effortlessly, leading to a global rise in countries exporting their goods—and where goods connect, so do people. More than 250 million people relocate their lives each year internationally, and even more travel for work or play. Industry data shows 4.1 billion passenger trips in 2017, up 7.3 percent from 2016. Global connectivity shapes the ways we work and live.

Nighttime satellite views, here of the Gulf coastline from Texas to Alabama, show how interconnected our world is today.

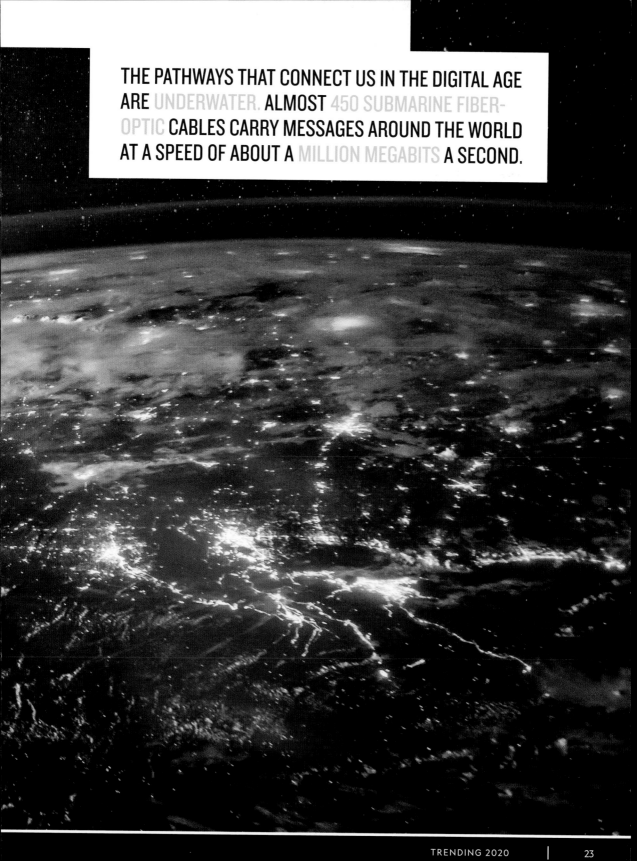

THE PATHWAYS THAT CONNECT US IN THE DIGITAL AGE ARE UNDERWATER. ALMOST 450 SUBMARINE FIBER-OPTIC CABLES CARRY MESSAGES AROUND THE WORLD AT A SPEED OF ABOUT A MILLION MEGABITS A SECOND.

GLOBAL CONNECTIVITY

AS ACCESS INCREASES, SO DO CONTROLS

UNITED STATES
Passage of the USA Patriot Act after September 11, 2001, expanded government surveillance of individuals. Civil liberties groups argued that privacy safeguards in the 2015 Freedom Act did not go far enough.

NORTH AMERICA

SOUTH AMERICA

Access to the Internet, 2016
Percent of population

- 80–100%
- 60–79%
- 40–59%
- 20–39%
- 1–19%
- 0 or no data

Government Restrictions to the Internet, 2016–17

- ☐ Government restricted internet access through blocking websites and internet blackouts.
- ☐ Government restricted internet access through monitoring email and social media and/or regulating published content.
- ☐ Government did a combination of both.

BOLIVIA AND PARAGUAY
Landlocked countries without easy access to undersea fiber optic cables have found themselves trying to catch up, often by launching expensive communications satellites.

FALKLAND ISLANDS
More than 99% of the 3,000 people living in the Falkland Islands use the internet, the highest percentage in the world. Luxembourg comes in second.

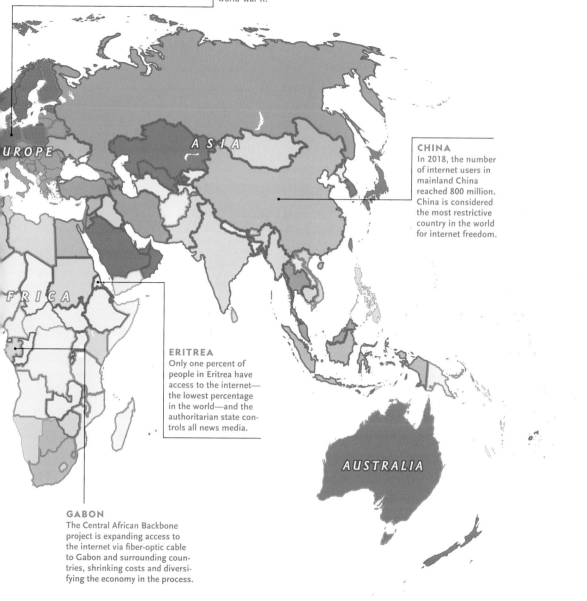

GERMANY
In Germany, laws monitoring and restricting fascist organizations and hate speech have been in place since the end of World War II.

CHINA
In 2018, the number of internet users in mainland China reached 800 million. China is considered the most restrictive country in the world for internet freedom.

ERITREA
Only one percent of people in Eritrea have access to the internet—the lowest percentage in the world—and the authoritarian state controls all news media.

GABON
The Central African Backbone project is expanding access to the internet via fiber-optic cable to Gabon and surrounding countries, shrinking costs and diversifying the economy in the process.

PIONEERING
WOMEN

THE FUTURE IS FEMALE

For eons, men have been the decision-makers in society, holding most of the leadership positions in politics, arts, and science. But things are changing. Events like the Women's March of 2017 have put a spotlight on women's interests, and a wave of female legislators have run for office. Today, more women than ever before are in positions of leadership. As of 2019, nearly a quarter of the U.S. Congress is made up of women—the highest portion in history. Around the world, women are challenging traditional expectations around gender and building a more inclusive future.

Millions around the world participated in January 2017 Women's Marches, here shown in Washington, D.C.

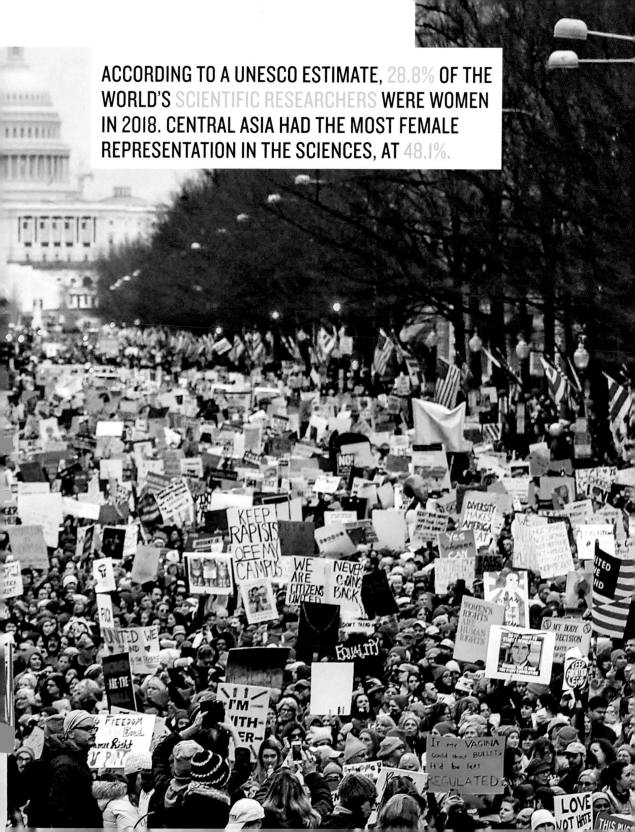

ACCORDING TO A UNESCO ESTIMATE, 28.8% OF THE WORLD'S SCIENTIFIC RESEARCHERS WERE WOMEN IN 2018. CENTRAL ASIA HAD THE MOST FEMALE REPRESENTATION IN THE SCIENCES, AT 48.1%.

WOMEN OF POWER

EXTRAORDINARY FEMALES PAST & PRESENT

Scidmore's photograph of Japanese girls and cherry blossoms

ARTS & CULTURE

JUANA INÉS DE LA CRUZ

In 1670, an immense library crowded the quarters of a Mexican nun, Sor Juana Inés de la Cruz. Sor Juana was a self-taught poet, a playwright, a scholar, and an advocate for women's education. Today, her former cloister is a college bearing her name.

MARGARET ATWOOD

Canadian writer Margaret Atwood's work includes 17 books of poetry, 16 novels, 10 nonfiction books, eight children's books, and a graphic novel. She's a powerful voice for environmentalism, and her dystopian work, *The Handmaid's Tale,* has reached millions.

EXPLORATION

ELIZA SCIDMORE

As the first female writer and photographer at National Geographic, Eliza Scidmore exemplified the brand in its first decades. Invited onto the governing board in 1892, she championed color photography. Her legacy persists around the tidal basin of Washington, D.C., where she helped bring much beloved cherry trees to the nation's capital.

BETH WALD

Beth Wald journeys around the world documenting how indigenous groups adapt to a changing world. She often treks far off the grid, where survival skills matter. Her work with National Geographic, the Wildlife Conservation Society, and other organizations has taken her from Nepal to Patagonia, Cuba to Alaska.

Margaret Atwood, whose fiction portrays women's issues

Donna Strickland, physicist and 2018 Nobel Prize winner

THE COUNTRY WITH THE HIGHEST PROPORTION OF FEMALE REPRESENTATIVES IS RWANDA, WHERE 61.3% OF SEATS IN THE LOWER HOUSE OF PARLIAMENT AND 38.5% IN THE UPPER ARE HELD BY WOMEN.

POLITICS

KATE SHEPPARD

New Zealander Kate Sheppard led the first successful effort to extend full voting rights to women. When the government granted women the vote in 1893, Sheppard became a titanic figure, traveling the world, inspiring women to follow her example and claim their natural rights.

ALEXANDRIA OCASIO-CORTEZ

When Alexandria Ocasio-Cortez decided to run for Congress, she was a bartender with no political experience challenging an incumbent nearly twice her age. With her surprise victory in 2018, 28-year-old Ocasio-Cortez became the youngest congresswoman in American history.

SCIENCE

WANG ZHENYI

In the feudal Qing dynasty of 18th-century China, women were not scholars. But Wang Zhenyi broke the mold. A scientist, poet, and author, she wrote at least 12 books, some to simplify mathematical ideas for the public and others to explain her own research on the astronomical movements of a solar eclipse. While much of her work has been lost, books of her poetry survive.

DONNA STRICKLAND

In 2018, Canadian scientist Donna Strickland became the third woman to win the Nobel Prize in Physics, joining the ranks of Maria Goeppert Mayer, a 20th-century expert in atomic structure, and Marie Curie. A self-described "laser jock," Strickland and her team found a new way to stretch and shape light into ultrafast, superstrong pulses. This work unlocked new fields of science in optics and has led to important advances in laser surgeries and laser-cut manufacturing.

AYCHECK FAIRNESS ACT
& Women: Same Job. Same Pay.

Alexandria Ocasio-Cortez, elected to Congress in 2018

INTO
OUTER SPACE

THE VOYAGE CONTINUES

Voyager 1 and Voyager 2 keep sailing on, out into deep space, past the edge of our solar system. Launched in 1977, their power systems will slowly decline over the next decade, but some data may flow back to Earth as late as 2036. The Voyager mission may be our first small step beyond our own star, but thanks in part to its success, we are one giant leap closer to understanding the universe beyond.

The two Voyager spacecraft led the way and have departed our solar system, while NASA's Juno stopped at Jupiter, returning this color-processed image of storms on the planet's surface.

VOYAGERS I AND 2 COMBINED HAVE EXPLORED JUPITER, SATURN, URANUS, AND NEPTUNE ALONG WITH 48 MOONS SURROUNDING THOSE PLANETS.

DEEP SPACE
OUTSIDE THE EDGES

WE EXPLORE DISTANT STARS AND GALAXIES IN AN ARRAY OF WAYS

Artist's concept of Voyager passing by the outer planets

SPACECRAFT TRAVEL THE DISTANCE

INTERSTELLAR TRAVELERS

A rare alignment of the outer planets of our solar system in the late 1970s and early 1980s inspired the Voyager mission. Twin craft launched in 1977, originally built to last five years and visit Uranus and Neptune, Voyager 1 and 2 have exceeded all expectations and lasted now more than 40 years, sending back information not only about the outer planets and their moons in our solar system but also about the space beyond.

Both Voyagers are now exploring what is termed interstellar space—the region beyond the reach of our sun's particles and magnetic force—with Voyager 1 nearly 13.5 billion miles and Voyager 2 more than 11 billion miles away from the sun.

SPACE TELESCOPES

OBSERVING DISTANT STARS

Earth's atmosphere can shimmer and distort the view from distant light sources—that's why stars seem to twinkle. Satellite telescopes orbit above the atmosphere, where they operate free from that distortion to create clearer images of distant stars, stellar nurseries, colliding galaxies, and the deepest reaches of space.

Orbiting cameras can be hard to maintain, and the Hubble, which launched in 1990, needs an upgrade. NASA's new James Webb Space Telescope, set to launch in 2021, will be able to see even farther and across a wider spectrum of light. It's expected to be able to photograph the first galaxies formed in our infant universe.

NASA's logo reflected in the James Webb's giant mirror

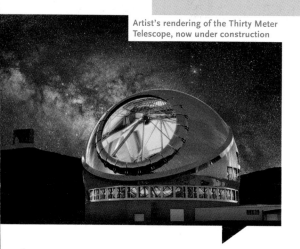

Artist's rendering of the Thirty Meter Telescope, now under construction

NASA IS PERFECTING A DEEP SPACE ATOMIC CLOCK—A MERCURY-ION TIME-KEEPER 50 TIMES MORE PRECISE THAN CURRENT NAVIGATIONAL DEVICES—THAT WILL GUIDE CRAFT AND CREW INTO DEEP SPACE IN THE COMING CENTURY.

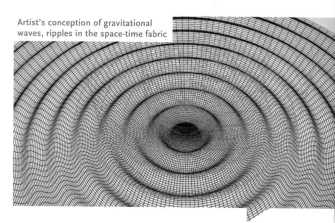

Artist's conception of gravitational waves, ripples in the space-time fabric

EARTHBOUND TELESCOPES

THE BIGGER THE BETTER

Land-based telescopes can be much larger and heavier than satellites, and for telescopes, a larger mirror means a better view. Spain's Gran Telescopio Canarias, located in the Canary Islands, has a single mirror, 34 feet across, made up of multiple segments that can be adjusted individually to eliminate atmospheric distortions. The new 39-meter telescope currently under construction in Hawaii will have 492 linked mirrors stretching almost 100 feet across, able to capture images 12 times as sharp as those from Hubble. The new telescope will join the Keck 1 and Keck 2 scopes atop Hawaii's Mauna Kea.

A WORD FROM

Listening for Others We are now, on an unprecedented scale, listening for radio signals from possible other civilizations in the depths of space. Alive today is the first generation of scientists to interrogate the darkness. Conceivably it might also be the last generation before contact is made—and this the last moment before we discover that someone in the darkness is calling out to us.

—**CARL SAGAN,** *astronomer*

GRAVITATIONAL WAVE OBSERVATORIES

REMNANTS OF THE ANCIENT UNIVERSE

The fabric of space-time is stiff. But according to Einstein's model of general relativity, that fabric ripples when certain events happen—titanic forces, such as black holes absorbing other black holes, ultra-dense neutron stars slamming into each other, or a massive supernova. The ripples are infinitesimal, though, by the time they reach Earth.

But thanks to gravitational wave observatories positioned on Earth, astronomers can now witness these waves. By 2018, 10 black hole mergers and one neutron star merger had been detected by coordinating signals received by laser interferometer observatories in Washington State, Louisiana, and Italy. Tracing the ripples in the fabric may give scientists new ways of obtaining information about deep space and the forces of galactic creation far, far away.

EXPLORATION & ADVENTURE

EXPLORATION | EXTREMES

Two bikers pedal across a natural sandstone arch in the desert near Moab, Utah.

QUIZ
MASTER

Intrepid Explorer? Does your spirit carry you to all corners of the globe? Which are you—sophisticated traveler or courageous adventurer? Either way, you'll journey to even more destinations in this chapter.

—CARA SANTA MARIA, *Our Favorite Nerd*

p51

HOW LONG CAN A DUGONG STAY UNDER-WATER?

WHICH TWO EXPLORERS WERE THE FIRST TO SUMMIT MOUNT EVEREST?

IN WHAT YEAR DID CAPTAIN JAMES COOK BEGIN EXPLORING THE PACIFIC OCEAN?

p74

p86

WHICH STADIUM HOSTED THE OLYMPICS IN 1948 AND ENGLAND'S WORLD CUP FINAL IN 1966?

p39

WHAT ICONIC WORLD LANDMARK WAS BUILT TO SERVE AS THE CENTERPIECE FOR THE 1889

p62

CHICHÉN ITZÁ WAS THE URBAN CENTER OF WHICH ANCIENT

HOW LONG WAS THE ROAD SYSTEM BUILT BY THE INCA EMPIRE IN THE 15TH

IN WHICH COUNTRY WILL YOU FIND **THE MAMMOTH-FLINT** RIDGE CAVE SYSTEM, **THE** LONGEST **IN THE WORLD?**

p53

IN WHICH REGION OF ITALY IS COOKING **CHICKEN** UNDER A **BRICK** A COMMON **CULINARY** TECHNIQUE?

p69

WHICH ENGLISH NATIONAL PARK DID **WILLIAM** THE CONQUEROR ONCE PROCLAIM A **ROYAL FOREST?**

p47

IN WHICH EUROPEAN NATIONAL PARK **CAN YOU** CLIMB THE DAUPHINÉ ALPS AND CYCLE A STAGE OF THE **TOUR DE FRANCE?**

p73

IN WHAT YEAR WAS THE FIRST HELICOPTER **BUILT?**

p63

WHICH SPORT DOES MIRNA VALERIO COMPETE IN?

p58

IN WHAT YEAR DID **BOB BALLARD** DISCOVER THE WRECK OF THE *TITANIC*?

p43

EXPLORATION
TIME LINE

PREHISTORY	2000 to 1 BC	AD 1 to 1000	1000 to 1500

PREHISTORY

■ **80,000 ya***
Homo sapiens moves out of Africa.

■ **ca 75,000 ya**
Modern humans reach Southeast Asia.

■ **ca 65,000 ya**
Humans reach Australia.

■ **ca 15,000 BC**
First settlements appear in North America.

■ **ca 8000 BC**
Dogs help pull sleds over snow.

■ **ca 6300 BC**
Earliest known boat is made.

■ **ca 2300 BC**
The earliest known maps are produced in Mesopotamia.

* *years ago*

2000 to 1 BC

■ **ca 2000 BC**
Austronesians settle on various islands in the South Pacific.

■ **ca 700 BC**
Celts are introducing Iron Age technology to Europe.

■ **240 BC**
Greek mathematician Eratosthenes calculates the circumference of the Earth.

■ **ca 115 BC**
Early trade agreements form between Chinese and European powers.

AD 1 to 1000

■ **150**
Ptolemy maps the world in his *Geography*.

■ **271**
A compass is first used in China.

■ **ca 400**
Polynesian seafarers settle the Hawaiian Islands.

■ **ca 600**
Silk Road is in full use, with China absorbing influences from the West.

■ **1000**
Viking longships under the command of Leif Eriksson cross the Atlantic and reach North America.

1000 to 1500

■ **1050**
Arab astronomers and navigators introduce the astrolabe to Europe.

■ **1271**
Marco Polo sets off on a four-year, 7,500-mile journey from Venice, Italy, to Shangdu, China.

■ **1331**
Arab traveler Ibn Battuta visits East Africa as part of a long voyage through the Islamic world.

■ **1492**
Christopher Columbus lands on a Caribbean island that he names Hispaniola.

■ **1499**
Italian navigator Amerigo Vespucci explores the northeast coastline of South America.

| 1500 to 1750 | 1750 to 1900 | 1900 to 1950 | 1950 to PRESENT |

1500 to 1750

1513
Ponce de León arrives in today's Florida, first of the Spanish conquistadors in the Americas.

1519
Ferdinand Magellan begins his circum-navigation of the globe.

1535
Jacques Cartier travels up St. Lawrence River to site of today's Montreal.

1595
Gerardus Mercator's first atlas is published.

1607
The English establish Jamestown on the James River in North America.

1722
The Dutch land on Easter Island.

1750 to 1900

1768
Britain's Capt. James Cook begins exploring the Pacific Ocean.

1799
The Rosetta Stone is discovered in Egypt.

1804–1806
Lewis and Clark run an expedition across the western territory of what is now the United States.

1841
The first wagon trains to cross the Rocky Mountains arrive in California.

1891
Construction begins on the Trans-Siberian Railroad.

1900 to 1950

1901
The city of Fairbanks is settled on the Alaskan frontier.

1904
Much of Chichén Itzá is discovered, in Mexico.

1909
Cmdr. Robert E. Peary and Matthew Henson lead the first expedition to the North Pole.

1937
Amelia Earhart disappears during an attempt at a flight around the world.

1946
Richard E. Byrd leads an expedition to the South Pole.

1950 to PRESENT

1953
Edmund Hillary and Tenzing Norgay reach Mount Everest's summit.

1957
The U.S.S.R. launches Sputnik 1, setting off a space race with America.

1960
Jacques Piccard becomes the first human to visit the Challenger Deep, the deepest point in the ocean.

1969
Apollo 11 lands men on the moon.

1990
The Hubble Space Telescope is put into operation.

2004
NASA's Spirit and Opportunity rovers land on Mars.

NAT GEO EXPLORERS

THE NEXT GENERATION

These explorers are using conservation, photography, science, and innovation to better understand our world and work toward improving it.

ANNE PRINGLE
UNITED STATES
Pringle, a fungal biologist, works with urban arborists and mycologists in the U.S. and Colombia to assess the health of city trees, including which mycorrhizal fungi are present, and plans to generate a globally applicable approach.

ELLA AL-SHAMAHI
UNITED KINGDOM
Al-Shamahi is a paleoanthropologist who searches for fossils in Paleolithic caves in the world's most hostile areas—including Syria, Iraq, and Yemen. Scientists avoid many of these spots, which increases Al-Shamahi's chances of making an important discovery.

THER WINT AUNG
UNITED STATES
An environmental health researcher working with young citizen scientists on issues of energy poverty in Myanmar, Ther Aung studies the effects of household air pollution associated with cooking and ambient air pollution from sources including industrial emissions.

JAMAL ALLEN GALVES
BELIZE
Passionate about manatee conservation since he was 11 years old, Galves joined the nonprofit Sea to Shore Alliance to advance the health and safety of these marine mammals, earning a Meritorious Service Award from the governor-general of Belize.

NORA SHAWKI
EGYPT
Shawki works in the field of settlement archaeology, which focuses on remnants of community members' daily lives. She investigates the relationships between cities and satellite settlements, as well as the domestic and religious habits of people in those settlements.

EMILIANO DONADIO
ARGENTINA
As mining expands in the Andes, Donadio, a conservation biologist, is studying the effects of this development on canyons and meadows used by migrating guanacos (close relatives of the llama) and proposing strategies to protect these animals.

NORTH AMERICA

SOUTH AMERICA

PACIFIC OCEAN

ATLANTIC OCEAN

MARTIN C. WIKELSKI
GERMANY
By tracking intercontinental migrant songbirds via satellite, physiological biologist Wikelski seeks to identify the factors behind their shrinking populations—for these same factors may give insight into challenges facing other life-forms and lead to conservation strategies.

❝ BELIEVE IN YOURSELF, AND STRIVE TO MAKE A DIFFERENCE. PUSH BOUNDARIES, MEET PEOPLE, TRAVEL, AND UNDERSTAND THE WORLD AROUND YOU.❞ —TASHI DHENDUP, CONSERVATION BIOLOGIST

ARCTIC OCEAN

TASHI DHENDUP
BHUTAN
A conservation biologist and forestry officer, Dhendup uses noninvasive camera traps and genetic sampling in Bhutan to educate local communities, reduce human-wildlife conflict, and strategize local conservation initiatives, with a particular focus on tigers.

EUROPE

ASIA

PACIFIC

OCEAN

ERINA PAULINE MOLINA
PHILIPPINES
Focusing on conservation and community, Molina uses knowledge gleaned from local fishermen to identify vulnerable or locally extinct reef fish species. She partners with communities to research ways to protect dugongs, a marine mammal.

AFRICA

INDIAN

OCEAN

FRIDAH KATUSHEMERERWE
UGANDA
To help preserve, respect, and nurture the resources in African communities, Katushemererwe, a linguist, is using modern language technology to document and share indigenous beliefs, taboos, and proverbs that promoted sustainable practices in previous generations.

AUSTRALIA

HOLLY JONES
AUSTRALIA AND NEW ZEALAND
Islands are home to 20 percent of species but account for 60 percent of contemporary extinctions. Jones, a restoration ecologist, is a pioneer in the area of invasive-pest eradication and how island size affects outcomes.

HANS COSMAS NGOTEYA
TANZANIA
Ngoteya cofounded an organization that promotes, supports, and improves community livelihoods through sustainable environmental practices. He also created a youth-focused project that provides conservation education and alternative livelihood options to reduce pressure on natural resources.

ROBERT BALLARD
MARINE GEOLOGIST

A BOY'S DREAM COME TO LIFE

Twenty Thousand Leagues Under the Sea and a childhood in San Diego, California, awakened in Bob Ballard a love of the ocean and its mysteries. That love eventually led to his discoveries of hydrothermal vents in the Galápagos Rift and numerous shipwrecks, including the *Titanic*. In all, he has conducted more than 150 expeditions coaxing secrets from the world's oceans.

Bob Ballard stands next to the *Hercules* vehicle, which can descend to underwater depths of 2.5 miles.

Before setting the gold standard for ocean exploration, Ballard studied marine geology and served in the U.S. Navy as an oceanographer. In 1985, he returned to temporary active duty for a top-secret Navy-funded mission to assess two sunken nuclear submarines. When he finished that task with 12 days to spare, Ballard was granted permission and resources to spend the remaining days attempting to locate the *Titanic*—which he did.

REWRITING TEXTBOOKS

Between those Navy assignments, Ballard's discoveries changed the way scientists understood not just the ocean but Earth and the universe as well. First, in 1975, Ballard and his colleagues explored the Mid-Atlantic Ridge, the largest mountain range beneath the sea. Their discoveries helped confirm the newly emerging theory of plate tectonics that explains how planet Earth works.

Two years later, Ballard was co-chief scientist on a team that made one of the greatest deep-sea discoveries ever when they found thermal vents off the Galápagos Islands and first reported on the exotic life-forms that live at these vents, using methane—the energy of Earth—instead of light—the energy of the sun—to survive. This discovery changed our definition of life, and that is now helping to guide our search for life elsewhere in the solar system and beyond.

All along, Ballard has been designing remote-controlled, camera-equipped submersibles such as *Jason* and *Hercules,* which can remain on the ocean floor for days on end, beaming their high-definition images to the surface in real time and then via satellite to anyone in the world. Online, 24/7, observers can now watch with Ballard's team on the research vessel *Nautilus* as their deep-sea subs explore the ocean floor.

> **" I THINK THE MOST FASCINATING THING I EVER SAW WERE THE CREATURES LIVING IN AND AROUND DEEP-SEA VENTS."**

The aged bow of the R.M.S. *Titanic,* first discovered by Bob Ballard

KEY DATES

Some of Ballard's
ACHIEVEMENTS

- **1973**
  Explores Mid-Atlantic Rift

- **1977**
  Discovers deep-sea vents and new life-forms

- **1985**
  Finds the *Titanic*

- **1989**
  Finds German battleship *Bismarck*

- **1998**
  Finds aircraft carrier *Yorktown*

- **1999–2000**
  Finds ancient shipwrecks in Black Sea and off Sinai

- **2002**
  Finds JFK's *PT 109*

- **2009**
  Launches exploration vessel E/V *Nautilus*

EXPLORING DEEP OCEANS

95 PERCENT OF EARTH'S LARGEST HABITAT IS UNEXPLORED

Deepsea Challenger sub carries James Cameron to Challenger Deep.

NEW TECHNOLOGY

A DIFFERENT KIND OF SPACECRAFT

The ocean, many say, is the next frontier for humans to explore, map, and exploit. This sentiment takes on urgency when one considers how the negative effects of our presence—pollution, climate change, mining, and fishing—are changing the seas and the creatures in them. Though we are eager to mount expeditions into space as quickly as possible, the cosmos will remain largely unchanged in the meantime. We may, however, have only centuries or even decades to explore our oceans before they are irreversibly altered—as widespread coral reef die-offs make evident. Demand is growing for submersible remotely operated vehicles, cameras, and other instruments that are resilient enough to withstand the pressures, temperatures, and trip durations that make some destinations inhospitable to humans.

DEEP-SEA CREATURES

LUMINOUS LIFE

As scientists explore the deeper reaches of the sea, they discover previously unknown luminous species, such as "green bombers"—deep-sea swimming worms that release sacs of bright green light when attacked—which were identified and described by marine biologists at the Monterey Bay Aquarium Research Institute. They estimate that three-quarters of the animals dwelling in depths up to two and half miles have bioluminescence. Near the surface are jellyfish, followed deeper down by worms and then larvaceans, a zooplankton resembling tadpoles. Some upcoming challenges in this growing field of research include measuring bioluminescence and understanding how these creatures will be affected by changing oxygen levels due to climate change.

A pink helmet jellyfish glows in the Arctic Ocean.

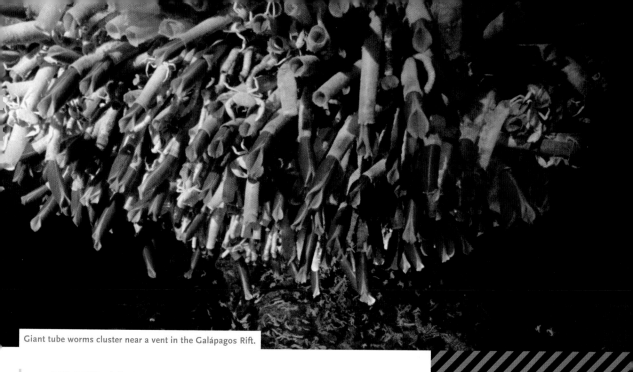

Giant tube worms cluster near a vent in the Galápagos Rift.

THERMAL VENTS

UNEXPECTED COLONIES

The study of hydrothermal vent ecosystems has redefined our understanding of the requirements for life. It was thought that all life on Earth depended on the sun's energy, through photosynthesis. But in 1977, while exploring the Galápagos Rift, scientists came across hydrothermal vents and, shockingly, a robust local community of creatures. Despite extreme temperatures and pressures, toxic minerals, and lack of sunlight, life was thriving because it generated food via chemosynthesis: the absorption of chemicals found in vent water to make organic carbon. Since then, 550 active hydrothermal vent sites have been identified.

Continued exploration of these ecosystems is also challenging models of how life began on Earth. Some scientists say that Charles Darwin's pond-and-lightning model should be replaced by the high-pressure environment found near a vent. In fact, the oldest fossils of living organisms ever found, which could be over four billion years old, come from rock in northern Quebec, Canada, that was once on the ocean floor and likely near a hydrothermal vent.

Modern Exploration of
DEEP SEAS

■ **1872–1876**
H.M.S. *Challenger* circles the globe conducting research for the Royal Society of London, laying the groundwork for modern oceanography.

■ **1943**
Jacques Cousteau and Émile Gagnan engineer the Aqua-Lung, forever changing the course of human-sea interaction.

■ **1961**
The Scripps Institution of Oceanography develops the Deep Tow System, the forerunner of all remotely operated unmanned oceanographic systems.

■ **1977**
Hydrothermal vents are discovered, along with an ecosystem that survives without the energy of the sun, by a team led by Robert Ballard.

■ **2010**
The first ever Census of Marine Life catalogs the diversity, abundance, and distribution of marine species in an online database.

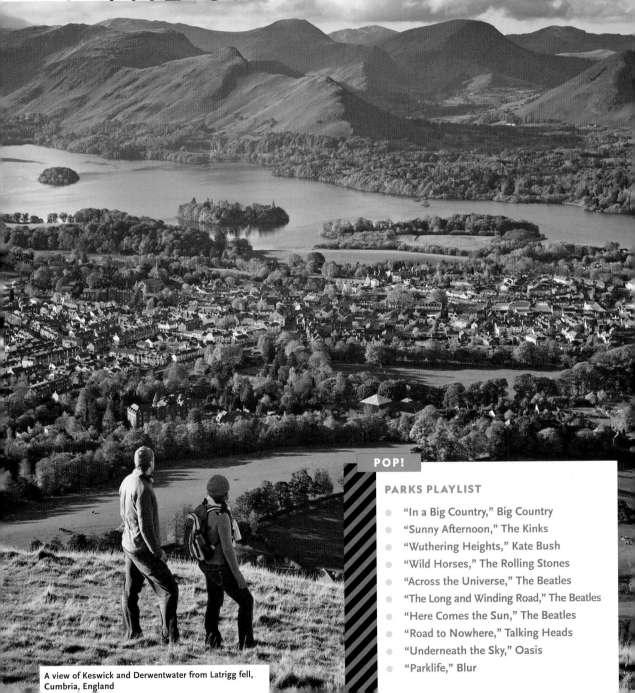

NATIONAL PARKS OF
THE U.K. & IRELAND

POP!

PARKS PLAYLIST

- "In a Big Country," Big Country
- "Sunny Afternoon," The Kinks
- "Wuthering Heights," Kate Bush
- "Wild Horses," The Rolling Stones
- "Across the Universe," The Beatles
- "The Long and Winding Road," The Beatles
- "Here Comes the Sun," The Beatles
- "Road to Nowhere," Talking Heads
- "Underneath the Sky," Oasis
- "Parklife," Blur

A view of Keswick and Derwentwater from Latrigg fell, Cumbria, England

BRECON BEACONS NATIONAL PARK

The Brecon Beacons mountain range in southern Wales sweeps down toward the valleys, celebrated in song as "The Green, Green Grass of Home." The park's sandstone peaks face north over sheer cliffs.

BROADS NATIONAL PARK

The Broads are one of Britain's secret gems. Under wide skies and open horizons, the park's marshy fens offer boaters, fishers, and bird-watchers a labyrinth of waterways, ideal for the leisurely study of the park's incredible biodiversity.

CAIRNGORMS NATIONAL PARK

Cairngorms rewards hikers with a highland spectacle of light glistening on glassy granite rocks, and shimmering corries (mountain lakes) that mirror the eagles and ospreys soaring above. Take the train to the peak and enjoy a bird's-eye view.

CONNEMARA NATIONAL PARK

A signature Irish dreamscape of cliffs, bogs, rolling mists, and wild Atlantic weather, Connemara is as wild and enchanting as the traditional jigs and reels of Ireland. The wild, rugged countryside, much of it in Ireland's largest Gaeltacht (Gaelic-speaking area), is framed by the magnificent Maumturk Mountains.

DARTMOOR NATIONAL PARK

In the haunting landscapes of Dartmoor National Park, you'll pass tall granite tors (exposed rocky hilltops) pointing upward from lonesome moorlands and heathery cleaves (valleys) toward skies that darken stormily and suddenly.

LAKE DISTRICT NATIONAL PARK

There are few more iconic British landscapes than the waters, forests, and fells of the Lake District. The sheer beauty of lakes such as Wastwater and Windermere inspired writers to craft their art in homage to nature's great wonders. For many nature lovers, this *is* England.

LOCH LOMOND & THE TROSSACHS NATIONAL PARK

Centered around the "bonny, bonny banks" of Britain's largest inland lake, this celebrated park bridges Scotland's lowlands and its highlands and encompasses 21 munros (Scottish mountains), two forest parks, 22 lochs, and conservation sites that host a rich range of wildlife.

NEW FOREST NATIONAL PARK

The New Forest embodies much English history. Proclaimed a royal forest by William the Conqueror, it provided wood for Britain's Royal Navy as the empire expanded. Today, you might still meet a verderer, an unpaid officer who enforces the rights of common pasture passed down from medieval times, when the New Forest was noted in the Domesday Book.

NORTH YORK MOORS NATIONAL PARK

Picture a brooding moorland that sweeps down to spectacular cliffs. North York Moors evokes the stormy world of Emily Brontë's *Wuthering Heights.* The village of Whitby was the vampire's landfall in Bram Stoker's *Dracula.* After a windswept hike, try the town's local delicacy: salty smoked kippers.

NORTHUMBERLAND NATIONAL PARK

Northumberland is a hiker's paradise, and home to England's wildest national park, spanning centuries of history. A walk along Hadrian's Wall evokes the Roman occupation of Britain. Beyond this point, the wild Celtic tribes of Scotland and Hibernia (Winterland—now Ireland) were never conquered.

The Staple Tors in Cornwall's Dartmoor National Park

SNOWDONIA NATIONAL PARK

A spirit of adventure lives large in the rugged mountains of North Wales. Sir Edmund Hillary and his team practiced here before their 1953 ascent of Everest. Look for the soaring red kite, the national bird of Wales, and listen for the lovely lilt of spoken Welsh.

THE BURREN NATIONAL PARK

At first glance, this park in County Clare looks like a haunting lunar landscape, devoid of any signs of life. Yet look a little closer to find Ireland's greatest diversity of wildflowers — arctic, alpine, and Mediterranean.

WICKLOW MOUNTAINS NATIONAL PARK

A mosaic of blanket bogs and woodlands spreads out atop the elevated eastern county known as the "Garden of Ireland." Hike the winding Wicklow Way to Glendalough (the glen of the two lakes), site of a sixth-century monastic settlement.

YORKSHIRE DALES NATIONAL PARK

The Yorkshire Dales lure travelers with gritstone and limestone valleys and bucolic villages. The karst landscape is pocked by caves and potholes, making the Dales popular with subterranean adventurers.

BEST OF @NATGEO

TOP PHOTOS OF ADVENTURE

@jimmychin | JIMMY CHIN
After his free-solo ascent of Yosemite's El Capitan, Alex Honnold examines the state of his hands.

@renan_ozturk | RENAN OZTURK
Pilots steer an ultralight trike—a type of powered hang glider—over the sandstone formations of Monument Valley in Utah.

@carltonward | CARLTON WARD
The Florida Wildlife Corridor Expedition team paddled, hiked, and biked more than a thousand miles from the northern Everglades to southern Georgia.

@pedromcbride | PETE MCBRIDE
A hockey player skates across fresh black ice in the stark cold of an early morning.

@jimmychin | JIMMY CHIN
Mountaineer Conrad Anker looks over the landscape on a bright end of day in Antarctica when there is no sunset.

@salvarezphoto | STEPHEN ALVAREZ
An adventurer makes the 600-foot drop into one of the world's largest caves, Majlis al Jinn in Oman.

@renan_ozturk | RENAN OZTURK
Ice climber Anna Pfaff makes her way up the side of Iceland's Vatnajökull glacier, the largest in Europe.

@paulnicklen | PAUL NICKLEN
Sunlight illuminates water from above as a diver explores a deep sinkhole in Mexico.

A HISTORY OF CLIMBING EVEREST

PROPELLED BY AMBITION AND AWE

For generations, the mountain we know as Everest was a presence to be honored, not conquered. But once British mountaineers attempted to reach its summit in 1922, Everest became an irresistible challenge to climbers from all over the world, forever altering the lives of people living around it. Adventurers have brought wealth and high-tech gear to the region, but they've also introduced pollution and a demand for guides willing to endure dangerous treks. Many hope that, in light of recent tragedies, ambition will be tempered by care and caution.

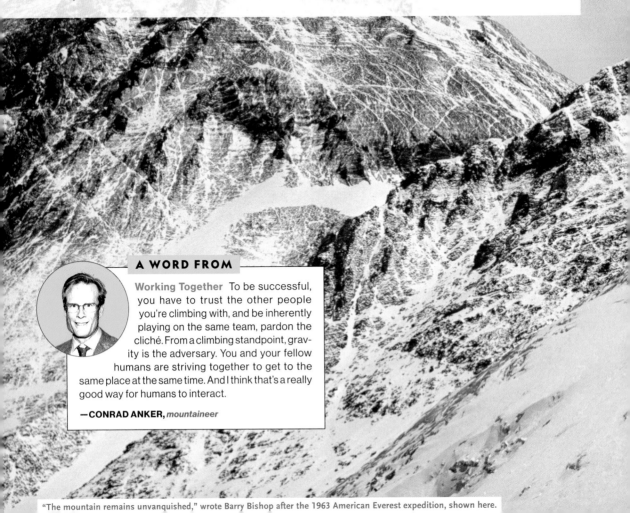

A WORD FROM

Working Together To be successful, you have to trust the other people you're climbing with, and be inherently playing on the same team, pardon the cliché. From a climbing standpoint, gravity is the adversary. You and your fellow humans are striving together to get to the same place at the same time. And I think that's a really good way for humans to interact.

—CONRAD ANKER, *mountaineer*

"The mountain remains unvanquished," wrote Barry Bishop after the 1963 American Everest expedition, shown here.

Setting Records on
EVEREST

■ **MAY 1953 (SOUTH FACE)**
Edmund Hillary (New Zealand) and
Tenzing Norgay (Nepal) accomplish
the first recorded summit of Everest.

■ **MAY 1963 (WEST RIDGE AND
NORTH FACE)**
First successful American expedition:
Team members Thomas Hornbein
and Willi Unsoeld traverse Everest
via West Ridge.

■ **MAY 1975 (SOUTH FACE)**
Junko Tabei (Japan) becomes first
woman to reach summit—just 12 days
after being injured in an avalanche.

■ **AUG. 1980 (NORTH FACE)**
Reinhold Messner (Italy) makes
first solo ascent—notably without
supplementary oxygen, as on his
previous summit in May 1978.

■ **SEPT. 1988 (SOUTH RIDGE)**
Jean-Marc Boivin (France) accomplishes
the first paraglider descent from the
summit, thus also clocking the fastest
descent ever.

■ **MAY 2010 (NORTH FACE)**
Jordan Romero (U.S.) becomes the
youngest person to summit, at 13 years
and 10 months old.

■ **MAY 2012 (NORTH FACE)**
Tamae Watanabe (Japan) becomes the
oldest female to summit, at age 73 years
and 180 days—breaking her own record.

■ **MAY 2013**
Yuichiro Miura (Japan) reclaims title
of oldest man to summit, at age 80.

■ **MAY 2013**
Dave Hahn (U.S.) sets a new
record, 15, for number of ascents
by a non-Sherpa.

■ **MAY 2018**
Kami Rita Sherpa, age 48, sets record for
number of summits by accomplishing
his 22nd.

EARTH'S EXTREMES

PUTTING THE AWE BACK IN AWESOME

Sunrise over Lake Superior

WATER RECORDS

LARGEST FRESHWATER LAKE

Lake Superior stretches across 31,700 square miles of the United States and Canada, making it the largest lake by surface area. It was formed about 10,000 years ago.

LOWEST POINT

The Challenger Deep in the Pacific is the lowest point on Earth: 36,037 feet below sea level. Mount Everest could be sunk into its depths and still be covered by more than one mile of water.

DEEPEST LAKE

Russia's Lake Baikal is both the deepest lake, at 5,387 feet, and the oldest, at 25–30 million years old. It is part of a rift valley, where tectonic plates are breaking apart.

LARGEST RIVER

There is no competition here: The Amazon River and its tributaries flow through Peru, Bolivia, Venezuela, Colombia, Ecuador, and Brazil before emptying into the Atlantic Ocean. The next largest, India's "Mother Ganges," discharges a significantly lower volume of water than the Amazon does.

LONGEST RIVER

Calculating the length of rivers is a complicated and controversial process. Freshwater scientists often cannot agree on a river's precise source or on how far to extend its watershed boundaries. But most agree that the Nile, stretching through northeast Africa, is the longest in the world at 4,160 miles. The Amazon is a close second at 4,150 miles and the Yangtze clocks in at 3,880 miles long.

The Nile in Sudan

The Valle de la Luna in Chile's Atacama Desert

SCIENTISTS THINK THE DRY VALLEYS OF ANTARCTICA MAY BE THE CLOSEST OF ANY ENVIRONMENT ON EARTH TO THE PLANET MARS.

Bore hole inside Mammoth Cave

LAND RECORDS

DRIEST PLACE

Parts of the high plateau of the Atacama Desert in Chile and the Dry Valleys of Antarctica have never recorded a drop of rain. They are ringed by high mountains that prevent moisture from reaching the dry basins.

HIGHEST POINT

Mount Everest is the world's highest elevation, 29,035 feet above sea level—a figure that increases as the Indian subcontinent crashes into Asia. Hawaii's Mauna Kea is the world's tallest mountain, 33,000 feet from seafloor to summit.

WETTEST PLACE

Asian monsoons make the Indian state of Meghalaya the rainiest place in the world. The town of Mawsynram received about 83 feet of rain in 1985. In 1861, nearby Cherrapunji received 86.6 feet.

FARTHEST FROM THE OCEAN

About 200 miles north of Urumqi, a city in Xinjiang, China, is a "pole of inaccessibility"—a location that is "challenging to reach owing to its remoteness from geographical features that could provide access." The most remote pole of inaccessibility—the place farthest from the ocean—is also in Xinjiang, about 1,644 miles from the coast.

LONGEST CAVE SYSTEM

The Mammoth-Flint Ridge cave system in Kentucky stretches about 400 miles, nearly twice the length of the next longest cave system, Mexico's Sac Actun underwater cave.

HOTTEST PLACE

The temperature at Furnace Creek Station in Death Valley National Park, which straddles California and Nevada, reached 134°F (56.7°C) on July 10, 1913. However, the Danakil Depression—which reaches into Eritrea, Djibouti, and Ethiopia—has the highest average year-round temperature—93.92°F (34.4°C).

COLDEST PLACE

A region near Vostok Station, a Russian research station in Antarctica atop ice almost two and a half miles thick, set the world record on August 10, 2010, when the temperature dipped to minus 135.8°F (−93.2°C).

UNDERWATER
MUSEUM

SWIMMING WITH SCULPTURE

A barren sand flat does not typically inspire creativity, but it happens to be a perfect setting for the first Underwater Museum of Art (UMA) in the United States. Located just off the Florida Panhandle, near Walton County's Grayton Beach State Park, the UMA installed its first seven sculptures in 2018. Over time, the collection will become a marine habitat. As at similar projects near Cancún and the Canary Islands, the experience is best suited for scuba divers. On clear days, snorkelers will also be able to enjoy the submerged journey, which sits at a depth of around 60 feet.

A school of gray snappers swims among the sculptures at the Underwater Museum of Art in Cancún, Mexico, precursor to the new one in Florida.

POP!

MOVIES WITH UNDERWATER WORLDS

- *The Little Mermaid* (1989)
- *Sphere* (1998)
- *Atlantis: The Lost Empire* (2001)
- *Finding Nemo* (2003)
- *Deepsea Challenge* (2014)
- *Aquaman* (2018)
- *Avatar 2 and 3* (in production)

Inaugural Class of
SUBMERGED ART

■ ANAMORPHOUS OCTOPUS
This perforated steel sculpture was created by artist Allison Wickey, who first proposed the museum. Her painter's eye is evident in the textured, shaded surface of her piece.

■ CONCRETE ROPE REEF SPHERES
With a goal of supporting oyster colonies, architecture professor and artist Evelyn Tickle developed a concrete formula that matches the constitution of oyster shells and used it to make the nooks and crannies of her creature-friendly tangled sculpture.

■ THE GRAYT PINEAPPLE
In the American colonies, rare and expensive pineapples symbolized hospitality. Artist Rachel Herring's steel sculpture is welcoming to small fish in particular. Its name refers to Grayton Beach.

■ JYC'S DREAM
In a nod to explorer Jacques Cousteau's Aqua-Lung, designer Kevin Reilly created this oversize stainless-steel depiction of a diver's head gear with rising bubbles—some containing children's art.

■ PROPELLER IN MOTION
Furniture designer Marek Anthony based his stainless-steel sculpture on a ship's propeller to elicit thoughts of motion and of nature reclaiming what humans have discarded. Swimming creatures can easily move through the hollow blades.

■ SELF PORTRAIT
Justin Gaffrey's eight-foot-tall stag evokes the stillness of an encounter on land. Its steely presence invites parallels between the underwater setting and a forest scene—with dashing fish instead of scurrying forest animals.

■ SWARA SKULL
The steel, cement, and limestone hollow skull created by film designer (and divemaster) Vince Tatum aims to attract corals and reclusive marine life. (SWARA stands for South Walton Artificial Reef Association.)

The Speed of Innovation

Progression of 100-meter dash world record,
1910-2018

KEY

Women

Men

Manually timed record

Electronically timed record

Male and female runners have bested world records in the 100-meter dash over the past century. But the gear and the track infrastructure are what have changed most dramatically since the first competitions were run with the help of nails driven into the soles of dress shoes.

Stronger starts
Early racers dug holes into the tracks, which were usually laid with cinders. The introduction of solid starting blocks in the late 1920s led to new world records.

Lighter shoes
The first running shoes were simply leather dress shoes, with nails to provide grip. Today's shoes boast nylon, fiberglass, and single-use spikes.

10.6 seconds
Donald Lippincott, U.S.
July 6, 1912

10.2
Jesse Owens, U.S.
June 20, 1936

13.0

12.5

12.0

11.5

11.0

10.5

10.0

1910   1920   1930   1940   1950

ATHLETIC ACHIEVEMENTS IMPROVED FOR DECADES, IN PART BECAUSE OF NEW TECHNOLOGY AND THE USE OF PERFORMANCE-ENHANCING STEROIDS. WITH ATHLETES UNDER INCREASED SCRUTINY, WORLD RECORDS ARE STILL GETTING BROKEN—BUT NOT INCREMENTALLY, SUGGESTING THAT WE ARE PUSHING THE LIMITS OF OUR ATHLETIC POTENTIAL.

Faster tracks
Polyurethane tracks debuted at the 1968 Olympics. The tracks are bouncier and return energy to a runner; cinder tracks absorbed energy.

10.49
Florence Griffith-Joyner, U.S.
July 16, 1988

Fastest time since Griffith-Joyner:
10.64
Carmelita Jeter
September 20, 2009

Better timekeeping
Early stopwatches measured only fifths of a second. It wasn't until 1977 that fully digital timekeeping—to the hundredths of seconds—became mandatory.

The unbeatable FloJo
The top three women's times are held by Florence Griffith-Joyner. She never tested positive for steroids, but her 1988 record—still unbroken today—shows how great performances can raise suspicion.

Lightning strikes thrice
Usain Bolt broke the men's world record twice in 2008 and again in 2009, dropping it by 0.14 seconds, more than any man in the modern era.

9.72
9.69
9.58
Usain Bolt, Jamaica
August 16, 2009

1970   1980   1990   2000   2010

MIRNA VALERIO
ULTRA RUNNER

CHARTING A COURSE FOR EVERY BODY

"I'm good in my big body." That's what Mirna Valerio—ultramarathon runner, author, and educator—wants her naysayers to know. A few years after starting her blog, Fat Girl Running, Valerio's story went viral, subjecting her to both praise and public scrutiny. Despite racism and body-shaming, she continues challenging stereotypes and inspiring others to do the same.

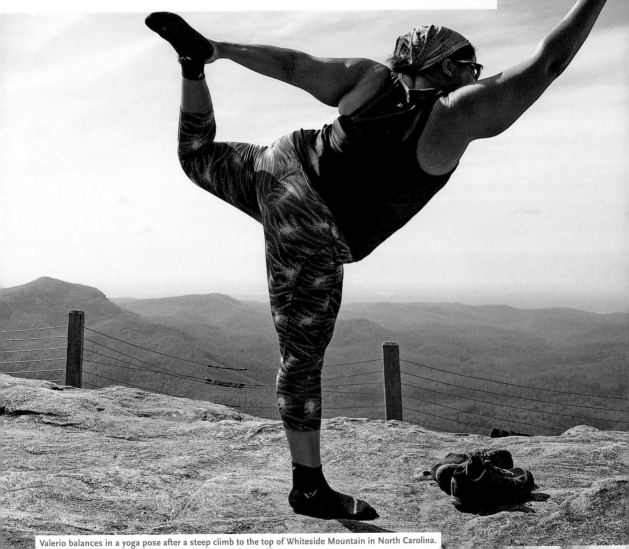

Valerio balances in a yoga pose after a steep climb to the top of Whiteside Mountain in North Carolina.

With an unwavering spirit that solidified her place as a 2018 National Geographic Adventurer of the Year, Mirna Valerio is challenging stereotypes in the running world and bringing a community of body-positive athletes along with her.

Valerio discovered her own athleticism and love of the outdoors at overnight camp in the Catskill Mountains when she was eight years old. She played high school sports and kept running through her college years. But over time, Valerio's exercise routines fell away—until a health scare in 2008. When she came back to running, she weighed more than 300 pounds. Even with running 25 to 35 miles a week and frequently participating in marathons and ultramarathons, Valerio's weight has plateaued at about 240 pounds.

WHAT DOES FIT LOOK LIKE?

This raises the question: Is a BMI score the best indicator of health? "I think that people are really having trouble grappling with the idea that fit comes in many forms," Valerio says, "and that people can still participate in athletics no matter what kind of body they have."

Her blog gained national attention, giving voice to her determination, positivity, and insistence that people of all sizes can be fit. Her message is so inspiring that she has been given a platform and held up as a role model by corporations and media alike.

"We are much more than our bodies. Whether it's body image, our choices to be moms or not, our career choices—we are more than our bodies," Valerio says. "We're so powerful beyond our wildest dreams."

> " I KNOW THERE'S GOING TO BE UPS AND DOWNS. THAT'S THE BEAUTIFUL CHALLENGE OF RUNNING LONG RACES. I THINK THEY REALLY PREPARE YOU FOR DIFFICULT THINGS IN LIFE."

Valerio started training for her first marathon in 2011.

KEY DATES

Mirna Valerio's
JOURNEY

DEC. 2011
Completes first marathon, Marine Corps Marathon, Washington, D.C.

OCT. 2015
Completes Javelina Jundred, her first 100k run, Fountain Hills, AZ

2016
Named ambassador for Merrell

OCT. 2017
Publishes memoir, *A Beautiful Work in Progress*

2017
REI releases documentary short, *The Mirnavator*

MARCH 2018
Named a National Geographic Adventurer of the Year

REDEFINING
WHAT IS POSSIBLE

PERFORMANCES THAT SET WORLD & OLYMPIC RECORDS

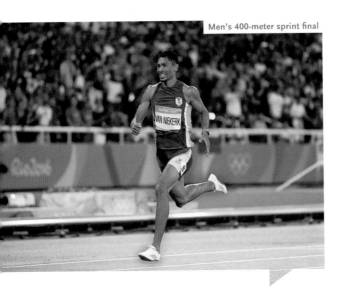

Men's 400-meter sprint final

2016 SUMMER GAMES

RECORD FINALLY FALLS

Sprinter Wayde van Niekerk of South Africa set a new world record at the 2016 games in the 400-meter race, coming in at 43.03 seconds. The previous record of 43.18 had been set in 1999 by Michael Johnson of the U.S.

DOMINANCE

In cycling's men's team pursuit, Great Britain set four world records between 2008 and 2012. In 2016, Great Britain set new world and Olympic records twice—in the first round (3:50.570) and again in the final (3:50.265). With the 2016 gold medal, his seventh, Bradley Wiggins became his country's most decorated Olympic athlete.

PUSHING THE ENVELOPE

A single event saw three new world and Olympic records during the Rio games: women's team pursuit cycling, a four-person 4-kilometer race. Great Britain clocked in at 4:13.260 in the qualifying round, 4:12.152 in the first round, and 4:10.236 in the final.

STRONG SHOWING

In the women's 63 kg weightlifting competition, Deng Wei of China exceeded her own world record in the clean and jerk portion (147 kg, up from 2015's 146 kg) and set a world record with her final tally of 262 kg.

HAMMER TIME

Polish hammer thrower Anita Włodarczyk set four world records between 2009 and 2015. In Rio, she set a world and Olympic record with her 270.0-foot throw. Just two weeks later, she bested that with a 272.2-foot throw.

Women's hammer throw final

Men's 500-meter speed skating quarterfinals

2018 WINTER GAMES

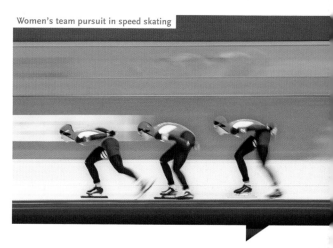

Women's team pursuit in speed skating

FIRE ON ICE

Chinese speed skater Wu Dajing broke the Olympic record in men's short track 500-meter speed skating in his heat and then went on to set two new world records in both the quarterfinal and final races (clocking in at 40.264, 39.800, and 39.584 seconds, respectively).

BESTS, NOT RECORDS

At the Pyeongchang Winter Games in 2018, only speed skating saw world and Olympic records broken at the same time. Performances at high elevations, as in Pyeongchang, tend to be better than those at sea level, so the latter may be designated world bests instead of world records. In the 2018 games, three world records and five world bests were recorded.

NO GOLD FOR FASTEST

In women's short track skating, the Netherlands' team set a new world record in the 3,000-meter relay, with a time of 4:03.471. But because they weren't among the top four teams competing for medals, they were almost sent home empty-handed. When other teams were disqualified, they ended up with the bronze medal—despite besting South Korea, the gold medal winners, by almost 4 seconds.

ONE AFTER ANOTHER

The Netherlands had another world best in the quarterfinals of the women's team pursuit with a time of 2:55.61, but two days later, Japan broke both records by finishing in 2:53.89. Japan also holds the world record for this event, set at the 2017 World Cup held in Salt Lake City, with a time of 2:50.87.

À LA CARTE

Jorien ter Mors of the Netherlands set world best and Olympic records for the women's 1,000-meter race with a time of 1:13.56. Ter Mors was also a member of the world-record-setting 3,000-meter relay team.

UNSTOPPABLE

In women's 500-meter speed skating, Japan's Nao Kodaira finished in 36.94 seconds, setting the world best and Olympic records—and earning her first gold medal. She also holds three world records, in the 500-meter x 2, 1,000-meter, and sprint combination events.

TRANSPORTATION
TIME LINE

PREHISTORY	1700 to 1 BC	AD 1 to 1000	1000 to 1700

PREHISTORY

■ **ca 65,000 ya***
Modern humans reach New Guinea and Australia by boat.

■ **ca 14,700 ya**
Humans are present in the Americas.

■ **ca 10,000 ya**
Dugout canoes are in use in Europe.

■ **ca 5500 BC**
Humans use bits and reins to manage horses for riding.

■ **ca 3500 BC**
The wheel is invented in Mesopotamia.

■ **ca 2500 BC**
Mesopotamians waterproof boats and buildings with tar.

* *years ago*

1700 to 1 BC

■ **ca 1700 BC**
Horses and chariots are introduced to Egypt.

■ **691 BC**
Assyrians build an aqueduct to carry water to their capital, Nineveh.

■ **312 BC**
Rome builds its first major road, the Appian Way.

■ **110 BC**
Romans use rudimentary horseshoes.

AD 1 to 1000

■ **415**
In India, suspension bridges are built using iron chains.

■ **ca 660**
Camel herds support a nomadic way of life among people living in the Sahara.

■ **ca 700**
Europeans begin to adopt the use of stirrups for riding horses.

■ **ca 800**
Roads in Baghdad, Iraq, are paved with tar extracted from nearby oil fields.

■ **ca 860**
Viking longships venture as far west as Iceland.

1000 to 1700

■ **ca 1088**
Shen Kuo first describes a magnetic compass used for navigation.

■ **ca 1450**
The Inca construct a road system 20,000 miles long to unite their empire.

■ **1457**
The first four-wheel passenger coach is built in Hungary.

■ **1500**
Chinese scientist Wan Hu attempts to make a flying machine out of rockets tied to a chair.

■ **1692**
In France, the 32-mile Canal du Midi, linking the Mediterranean Sea with the Atlantic Ocean, is completed.

1700 to 1900

■ 1769
James Watt patents the modern steam engine.

■ 1783
French brothers Joseph and Jacques Montgolfier first demonstrate the hot air balloon.

■ 1869
The Suez Canal is completed in Egypt.

■ 1869
The U.S. Transcontinental Railroad is completed.

■ 1879
Karl Benz runs the first gas-powered automobile.

■ 1891
Construction begins on the Trans-Siberian Railroad.

1900 to 1930

■ 1903
Orville and Wilbur Wright fly a powered airplane at Kitty Hawk, North Carolina.

■ 1904
The first portion of the New York City subway opens.

■ 1908
The first Model T Ford comes off the assembly line.

■ 1909
French aviator Louis Blériot flies across the English Channel.

■ 1927
Charles Lindbergh flies the *Spirit of St. Louis* nonstop from New York to Paris.

1930 to 1960

■ 1933
The first modern airliner, the Boeing 247, enters service.

■ 1937
The *Hindenburg* dirigible bursts into flames when attempting to dock after a transatlantic flight.

■ 1939
Inventor Igor Sikorsky builds the first helicopter.

■ 1945
James Martin designs the ejector seat.

■ 1947
American airman Charles "Chuck" Yeager makes the first supersonic flight.

■ 1958
Australian engineer David Warren invents the "black box" flight data recorder.

1960 to PRESENT

■ 1961
Soviet cosmonaut Yuri Gagarin becomes the first man in space.

■ 1969
The British-French supersonic airliner Concorde takes its maiden flight.

■ 1969
NASA's Apollo 11 makes the first piloted moon landing.

■ 1998
English inventor David Baker patents the Land Shark, a high-speed amphibious car.

■ 2010
Self-driving cars make their first test drives on public streets.

ICONIC
DESTINATIONS

JOURNEYS THAT SHOULD BE ON EVERY BUCKET LIST

NASHVILLE
U.S.
Immerse yourself in Americana at the Country Music Hall of Fame and Hatch Show Print. Then make a pilgrimage to the Ryman Auditorium and Music Row.

DUTCH BULBFIELDS
Netherlands
In spring the famed bulbfields in South Holland become a blaze of color. Cycle around fields of brilliant hues, and then visit world-famous gardens.

PACIFIC COAST HIGHWAY
U.S.
Savor the sweeping Pacific vistas and hairpin bends of the highway that clings to America's western edge. Cruise north from Hearst Castle to historic Monterey.

NORTH AMERICA

HANA HIGHWAY
U.S.
A restorative for mind and body, Maui's Hana coast—with black-sand beaches, plunging waterfalls, limpid pools, and rainbow eucalyptus—unspools for 52 miles.

ATLANTIC

OCEAN

PACIFIC

TAHITI & BORA BORA
French Polynesia
A stroll along a black-sand beach, a dive into a translucent lagoon, or a visit to palm-shaded coral atolls will show you why these islands are considered paradise.

OCEAN

GALÁPAGOS
Ecuador
Visit for a day or more to see the lava fields, white-sand strands, and giant cliffs that are home to the abundant wildlife that inspired Charles Darwin.

SOUTH AMERICA

PYRAMIDS OF GIZA
Egypt
The lone survivor of the original Seve Wonders of the World, these tombs have been astonish ing visitors since they were firs erected in the 26th century BC.

> ❝ TRAVEL IS MORE THAN THE SEEING OF SIGHTS; IT IS A CHANGE THAT GOES ON, DEEP AND PERMANENT, IN THE IDEAS OF LIVING. ❞
>
> —MIRIAM BEARD, HISTORIAN AND ACTIVIST

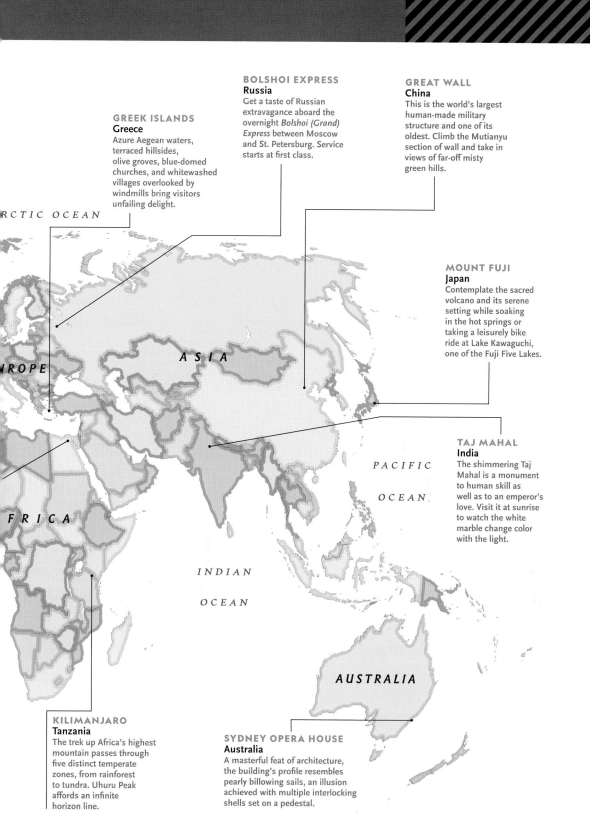

GREEK ISLANDS
Greece
Azure Aegean waters, terraced hillsides, olive groves, blue-domed churches, and whitewashed villages overlooked by windmills bring visitors unfailing delight.

BOLSHOI EXPRESS
Russia
Get a taste of Russian extravagance aboard the overnight *Bolshoi (Grand) Express* between Moscow and St. Petersburg. Service starts at first class.

GREAT WALL
China
This is the world's largest human-made military structure and one of its oldest. Climb the Mutianyu section of wall and take in views of far-off misty green hills.

MOUNT FUJI
Japan
Contemplate the sacred volcano and its serene setting while soaking in the hot springs or taking a leisurely bike ride at Lake Kawaguchi, one of the Fuji Five Lakes.

TAJ MAHAL
India
The shimmering Taj Mahal is a monument to human skill as well as to an emperor's love. Visit it at sunrise to watch the white marble change color with the light.

KILIMANJARO
Tanzania
The trek up Africa's highest mountain passes through five distinct temperate zones, from rainforest to tundra. Uhuru Peak affords an infinite horizon line.

SYDNEY OPERA HOUSE
Australia
A masterful feat of architecture, the building's profile resembles pearly billowing sails, an illusion achieved with multiple interlocking shells set on a pedestal.

RCTIC OCEAN

ROPE

ASIA

PACIFIC

OCEAN

FRICA

INDIAN

OCEAN

AUSTRALIA

SAVOR THE WORLD'S
BEST CITIES

Puerto Madero, Buenos Aires

MARRAKECH

GREEN OASES

Marrakech is known for its gardens, particularly the Jardin Majorelle (Rue Yves Saint Laurent), a breathtaking landscape of exotic plants, trees, pools, and fountains. But few realize its haute couture legacy. Fashion legends Yves Saint Laurent and Pierre Berg bought and restored the garden in 1980, saving it from becoming part of a hotel complex.

READ AHEAD

Lords of the Atlas by Gavin Maxwell (1966), an account of the ruling Glaoua clan, who maintained a near-medieval fiefdom in southern Morocco from 1893 to 1956, is a must-read.

BUENOS AIRES

LIKE A LOCAL

Calle Florida in downtown Buenos Aires has been at least partly pedestrianized since 1913. Now totally off-limits for vehicles, it's one of the city's biggest tourist attractions, with shops and arcades selling leather, jewelry, and souvenirs.

READ AHEAD

The translated short stories of Argentina's most important writer, Jorge Luis Borges, are a great way to learn about the city, especially the tumultuous dark underworld of the *compadritos,* gangsters, of the 1920s and 1930s. Pick up his *Collected Fictions* (1999).

Jardin Majorelle in Marrakech

Aerial view of Paris at night

Yu Garden in Shanghai

PARIS

LA TOUR MAGNIFIQUE

The Eiffel Tower—built as the centerpiece for the 1889 World's Fair—is France at its best: confident, brilliant, putting on a show for the world. Glass-roofed shopping arcades are another Paris invention, also from the 19th century. The ones that survive, mostly around the old Bibliothèque Nationale, are utterly charming; some are packed with old bookstores and curiosity shops, others with chic galleries and boutiques.

FLEA MARKETS

No trip to Paris is complete without a day at the 17-acre, 3,000-stall Marché aux Puces de Saint-Ouen on the city limits. You might score vintage French cookery or antique tomes at the centrally located Marché aux Puces d'Aligre. A visit to the intimate and friendly Marché aux Puces de Vanves is like rummaging through the attic of the French grandparents you never had.

READ AHEAD

All of Georges Simenon's Maigret detective stories are great for evoking Parisian life, both high and low. *Maigret at the Crossroads* (1931) is regarded as one of the best.

SHANGHAI

VISIT THE PAST

Take a break from the busy streets and glitzy skyscrapers and lose yourself in ancient China at the 400-year-old Yu Garden in the Huangpu District. The complex was a private garden in the Ming dynasty and has become one of Shanghai's most famous sites. See exquisite Chinese sculptures, carvings, garden pavilions, pagodas, and pools. Outside you'll find the bustling Yuyuan Bazaar with souvenir shops, teahouses, and restaurants.

READ AHEAD

Man's Fate (1933), which many consider to be André Malraux's best novel, follows two communist conspirators and two foreigners during the violent crackdown of the communist insurrection in 1927 Shanghai.

A TASTE OF ITALY

ABBONDANZA DELIZIOSA

Central Italy—its mountains, plains, valleys, and merry coastline—is both civilized and down to earth. Home of the Renaissance, this most visited part of Italy, along with its celebrated culture and cuisine, is what most travelers think of as "Italian." Indeed, the central Italian kitchen, which takes simplicity to a high level, characterizes much of what generally makes Italian food so special. That finesse is derived from two things: an ancient cosmopolitan heritage and a fidelity to high-quality ingredients that are locally grown or produced.

A WORD FROM

Traveling via Flavors The real Italy is so much more multifaceted, and so much more remarkable, than the Italy that lives on in popular imagination. For the traveler to Italy, this diversity means an incredible range of experiences and tastes, from heavenly white truffles in Alba to musky blood oranges in Sicily. These locally produced ingredients . . . shape the local cooking and produce the wide variety of regional cuisines . . . And 21st-century transport means these artisanal ingredients are likely available at your local market.

—JACK BISHOP, *chief creative officer of America's Test Kitchen*

Parmesan cheese and Bolognese sauce top homemade fettucine.

Traditional Dishes From
CENTRAL ITALY

■ **CHICKEN UNDER A BRICK**
(POLLO AL MATTONE)
This Tuscan technique ensures even cooking, speeds up the process, and maximizes contact with the cooking grate for perfectly crisp skin.

■ **FRIED STUFFED OLIVES**
(OLIVE ALL'ASCOLANA)
Crisp-coated, salty fried olives with a rich meat filling are a culinary marvel from the town of Ascoli Piceno in Le Marche.

■ **ORECCHIETTE WITH
SAUSAGE AND CREAM**
(ORECCHIETTE ALLA NORCINA)
The black pigs of Umbria are prized for their superlative flavor, owing to their diet of plants, herbs, and truffles.

■ **ROMAN GNOCCHI**
(GNOCCHI ALLA ROMANA)
Semolina gnocchi—no potatoes here—is appealingly creamy and slightly dense, similar to polenta.

■ **SEAFOOD SOUP**
(BRODETTO ALL'ANCONETANA)
Ancona's trademark dish has long served as a way for fishermen to use the bycatch remaining after selling the day's haul.

■ **SPRING VEGETABLE STEW**
(VIGNOLE)
Spring vegetables abound in Abruzzo's inland, and *vignole* is a vibrant (and speedy) braise that celebrates them.

■ **TUSCAN TOMATO AND BREAD SOUP**
(PAPPA AL POMODORO)
This is a tomato-bread soup finished with basil. In the pot, the ingredients meld to form a fragrant porridge-like stew that's downright luxurious.

■ **VEGETABLE AND FARRO SOUP**
(MINESTRA DI FARRO)
Umbrians use coarsely ground farro, a staple of Umbria that predates common wheat, to thicken and flavor soups.

GREATEST EXPEDITIONS

FOLLOW HISTORY'S PATHWAYS AROUND THE WORLD

Passengers traverse Switzerland's Landwasser viaduct.

BY TRAIN

SWISS ALPS AND ITALIAN LAKE DISTRICT

Climb aboard the unhurried *Glacier Express* and savor the panorama of snowcapped peaks, dense forests, rushing rivers, Alpine meadows, and mountain villages near Switzerland's southern borders.

CANADIAN ROCKIES

Take the *Rocky Mountaineer*'s dramatic route through the Canadian Rockies—rocky gradients, soaring pine trees, spiraling tunnels—from Vancouver to Banff.

SHINKANSEN TRANS-SIBERIAN RAILWAY

A weeklong Moscow-Beijing route via Mongolia weaves though the Russian hinterlands of Siberia, the wilderness of Mongolia, and the wastes of the Gobi, within sight of Lake Baikal and the Great Wall.

ACROSS LAND

MOROCCO'S CITIES OF LEGEND

A journey along age-old trade routes—from Ceuta (officially part of Spain) to the tiny fishing port of Tarfaya—immerses you in ancient cultures, exotic markets, and imposing mountain and desert scenery.

NEW ZEALAND NORTH TO SOUTH

The unspoiled (but accessible) landscape between Karamea and Jackson Bay includes two glaciers, exceptional ocean vistas, and alpine scenery.

PILGRIMAGE TO BHUTAN

One enchanted tour includes a trek into Trashi-yangtse, a stunning "lost" valley, with a monastery, a wildlife sanctuary, a shrine, and welcoming locals.

Prayer flags frame Bhutan's mythic Taktsang Monastery.

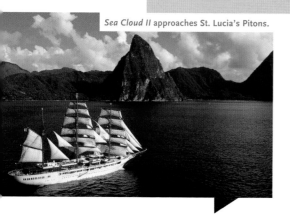

Sea Cloud II approaches St. Lucia's Pitons.

TOGETHER, TOURISTS FROM CHINA AND THE UNITED STATES SPEND ALMOST $400 BILLION A YEAR ON TRAVEL.

BY SEA

CARIBBEAN DREAMING

These legendary islands are synonymous with paradise: idyllic beaches, water sports, and rum cocktails. A cruise through the breathtaking waters offers luxury, shopping, and outdoor fun.

EPIC POLYNESIA

During one seven-day excursion around Tahiti and nearby islands, guests can kayak, dive, snorkel, hike, or sunbathe. Inland spots to visit include an archaeological site and a vanilla plantation.

ANTARCTIC CRUISING

You'll be comfortable aboard an ice-reinforced vessel as icebergs float past, some of them as large as ships themselves. Time your trip right to catch sight of seals, whales, and penguins.

Zebras and wildebeests graze in Tanzania's Serengeti National Park.

ON SAFARI

TANZANIA'S GREAT MIGRATION

On the ground, in the trees, along rivers, and in the sky—more than 1,000 bird species can be found here, and it's possible to see 100 species in a day. Birding is good year-round, but fall migration is spectacular.

BOTSWANA GAME RESERVE

On a guided safari, guests of the national parks shoot the "big five" of African wildlife—lion, leopard, buffalo, rhino, and elephant—with cameras rather than guns.

VICTORIA FALLS

On a microlight aircraft, there's not much between you and the tree-covered islands that dot the Zambezi River as it approaches Victoria Falls. Want to see wildlife? Book a flight over the nearby national park.

A WORD FROM

Overtourism According to figures from the United Nations World Tourism Organization, international tourism has grown 40-fold since commercial jet traffic began some six decades ago. The places that these people visit, however—the museums, the archaeological ruins, the natural attractions, the narrow medieval streets of historic cities—are still the same physical size.

—JONATHAN TOURTELLOT,
sustainable tourism expert

EUROPE'S
NATIONAL PARKS

PLAN YOUR NEXT CONTINENTAL OUTDOOR ADVENTURE

A crystalline lake reflects the Dauphiné Alps in France's Écrins National Park.

NATURE BECKONS

Taking inspiration from the American system of national parks, first established in 1916, Europeans have selected their own treasured landscapes to delineate, preserve, and cherish. Each of these parks has character all its own, but each also represents the beauty and spirit of the country in which it is found. From the Pyrenees to the Dutch lowlands, from the Côte d'Azur to the Black Forest—when you visit these wildlands, you travel back to the time when nature prevailed.

ÉCRINS NATIONAL PARK (FRANCE)

Climb the Dauphiné Alps, hike the vie ferrate (fixed-rope trails), cycle a Tour de France stage, or go gorge walking and canyoning in this alpine wonderland.

PORT-CROS NATIONAL PARK (FRANCE)

Two Mediterranean islands with an undersea trail for divers are your passport to a parade of marine life on the Côte d'Azur.

PYRENEES NATIONAL PARK (FRANCE)

This is France writ large: Hike, ski, and enjoy a plethora of protected wildlife or just take a deep breath of the pure air.

HOGE VELUWE NATIONAL PARK (NETHERLANDS)

The Hoge Veluwe is a maze of marshlands, sand dunes, heathlands, and pinewoods on an estate with a renowned Van Gogh museum.

ZOOM-KALMTHOUTSE HEIDE NATIONAL PARK (BELGIUM/NETHERLANDS)

Walk the 20-mile (32-km) Grenspark-route for a sense of the diversity within this expansive transborder park that transects the lowlands.

Ludwig II's castle, Schloss Neuschwanstein, in the Bavarian Alps

BAVARIAN FOREST NATIONAL PARK OR BLACK FOREST NATIONAL PARK (GERMANY)

Take the Baumwipfelpfad, the mile-long (1.6-km) treetop elevated trail above the spruces, beeches, and firs of the Bavarian Forest. Welcome to "Europe's Green Roof."

LOWER SAXON WADDEN SEA NATIONAL PARK (GERMANY)

Walk or horse-ride across mudflats and salt marshes to study the floor of Earth's second most fecund ecosystem, the food-rich habitat of the Wadden Sea.

SAXON SWITZERLAND NATIONAL PARK (GERMANY)

Follow the Elbe River through a fantasia of palaces and castles; then cross the Bastei bridge between the dramatic sandstone outcrops of Saxon Switzerland.

SWISS NATIONAL PARK (SWITZERLAND)

This soaring alpine ecosystem cradles many of Europe's most dramatic wildlife and wildflowers, from the high-climbing ibex to the delicate edelweiss.

> " TRAVEL IS FATAL TO PREJUDICE, BIGOTRY, AND NARROW-MINDEDNESS, AND MANY OF OUR PEOPLE NEED IT SORELY ON THESE ACCOUNTS."
>
> —MARK TWAIN

AUSTRALIA'S BARRIER REEF

UNDERWATER WONDERS

You can spend a lifetime exploring the Great Barrier Reef and still not see it all. Sprawling off the east coast of Queensland, Australia, it stretches over 1,250 miles and covers some 135,000 square miles in total. The magnificent structures we see today—the largest structure on Earth built by living organisms—were produced by a slow process played out over millions of years. Home to a staggering diversity of plant and lower animal life, this colorful aquatic ecosystem is also frequented by larger species like dugongs, sea turtles, sharks, and dolphins.

Great Barrier's Opal Reef, shallow and easy to snorkel, can be a crowded destination.

THE GREAT BARRIER REEF MARINE PARK HOSTS 5,000 TYPES OF MOLLUSKS, 1,800 SPECIES OF FISH, 125 KINDS OF SHARKS, AND INNUMERABLE MINIATURE ORGANISMS.

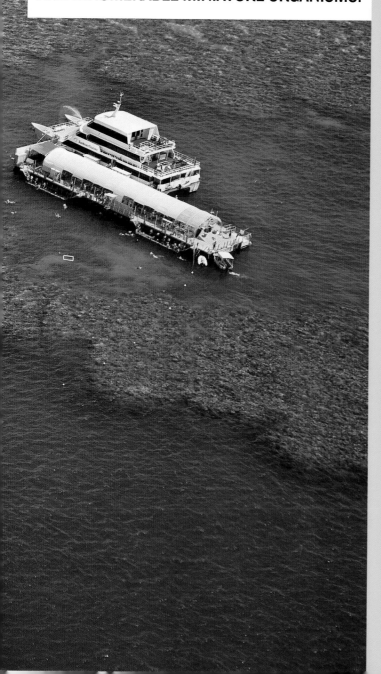

Varieties of
REEF LIFE

DUGONG
These enormous vegetarians are related to manatees, yet with a tail fluked like a whale's. They graze on underwater grasses and can stay underwater as long as six minutes.

CLOWNFISH
Bright orange with three white bars, just over four inches long, these are real-life Nemos. They nestle into color-ful sea anemones, immune from their lethal sting.

GREEN SEA TURTLE
Among the largest sea turtles in the world, these can weigh up to 700 pounds. Herbivorous as adults, the juveniles may also eat crabs, jellyfish, and sponges.

SALTWATER CROCODILE
Opportunistic predators, these creatures can weigh as much as a ton. They lurk under the water, seeking prey at the water's edge, but also swim into open water.

WHITE-BELLIED SEA EAGLE
One of the largest raptors in Australia, this bright white and ash-gray bird's wing-span may measure six feet as it soars over the coastline and inland as well.

HUMPBACK WHALE
These legendary singers feed on krill, plankton, and small fish. Found near the poles in summer, they migrate toward the Equator in winter.

BLACKTIP REEF SHARK
These small sharks glide through lagoons and in and out of coral reefs, their iconic black dorsal fin sticking up above the water.

SMOOTH CAULIFLOWER CORAL
With colors ranging from cream and pink to yellow and green, this coral grows short branches from which tentacles extend at night.

BEST OF @NATGEO

TOP PHOTOS OF TRAVEL

@jenniferhayesig | JENNIFER HAYES
n the Philippines, a whale shark swims to the surface, drawn
by krill that a tour guide dropped into the water.

@irablockphoto | IRA BLOCK
A nun watches the sun set behind a statue of Buddha at the
Fo Guang Shan Buddha Museum in Kaohsiung, Taiwan.

@simonnorfolkstudio | SIMON NORFOLK
The Meidan Emam is a public square in Isfahan, Iran, originally built at the turn of the 17th century.

@stephenwilkes | STEPHEN WILKES
A composite photo shows Paris's Eiffel Tower and Trocadéro
transition from day into night.

> **"THE** MORE PLACES **I SEE AND** EXPERIENCE, **THE BIGGER I REALIZE THE WORLD TO BE."** —ANTHONY BOURDAIN

@paolowoods @gabrielegalimbertiphoto
PAOLO WOODS & GABRIELE GALIMBERTI
A man floats in a rooftop swimming pool, Singapore.

@juanarre | **JUAN ARREDONDO**
Outside St. Peter's Basilica in the Vatican City, a line of visitors waits in the rain to enter the historic church.

@dguttenfelder | **DAVID GUTTENFELDER**
Costumed go-kart drivers prepare for a tour around the streets of Tokyo's Ginza district.

@renan_ozturk | **RENAN OZTURK**
Redwood trees like these hold a special place in the history of the Yurok people, the largest Native American tribe in California.

TOKYO

WHERE OLD MEETS NEW

All eyes will be on Tokyo for the 2020 Summer Olympics. Japan's capital—the world's largest city, population 37 million—can feel energetic one moment and calm the next, and that kind of mishmash is one of the city's endearing qualities. Plan to see some of the old and some of the new, some urban and some rural, and leave room in your itinerary for spontaneity so you can take part in a festival, sample street food, and explore alleyways.

A WORD FROM

Pace of Change Just 26 years—that's the average life span of a Tokyo building. As a result, there are fewer historical landmarks in Tokyo. In places like Kyoto, there are more traditional buildings, but everything that is really vital in Tokyo is so because of its newness and its sense of change. The environment here transforms constantly to make way for the future.

—**DARRYL JINGWEN WEE,** *lead consultant, Tokyo Tomo*

Pedestrians flood the streets of Tokyo's Shibuya shopping district.

What to Do in
TOKYO

1 **WILDLIFE** Off the Izu Islands, teeming with birds, you might see dolphins, humpback whales, and sperm whales.

2 **OFFBEAT** Trails wind through mountain scenery in Tanzawa-Oyama Quasi-National Park. Historical treasures await at the foot of Mount Oyama.

3 **HISTORY** The Edo-Tokyo Museum brings to life Edo-era Tokyo (1603–1868) with reconstructions of Edo housing and dioramas of the city.

4 **MOST ICONIC PLACE** Nothing else encapsulates modern Tokyo like the Shibuya Crossing at night: Crowds cross from six directions against a neon-lit high-rise backdrop.

5 **LATE NIGHT** Unleash your inner diva at karaoke. Rent a booth at a karaoke chain for a private space and order from the long menu of party food and drinks.

6 **NATURAL BEAUTY** Take the 26-hour ferry to the Ogasawara Islands, designated for their rich ecosystems, with 195 endangered bird species and over 400 native plant taxa.

7 **HIP NEIGHBORHOOD** Kichijoji has used clothing stores, record shops, craft breweries, street performers, and the acclaimed anime-themed Ghibli Museum.

8 **TIMELESS GARDEN** Founded in the 1600s, the Koishikawa Korakuen garden is an example of traditional landscaping, with paths, ponds, and gorgeous seasonal foliage.

9 **ART** The Tokyo Metropolitan Art Museum brings art from Japan and the rest of the world together in the heart of the capital.

10 **VIEWS** The Tokyo Skytree is the second tallest structure in the world, with a 360-degree view of the sprawling city from its upper observation deck.

SUSTAINABLE TRAVEL

RESPONSIBLE AND SPECTACULAR: UNIQUE LODGES OF THE WORLD

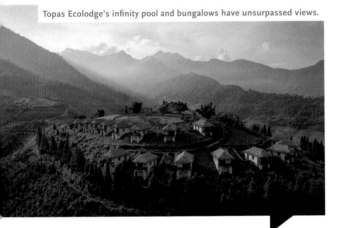

Topas Ecolodge's infinity pool and bungalows have unsurpassed views.

MOUNTAIN

SA PA, VIETNAM
Topas Ecolodge—a cluster of mountain bungalows north of Hanoi—organizes treks into Hoang Lien National Park, a global biodiversity hot spot.

ARISTI, GREECE
Crystal rivers, deep gorges, and soaring peaks combine with village life at Aristi Mountain Resort & Villas.

COCHRANE, CHILE
The Lodge at Valle Chacabuco, in Chile, sits in the heart of Patagonia Park, a conservation initiative protecting nearly 200,000 acres.

HIGH ATLAS MOUNTAINS, MOROCCO
Kasbah du Toubkal is a tribute to Berber culture and hospitality built upon the ruins of an ancient kasbah.

DESERT

NORTHERN TERRITORY, AUSTRALIA
The Longitude 131° lodge is built into the curve of a sand dune, isolated from everything but the raw beauty of Uluru-Kata Tjuta National Park.

GOBI, MONGOLIA
The Three Camel Lodge, a scattering of traditional felt-covered Mongolian tents, celebrates the traditions of Mongolia's nomads while seeking to preserve its awe-inspiring surroundings.

TRUTH OR CONSEQUENCES, NEW MEXICO
Ted Turner's Sierra Grande Lodge is on over half a million acres of private wilderness, part of the conservation crusader's efforts to rewild America.

The spa at Sierra Grande Lodge includes pools fed by hot springs.

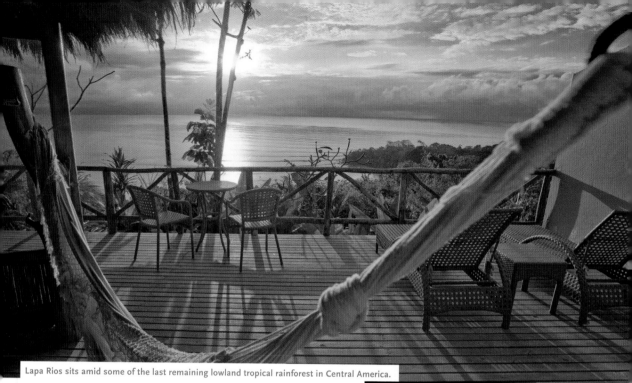

Lapa Rios sits amid some of the last remaining lowland tropical rainforest in Central America.

SEASIDE

OSA PENINSULA, COSTA RICA
The Lapa Rios Lodge has long been a conservation icon in this lowland tropical rainforest, where guests are sure to spot plenty of local wildlife.

FÉLICITÉ, SEYCHELLES
Guests at the Six Senses Zil Pasyon can kayak to Cocos Island National Park. The resort is committed to habitat restoration, ridding the island of invasive species, and propagating rare local plants.

TETIAROA, FRENCH POLYNESIA
The Brando is late actor Marlon Brando's eco-dream brought to life: a private tropical island run on 100 percent renewable energy sources, including solar power and coconut oil.

KENAI PENINSULA BOROUGH, ALASKA
Nestled amid old-growth Sitka spruces at the mouth of a miles-long fjord, the Tutka Bay Lodge is a wilderness lodge with deep roots and a culinary twist.

EARTH DAY EVERY DAY

Tips for Eco-Conscious
TRAVELERS

AVOID THE PLANE
Go to fewer places and stay longer.

GIVE—THE RIGHT WAY
Identify reputable local organizations that work on social welfare programs.

SAY NO TO PLASTIC
Opt for locally purified water in recyclable glass bottles (or drink coconut water), and carry tote bags to use while perusing street markets and shops.

RESEARCH TOUR OPERATORS
Ask about environmentally friendly practices, examples of supporting wildlife or culture, and employment of local guides.

SUPPORT LOCAL ECONOMIES
Purchasing locally made crafts has a direct and positive impact.

REFUSE WILDLIFE PRODUCTS
Be wary of souvenirs that create demand for endangered wildlife products.

MARVELS
OF THE MAYA

SATISFYING AN EXPLORER'S SPIRIT

The tip of the Yucatán Peninsula is best known for the resort city of Cancún. But the region has a wealth of natural and historic attractions away from the tourist traps, including two UNESCO World Heritage sites: Chichén Itzá and the Sian Ka'an Biosphere Reserve. Come for the picturesque beaches and the turquoise cenotes (pools formed by inland sinkholes) but stay for the history—grand ruins of the sprawling Maya Empire, which thrived here for centuries.

Built facing east, Tulum may have originally been called Zama, meaning "dawn."

LIDAR SCANNING TECHNOLOGY RECENTLY DISCOVERED MORE THAN 60,000 MAYA STRUCTURES, BEFORE UNKNOWN, SUGGESTING A CIVILIZATION AS COMPLEX AS ANCIENT GREECE.

OFF THE
BEATEN PATH

PUT ADVENTURE BACK IN YOUR TRAVEL PLANS

CANADA
British Columbia
In British Columbia's Yoho National Park, you can hike, snowshoe, spot wildlife and wild orchids, kayak on Emerald Lake, and explore the Burgess Shale fossil beds without bumping into busloads of tourists.

GREECE
Lousios Gorge
Traverse rugged hiking trails in this region of the Peloponnese peninsula amid towering cypress trees, olive groves, terra-cotta-rooftop towns, medieval villages, and mountaintop monasteries—like the Prodromos Monastery, built precariously into the rock face.

NORTH AMERICA

ATLANTIC OCEAN

PACIFIC OCEAN

SOUTH AMERICA

NICARAGUA
Lake Nicaragua
On a lake ringed by three volcanic peaks, the islets and lakeshores are shrouded in lush tropical forests that harbor myriad colorful bird and butterfly species. Nearby cities are awash with Spanish colonial splendor.

BRAZIL
Amazon Rainforest
Most of the action here takes place overhead. Eco-tourism companies will take you climbing and provide the ropes, harnesses, and hammocks you'll need in the canopy, where you'll observe diverse, thriving flora and fauna.

EGYPT
Sinai Peninsula
Curious about the life of a desert nomad? Book an expedition steeped in Bedouin culture along the Sinai Trail—from camels to desert dunes, slot canyons, and lush desert oases—ending at Mount Catherine, Egypt's highest peak.

MONGOLIA
Gobi Desert
Visit the protected Flaming Cliffs, the site of important paleontological discoveries, including the first nest of dinosaur eggs ever discovered. Hike up and slide down sand dunes, search out petroglyphs, photograph spectacular panoramas, and observe desert wildlife.

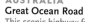

AUSTRALIA
Great Ocean Road
This scenic highway follows the coastline west of Melbourne for 151 miles through Victoria. You'll find coastal beauty like the magnificent Twelve Apostles rock formation, villages and lighthouses, and opportunities to learn about Aboriginal settlements.

MOZAMBIQUE
Vilankulo
After a coastal safari on horseback, sail out to the Bazaruto Archipelago—a 550-square-mile marine reserve recognized by the World Wildlife Fund as a "Gift to the Earth," home to coral reefs and rare manatee-like dugongs.

FOOTBALL'S BEST AWAY TRIPS

BRITAIN'S FOOTBALL GROUNDS ARE FUN DESTINATIONS

Tottenham Hotspur meets Newcastle United.

LONDON

SELHURST PARK, CRYSTAL PALACE

Palace's ground, in Croydon, was designed by Archie Leitch, a Scotsman who designed many stadiums in the early 20th century. In honor of their nickname, the Eagles host one of nature's great predators on match days, a bald eagle called Kayla.

TOTTENHAM HOTSPUR STADIUM, NORTH LONDON

Tottenham Hotspur Stadium opened in 2019 to replace White Hart Lane as the new home for the Spurs in North London. The Lane was a favored ground of away fans, instantly recognizable by its familiar cockerel on a football statue on the main stand. A newer version of the old bird still looks down on the fortunes of the Lilywhites on game day.

SOUTHERN ENGLAND

FRATTON PARK, PORTSMOUTH

This traditional south coast ground, affectionately known as "the Old Girl" by Pompey fans, is the only league ground that is *not* on mainland Britain; it is located on Portsea Island. A consoling or celebratory pint at the Good Companion pub is only a five-minute walk away.

WEMBLEY STADIUM, LONDON

The national football stadium, rebuilt in 2007, is recognizable from afar by its enormous arch. The old stadium witnessed so much history: the 1948 Olympics; Muhammad Ali beating Henry Cooper in 1963; England's World Cup win in 1966; and Live Aid in 1985.

Portsmouth fans celebrate victory.

East Stand of Manchester's Old Trafford

❝ CELTIC VS RANGERS IS ONE OF THE MOST EXPLOSIVE FIXTURES IN WORLD FOOTBALL. YOU CAN SMELL THE ATMOSPHERE, YOU CAN TASTE THE TENSION.❞

—DANNY DYER, ACTOR

Celtic fans show their support.

NORTHERN ENGLAND

OLD TRAFFORD, MANCHESTER

This huge cathedral of football sits between a railway line and a canal, an apt echo of Manchester's industrial past. The old stadium was bombed in World War II but rebuilt thanks to the resolve of its first great Scottish manager, Sir Matt Busby.

ELLAND ROAD, LEEDS

This stadium sits under Beeston Hill, once an industrial area, yet the North York Moors and the Yorkshire Dales are within easy driving distance to add to your trip. A word of advice: The Old Peacock pub is where Leeds fans congregate. Don't venture in wearing your colors!

A WORD FROM

Travel With the Team Football has taken me to places I never otherwise would have visited. And at every destination, you have an instant excuse to fall into conversation with strangers: "You going to the game?" Those five words can lead to some of most interesting days and nights spent with the most unexpected of traveling companions.

— **JUSTIN KAVANAGH,** *travel editor and sportswriter*

SCOTLAND

CELTIC PARK

The home of Glasgow's Celtic Football Club is a strange spiritual and geographic anomaly: a field in Britain that is considered a sacred piece of Irish soil. An Irish patriot laid the first shamrock-imbued turf, brought over from County Donegal, on Celtic's original ground.

MCDIARMID PARK, ST. JOHNSTONE

This small ground at Perth deserves a mention as a true groundbreaker. McDiarmid Park was Britain's first all-seater football stadium. In the season following the 1989 Hillsborough disaster, when a crush of fans resulted in 95 dead, it represented the future of British football parks, with no standing terraces.

ICELAND'S
HOT SPRINGS

IMMERSIONS IN ICELAND

Escape the throngs of tourists and enjoy aquamarine-colored water at Mývatn Nature Baths in northern Iceland. Traveling farther afield means fewer people in the pools and increases your chances of witnessing the aurora borealis. More adventurous travelers will enjoy the challenge of reaching the geothermal pools inside the caves of Grjótagjá—a setting so magical it's appeared in *Game of Thrones*—or the hot stream at Reykjadalur, just an hour outside Reykjavík.

Bathers soak in the hot springs at Mývatn Nature Baths, where sulfur gives the water its blue tint.

ICELAND USES ITS GEOTHERMAL FEATURES FOR HEAT AND POWER GENERATION. IN REYKJAVÍK, 90% OF HOMES CONNECT DIRECTLY TO A GEOTHERMAL DISTRICT HEATING SYSTEM.

The World's Best
HOT SPRINGS

1 **BEPPU, JAPAN** The ultimate *onsen*—Japanese for hot springs, here you'll find eight bathhouses.

2 **DECEPTION ISLAND, ANTARCTICA** An active underwater volcano offers a steamy caldera with penguins nearby.

3 **PÚCON, CHILE** Waterfalls, plunge pools, and a red boardwalk distinguish the Termas Geometricas in the Villarrica National Park.

4 **HOT SPRINGS, ARKANSAS, U.S.A.** Bathe your way into history on Bathhouse Row, the 19th-century main street now a national park.

5 **DUNTON, COLORADO, U.S.A.** Hot springs steam up this luxury destination, a reconstructed ghost town in the Colorado Rockies.

6 **BANFF, BRITISH COLUMBIA, CANADA** Gaze at the Canadian Rockies from the historic bathhouse, established in 1886.

7 **ROTORUA, NEW ZEALAND** The smell of sulfur infuses this region of the North Island, long deemed sacred by the Maori.

8 **PAMUKKALE, TURKEY** Naturally heated water cascades through 17 white limestone terraces, closed to bathers but still magnificent to view.

9 **MAREMMA, ITALY** Soak in mineral springs that once comforted Roman generals in Tuscany's Terme di Saturnia.

10 **BANJAR, BALI** Mineral-rich water spews from the mouths of intricately carved *naga*, mythical serpent demigods.

FURTHER

FOR A BETTER VIEW

Even earthbound spectators feel the frisson of triumph when an athlete like Pete Thompson accomplishes a feat like this, walking barefoot along a 411-foot-long highline off Mushroom Rock, a favorite lookout point above Carbondale, Colorado. Extreme sports—from classics like surfing and skateboarding to new high-tech ventures like wing suiting and zorbing—took off after ESPN's first Extreme Games in 1995. Now X Games happen all around the world, with millions of video viewers. Meanwhile, solitary achievers like Thompson push boundaries as well.

Highliner Pete Thompson appears to balance between the two peaks of Colorado's Mount Sopris.

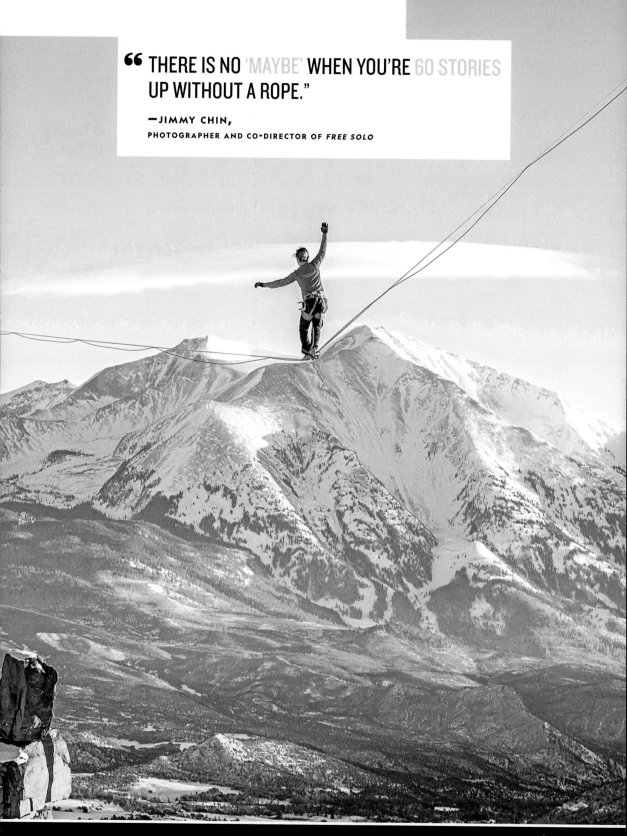

"THERE IS NO 'MAYBE' **WHEN YOU'RE** 60 STORIES **UP WITHOUT A ROPE."**

—JIMMY CHIN,
PHOTOGRAPHER AND CO-DIRECTOR OF *FREE SOLO*

THIS PLANET & BEYOND

PLANET EARTH | **EARTH, SEA & SKY**

Monsoon clouds hover above the Indian Ocean surrounding Madagascar.

THE SOLAR SYSTEM | THE UNIVERSE & BEYOND

QUIZ MASTER

Planetary Genius? How much do you know about our planet—Earth, sea, and sky? How about the solar system, universe, and beyond? Test your knowledge, and then read on for answers and general amazement.

—**CARA SANTA MARIA,** *Our Favorite Nerd*

IN WHAT YEAR WAS THE FIRST KNOWN MAP OF THE MOON PUBLISHED?

p96

ABOUT HOW MANY YEARS AGO DID *HOMO SAPIENS* FIRST APPEAR ON EARTH?

IN WHAT YEAR DID MOUNT ST. HELENS ERUPT MOST RECENTLY?

p126

p124

THE BIG AND LITTLE DIPPER STAR PATTERNS ARE ALSO KNOWN BY NAMES THAT TRANSLATE TO WHICH ANIMAL?

p108

p130

WHICH U.S. NATIONAL PARK CONTAINS A SUPERVOLCANO?

HOW MANY DWARF PLANETS ARE ESTIMATED IN OUR SOLAR SYSTEM?

IN WHAT YEAR WAS THE HUBBLE SPACE TELESCOPE LAUNCHED INTO ORBIT?

p108

p127

WHICH OF THESE MINERALS IS HARDER: SERPENTINE **OR** QUARTZ?

p147

WHAT IS THE **PLANET** IN OUR SOLAR **SYSTEM** NEAREST TO **THE SUN?**

p128

ABOUT HOW FAR FROM **EARTH IS THE** SUPERMASSIVE **BLACK HOLE** AT THE CENTER OF THE **MILKY WAY?**

p114

WHAT IS THE NAME FOR THE STRONGEST PART OF A HURRICANE?

p106

WHAT IS THE **NAME OF** THE TALLEST MOUNTAIN ON **MARS?**

p134

p152

IN WHICH DECADE WAS THE THEORY OF **DARK MATTER FIRST** INTRODUCED?

WHICH METEOROLOGICAL PHENOMENA IS TIM SAMARAS FAMOUS FOR STUDYING?

p110

EARTH SCIENCE
TIME LINE

4.6 to 2.3 BYA

■ **4.6 bya***

Planet Earth forms from the material that built the rest of the solar system.

■ **4.5 bya**

Earth's moon forms out of space debris.

■ **4.3 bya**

Liquid water appears on Earth.

■ **3.8 bya**

Single-celled life emerges on Earth.

■ **3 bya**

Earth's continental masses form.

■ **2.5–2.3 bya**

Oxygen levels in the Earth's atmosphere rise.

*** billion years ago**

2.3 BYA to 400 MYA

■ **2.1 bya**

More complex multicellular organisms evolve.

■ **720–635 mya***

The temperature on Earth falls, and the entire planet is covered in ice.

■ **541 mya**

Most major animal groups evolve in an event known as the Cambrian explosion.

■ **520 mya**

Animals with bilateral symmetry first flourish on Earth.

■ **470 mya**

Plant life first appears on land.

*** million years ago**

400 to 200 MYA

■ **360 mya**

Amphibious life emerges from the water to live on land.

■ **251 mya**

Massive numbers of marine and land species die off in the Permian extinction, the largest mass extinction in history.

■ **250 mya**

A single supercontinent called Pangaea emerges.

■ **240 mya**

The first dinosaurs appear on Earth.

■ **200 mya**

The supercontinent Pangaea breaks up into separate landmasses.

200 MYA to 20,000 YA

■ **130 mya**

Flowering plants, the most diverse group of land plants, emerge.

■ **65 mya**

Dinosaurs go extinct in the aftermath of the Chicxulub asteroid impact.

■ **2.6 mya**

Continents arrive at roughly their modern positions and a pattern of glacial and interglacial periods emerges.

■ **200,000 ya***

Homo sapiens first appear, and modern humans emerge.

*** years ago**

| 20,000 YA to AD 1 | AD 1 to 1800 | 1800 to 1920 | 1920 to PRESENT |

■ 11,700 ya
The Holocene,
the current geological
age, begins.

■ 10,000 ya
The last major
ice age ends.

■ ca 499 BC
Indian scientist Aryabhata
proposes that Earth
rotates on its axis.

■ 240 BC
Eratosthenes calculates
the circumference
of the Earth.

■ ca 1088
Chinese scientist
Shen Kuo first describes
a magnetic compass
used for navigation.

■ 1490s
Leonardo da Vinci begins
filling notebooks with
theories on astronomy,
Earth, physics, and more.

■ 1543
Copernicus publishes
ideas on heliocentrism.

■ 1595
Gerardus Mercator's
atlas of the world
is first published.

■ 1815
Explosion of Mount
Tambora temporarily
changes Earth's climate.

■ 1831
English explorer
James Ross locates
the position of the
north magnetic pole.

■ 1851
Léon Foucault constructs
Foucault's pendulum
to show Earth's rotation.

■ 1912
Alfred Wegener first
describes the theory
of continental drift.

■ 1913
Charles Fabry and Henri
Buisson discover
the ozone layer.

■ 1935
Charles Richter invents
the Richter scale
to measure earthquake
intensity.

■ 1960s
Scientists first describe
plate tectonics.

■ 1960
Jacques Piccard and Don
Walsh are first to visit
the deepest point in the
ocean, Challenger Deep.

■ 1970
The inaugural Earth Day
is held on April 22.

■ 2017
One of the largest
icebergs on record breaks
off from Antarctica's
Larsen C ice shelf.

CLARIFYING
CLIMATE

TO UNDERSTAND CLIMATE CHANGE, WE MUST UNDERSTAND CLIMATE

The climate of any location on Earth depends on latitude, elevation above sea level, proximity to the ocean, and the circulation patterns in the atmosphere and ocean. This map displays the Köppen-Geiger system of climate zones based on seasonal temperatures and precipitation.

WARMING ALPS
Climate change is expected to transform much of the European Alps from a snow to a warm temperate climate by the end of the 21st century.

ARC

NORTH AMERICA

ROCKY MOUNTAINS

TREES AT RISK
In the northern Rocky Mountains as summers get longer and hotter, trees at high altitudes will be especially vulnerable to drought, wildfire, and destructive insects.

CARIBBEAN HURRICANES
The Gulf Stream's warm ocean water intensifies the hurricanes that pass over it, often tracking the storms toward mainland North America.

PACIFIC OCEAN

ATLANTIC OCEAN

ANDES

SOUTH AMERICA

RAIN SHADOWS
The Rocky Mountains and Andes form the spine of the Americas, influencing climate by stopping moist ocean air from reaching the interior.

EXPANDING DESERT
In Algeria, the desert has gradually expanded and displaced much of the warm temperate region where most people live.

SOUTHERN AFRICA
The position of the island of Madagascar reduces the impact of wet trade winds on the mainland coast and lessens the chance of tropical cyclones landing there.

DISAPPEARING ICE
Scientists expect the largest shifts in climate zones in the 21st century to replace about 1% of polar zones with warmer snow zones.

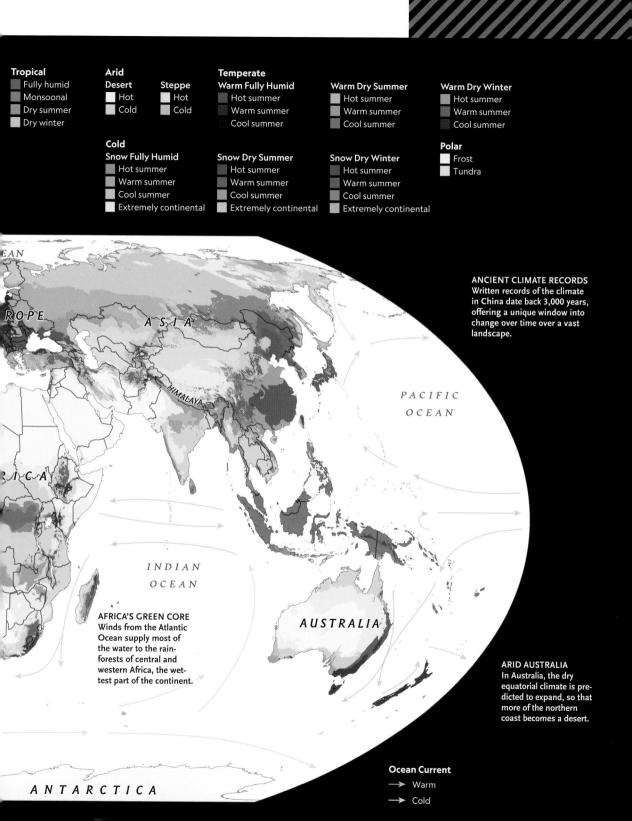

Tropical
- Fully humid
- Monsoonal
- Dry summer
- Dry winter

Arid
Desert
- Hot
- Cold

Steppe
- Hot
- Cold

Temperate
Warm Fully Humid
- Hot summer
- Warm summer
- Cool summer

Warm Dry Summer
- Hot summer
- Warm summer
- Cool summer

Warm Dry Winter
- Hot summer
- Warm summer
- Cool summer

Cold
Snow Fully Humid
- Hot summer
- Warm summer
- Cool summer
- Extremely continental

Snow Dry Summer
- Hot summer
- Warm summer
- Cool summer
- Extremely continental

Snow Dry Winter
- Hot summer
- Warm summer
- Cool summer
- Extremely continental

Polar
- Frost
- Tundra

EAN

ROPE

ASIA

PACIFIC
OCEAN

HIMALAYA

RICA

INDIAN
OCEAN

AUSTRALIA

ANTARCTICA

ANCIENT CLIMATE RECORDS
Written records of the climate in China date back 3,000 years, offering a unique window into change over time over a vast landscape.

AFRICA'S GREEN CORE
Winds from the Atlantic Ocean supply most of the water to the rainforests of central and western Africa, the wettest part of the continent.

ARID AUSTRALIA
In Australia, the dry equatorial climate is predicted to expand, so that more of the northern coast becomes a desert.

Ocean Current
→ Warm
→ Cold

DROUGHT

A WORLD WITHOUT WATER

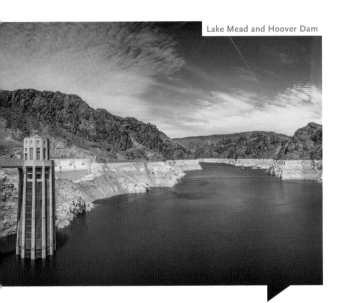

Lake Mead and Hoover Dam

DEFINING DROUGHT

DISAPPEARING WATER

On a planet where water is life, drought can be deadly. On almost every continent, cities, states, and countries are struggling to find water. As climate change alters rain patterns, seasonal monsoons, and heat waves, water is becoming harder to find. Droughts are getting worse. At Lake Mead, along the Colorado River, the sprawling reservoir is ringed by a bleached line of barren rock marking how far its once flowing waters have fallen. In South America, Bolivia's second largest lake, Lake Poopó, disappeared completely, transformed into a barren salt flat. In Australia, vast reaches of the island continent fell under the worst drought in living memory.

LOSING RESOURCES

NOT A DROP TO DRINK

In Cape Town, South Africa, the drought is so intense and reservoirs have gotten so low the government is considering radical measures. They even predicted "Day Zero," saying that when the reservoirs reached 13.5 percent capacity, the city would severely limit water for its four million people. That day never came. For the time being, dam levels have risen in Cape Town, allowing the city to ease restrictions, but experts believe such rationing is now inevitable. And Cape Town is not alone: Sections of Mexico City limit water use to only part of the day, while Jakarta is literally sinking as it drains the freshwater aquifer beneath the city. Half the world could face similar stresses by 2030, according to UN estimates.

Aerial view of Mexico City

BY THE TIME THE COLORADO RIVER REACHES MEXICO, MOST OF ITS WATER HAS BEEN SIPHONED OFF TO SUPPLY THIRSTY U.S. CITIES OR TO BE USED FOR IRRIGATION OR HYDROPOWER.

The Colorado River Delta in Mexico is often too dry to flow into the Pacific Ocean.

CHANGING CLIMATE

CHANGING RAIN

Changing weather patterns mean that farmers can no longer rely on traditional wisdom. The once predictable wet and dry seasons powered by the tropical monsoon rains have become erratic. A warming atmosphere holds more water, which means storms can be more intense. Warming oceans power more intense storms and hurricanes. Record-long droughts are followed by record rains and snows, creating a weather whiplash that stresses natural and man-made systems even more. Estimates say that this whiplash will become more likely as the climate continues to warm. Water planners who have worked to solve the problems of the past are staring into an uncertain future.

GETTING READY

PREPARING FOR DROUGHT

In Cape Town, conservation efforts fended off "Day Zero" as the city cut back on its water consumption. The average family cut its consumption in half, and farmers and other growers cut their consumption as well. Desalination plants designed to create drinkable water from seawater also help reduce the threat from future droughts for the South African city. Another solution might be found in Israel, where new technology helps reuse 85 percent of wastewater and policies have helped shift the agricultural focus away from water-hungry crops like cotton. Whatever the metric, more droughts are coming, and Day Zero may not be far away.

READING
THE CLOUDS

Looking Up Though we've always had clouds above, we are still coming up with new ways to categorize and name them. Changes in technology, especially the sharing of photos, is also leading to new identifications.

FAIR-WEATHER CUMULUS
Small, puffy, white

CUMULIFORM
Puffy, humid air condensing

ORTHOGRAPHIC
Precipitation near mountains

CIRRUS
Thin and transparent

CIRROCUMULUS
White patches of high clouds

CIRROSTRATUS
High and thin, hazy

ALTOCUMULUS
Puffy clouds with darker patches

LENTICULAR
Lens-shaped, over mountains

ALTOCUMULUS CASTELLANUS
Tall, narrow

STRATOCUMULUS
Spread across large areas

STRATUS
Featureless gray layers

ALTOSTRATUS
Thin, gray, highest sheet-type

NIMBOSTRATUS
Low, dark, gloomy

CUMULUS CONGESTUS
Cauliflower-like

CUMULONIMBUS
Anvil shape, brings thunderstorms

ALTOCUMULUS MAMMATUS
Hanging pouches

THE INTERNATIONAL CLOUD ATLAS RECOGNIZED A NEW CLOUD TYPE IN 2017: THE ASPERITAS, DAPPLED LIKE THE SEA SEEN FROM UNDERWATER.

Lightning begins as static charges in a rain cloud.

TOP TEN

Lightning
HOT SPOTS

1 **LAKE MARACAIBO**
Venezuela

2 **KAHUZI-BIEGA NATIONAL PARK**
Democratic Republic of the Congo

3 **SHABUNDA**
Democratic Republic of the Congo

4 **CÁCERES**
Colombia

5 **WALIKALE**
Democratic Republic of the Congo

6 **DAGGAR**
Pakistan

7 **EL TARRA**
Colombia

8 **NGUTI**
Cameroon

9 **BUTEMBO**
Democratic Republic of the Congo

10 **BOENDE**
Democratic Republic of the Congo

THUNDERSTRUCK

COUNTING THE FLASHES

Satellite data analyzed in 2016 identified 500 lightning "hot spots" around the world: the places where lightning flashes and strikes most often. Of those 500, more than half are in Africa, but the place that sees the most lightning—almost every night of the year—is Lake Maracaibo in Venezuela, South America's largest lake by area.

COMBATING A BLAZE

THE COMPLICATED BATTLE AGAINST WILDFIRES

Fighting wildfire is often likened to a military campaign, with personnel deployed strategically on the ground and air support striking from above. Planning an attack, as here in the northern Rockies, firefighters weigh three factors that drive the course of any blaze: topography, weather, and the type of fuel in the line of fire.

1 Fires can spread especially rapidly up slopes and suddenly explode up canyons, which act as natural chimneys. Southern slopes, sunnier and drier, are more likely to burn than northern exposures.

2 Dramatic winds brought on by cold fronts and storms can shift a fire's direction or cause flare-ups. Low humidity and high temperatures make fuel, especially grass and accumulated underbrush, drier and quicker to burn.

3 Air tankers and helicopters, called in by coordinators on the ground, drop water or chemical fire retardant.

4 A fire crew's priority is to find a man-made or natural barrier to the fire's advance—a road or a stream—and from that anchor point dig a perimeter fire line to contain the blaze.

5 Long days are spent digging a fire line down to bare earth, even if a bulldozer is available to help. The line is banked to catch rolling debris.

6 Drip torches are used to burn out fuel between the fire line and the fire, halting its advance.

7 Felling dead trees prevents them from collapsing across the fire line or on firefighters and helps keep flames from climbing into the canopy.

8 Homes that have edged into forest fire territory can't be guaranteed protection. And even if fire is stopped before reaching a house, airborne embers can drift through vents and burn it down from the inside out.

A WORD FROM

Devastating Embers A fire acts like a living organism. The same way a plant spreads its seeds, a fire creates wind to spread its embers. A fire causes hot air and smoke to rise rapidly, pulling in air along the ground to replace it. This creates a wind that will push the fire along, which creates a self-perpetuating cycle of fire that is impossible to stop.

—**MARK THIESSEN,** *photographer and wildland firefighter*

HURRICANES

SWIRLING STORMS OF DESTRUCTION

Hurricanes are massive storm systems, sometimes broadening to more than a hundred miles across and packing damaging winds and intense amounts of water. In 2018, it was estimated that Hurricane Florence was carrying 18 trillion gallons of water in its rain bands, enough water to fill the Chesapeake Bay, and several North Carolina towns reported more than 30 inches of rain. Hurricane Harvey in 2017 held 25 trillion gallons. Like the ocean currents, hurricanes move heat from the warm tropics up toward the poles. They wreak chaos and can leave utter destruction in their wakes, but they also help maintain the thermal balance in tropical oceans.

ANTI-CYCLONE
High above the eye of the storm, an atmospheric anti-cyclone rotates in opposition to the hurricane below. This acts as an exhaust pipe for the warm winds spiraling up inside the eye wall.

EYE WALL
The eye wall is the strongest part of the storm; winds here can reach over 200 miles per hour.

NEGATIVE SURGE
Just as the winds push the ocean higher in a storm surge, they can also "blow away the ocean" in a negative surge, lowering tides when the winds aim seaward.

Tropical Storm Lowell strengthens into a hurricane in the Pacific Ocean.

HURRICANE WILMA IN 2005 IS THE MOST INTENSE ATLANTIC HURRICANE RECORDED SO FAR, WITH WIND SPEEDS REACHING 185 MILES AN HOUR. IT CAUSED AN ESTIMATED $34.4 BILLION IN DAMAGES.

SPIN
Hurricane spin depends on the Coriolis effect caused by Earth's rotation. Northern Hemisphere hurricanes rotate counterclockwise, and Southern Hemisphere hurricanes rotate clockwise.

EYE
The calm eye is the center of the storm, a central core of warm air that draws heat from the ocean to create intense low pressure that powers the devastating winds.

STORM SURGE
A hurricane's powerful winds can push the ocean over 10 feet higher than the highest tide, leading to devastating flooding, erosion, and property damage.

VOLCANOES

WHEN EARTH ERUPTS

When we talk about volcanoes in the continental U.S., we probably think of Mount St. Helens, the "Mount Fuji of America," which erupted spectacularly in May 1980. We are less likely to think of Yellowstone, even with its geysers and hot mud, because although it is surrounded by mountains, it is not one itself. But our most famous national park sits squarely atop one of Earth's biggest volcanoes—a supervolcano—and it is not extinct. Volcanoes, as we tend to imagine them, form mountains. Supervolcanoes erase them.

Sleeping Giants

Beneath Yellowstone is a hellish column of superheated rock— mostly solid, some viscous, some molten. Experts say three major blasts, bigger than most known prehistoric eruptions, have shaken Yellowstone in its two million years atop the plume. The smallest of these ejected 280 times the volume of what Mount St. Helens projected.

The U.S. Geological Survey's Yellowstone Volcano Observatory monitors sensors and satellites, looking for changes in activity. Despite rumors, a supereruption like the one illustrated on the facing page is not imminent. For its part, the USGS puts the rough yearly odds of another massive Yellowstone blast at one in 730,000.

CALDERA
Buoyed by an expanding magma chamber, the caldera, formed by the last major eruption, has risen as much as 2.8 inches a year over the past decade.

PLUME
Beneath the caldera, a vast rocky zone of primordial heat emanates from the mantle. This plume feeds a magma chamber brimming with volcanic fuel just a few miles below the surface.

HOT POCKETS
Current seismic data and geological conditions suggest there may be smaller pockets of hot rock associated with the Yellowstone plume.

POP!

MOVIES STARRING VOLCANOES

- *The Last Days of Pompeii* (1935)
- *Stromboli* (1950)
- *Krakatoa: East of Java* (1969)
- *St. Helens* (1981)
- *Joe Versus the Volcano* (1990)
- *Dante's Peak* (1997)
- *Volcano* (1997)
- *Supervolcano* (2005)
- *Disaster Zone: Volcano in New York* (2006)
- *Volcano Zombies* (2014)
- *Pompeii* (2014)
- *Ixcanul* (2015)

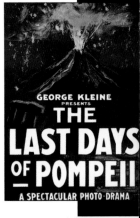

GEORGE KLEINE
PRESENTS
THE
LAST DAYS
OF POMPEII
A SPECTACULAR PHOTO-DRAMA

HOW DOES IT HAPPEN?

BEFORE THE ERUPTION Warning signs may appear years in advance. Pressure builds from below, driving seismic activity and doming of the land over the hot spot.

THE EARTH FRACTURES Gas-filled magma explodes upward; ash and debris soon rain down across hundreds of miles. Fiery ash flows clog rivers and carpet landscapes near and far.

ERUPTIONS CONTINUE Periodic blasts go on for weeks or even months, emitting pollutants and causing acid rain. Eventually, the land collapses and a new caldera is born.

World's Deadliest ERUPTIONS

1 **TAMBORA, INDONESIA**
Apr. 10, 1815: 92,000 killed
Largest in recorded history, with ejecta volume of 12 mi³

2 **KRAKATAU, INDONESIA**
Aug. 26, 1883: 36,417 killed
Ash layer lowered temperatures and affected global climate.

3 **PELÉE, MARTINIQUE**
May 8, 1902: 29,025 killed
Most deaths direct result of eruption and not tsunami, etc.

4 **RUIZ, COLOMBIA**
Nov. 13, 1985: 25,000 killed
Mudflows caused by melting snow and ice buried thousands.

5 **UNZEN, JAPAN**
May 21, 1792: 14,300 killed
Eruption followed by earthquake, landslide, and tsunami

6 **LAKI, ICELAND**
June 8, 1783: 9,350 killed
Lava flows and explosions continued for eight months.

7 **KELUD, INDONESIA**
May 19, 1919: 5,110 killed
Still active with hundreds killed in 1951, 1966, 1990, and 2014

8 **GALUNGGUNG, INDONESIA**
Oct. 8, 1882: 4,011 killed
Crater lake ejected boiling water and mud during eruptions.

9 **VESUVIUS, ITALY**
Dec. 16, 1631: 3,500 killed
Fatal pyroclastic flows followed a 30-mile-high cloud.

10 **VESUVIUS, ITALY**
79: 3,360 killed
Ash-covered Pompeii is famous for perfectly preserved victims.

TIM SAMARAS
STORM CHASER

HEAD FIRST INTO THE STORM

When tornadoes, one of nature's most powerful and least predictable disasters, come down from the sky, most people run away—but Tim Samaras went to work. Samaras faced the devastating force of a tornado more than 125 times in his life. But he wasn't a thrill seeker; he was a scientist. Under pelting hail and blinding rain, he braved the winds and flying debris to better understand the storm and, with that understanding, to save lives.

Tim Samaras deploys probes as a tornado approaches in South Dakota.

With winds almost 50 percent stronger than the strongest hurricanes, a tornado's power and potential to level towns and destroy lives is unmatched. The best hope for survival is to hide before it hits, but forecasters can give only 13 minutes' warning before a strike. Samaras's life goal was to increase the warning time for a tornado and, with it, the chance for survival. That meant he had to see into the heart of a twister and place himself in harm's way.

UNDERSTANDING TORNADOES

Storms were never far from Samaras's thoughts. He had a gift for reading the skies and understanding the behavior of storms. Despite never graduating from college, he was a gifted engineer. When the National Oceanic and Atmospheric Administration requested designs for a probe that could record data inside a tornado, Samaras combined his passions. After several failed attempts, he and his team succeeded when they deployed a hardened pressure sensor, nicknamed the "Turtle," in front of a tornado just 82 seconds before the twister struck. It was a meteorological milestone.

Samaras didn't take risk lightly. But for all his success, tornadoes remain unpredictable. On May 31, 2013, the tornado that Samaras was chasing suddenly doubled in size, stretching over 2.5 miles wide, the largest ever recorded. Samaras, his son, and their cameraman were caught inside, and all three perished. His life ended, but his work continues as storm chasers continue to travel across the plains every year to better understand these erratic, deadly storms.

> " I'M NOT SURE EXACTLY WHY I CHASE STORMS. PERHAPS IT'S TO WITNESS THE INCREDIBLE BEAUTY OF WHAT MOTHER NATURE CAN CREATE."

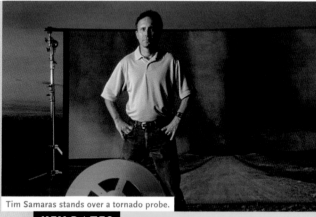

Tim Samaras stands over a tornado probe.

KEY DATES

Tim Samaras's
MILESTONES

1980
Begins selling storm footage to local news stations

1997
Builds first probe to gather data inside a tornado

1998
Founds the National Storm Chasers Convention

2003
First successful deployment of the tornado probe

2005
Named National Geographic Emerging Explorer

2009
Hosts *Storm Chasers* on the Discovery Channel

2013
Photographs lightning strike in slow motion at 150,000 frames per second

2013
Dies after being caught in the El Reno Tornado in Oklahoma

BEST OF @NATGEO

TOP PHOTOS OF EXTREME WEATHER

@ladzinski | KEITH LADZINSKI
A supercell thunderstorm gathers over a small town in Oklahoma. These powerful storms can reach nearly 70,000 feet tall.

@randyolson | RANDY OLSON
In the lower Omo River Valley in Ethiopia, water is scarce
because of an upstream dam and periods of drought.

@franslanting | FRANS LANTING
Flames overtake mountains near Santa Barbara, California,
in what was among the largest fires in the state's modern
history.

@chamiltonjames | CHARLIE HAMILTON JAMES
A rainbow appears in airborne ice crystals over Jackson
Hole, Wyoming, where below-zero temperatures are com-
mon in the winter.

> ❝ A CHANGE IN THE WEATHER IS SUFFICIENT TO CREATE THE WORLD AND OURSELVES. ❞
>
> —MARCEL PROUST, FRENCH NOVELIST

@yamashitaphoto | MICHAEL YAMASHITA
Heavy snowfall blankets a quiet forest on Hokkaido, the northernmost and coldest of Japan's main islands.

@franciscop777 | FRANCISCO J. PEREZ
A composite of long-exposure photographs shows a summer thunderstorm raging over the Grand Canyon.

@ladzinski | KEITH LADZINSKI
A tornado touches ground in Wyoming. Most twisters last for less than 10 minutes, but their destruction can be long lasting.

@carltonward | CARLTON WARD
A storm approaches Biscayne National Park in Florida. Afternoon showers are common on humid summer afternoons.

MINERALS
REVEALED

How Hard Is It? More than 4,000 naturally occurring minerals have been found on Earth. Geologists classify them according to hardness, using the Mohs' scale (opposite). All rocks are made of mixtures of minerals.

JASPER
Hardness: 6–7

FELDSPAR
Hardness: 6–7

OLIVINE
Hardness: 6.5–7

GARNET
Hardness: 6.5–7.5

EPIDOTE
Hardness: 6–7

STAUROLITE
Hardness: 7–7.5

TOURMALINE
Hardness: 7–7.5

PYROXENE
Hardness: 5–6.5

TALC
Hardness: 1

HORNBLENDE
Hardness: 5–6

BIOTITE
Hardness: 2.5–3

MUSCOVITE
Hardness: 2–2.5

KAOLINITE
Hardness: 2–2.5

SERPENTINE
Hardness: 3–6

DOLOMITE
Hardness: 3.5–4

CALCITE
Hardness: 3

GYPSUM & ANHYDRITE
Hardness: 2 & 3–3.5

MALACHITE
Hardness: 3.5–4

CHALCOPYRITE
Hardness: 3.5–4

GALENA
Hardness: 2.5–3

PYRITE
Hardness: 6–6.5

FLUORITE
Hardness: 4

MAGNETITE
Hardness: 5.5

HEMATITE
Hardness: 5–6

QUARTZ
Hardness: 7

Marble rates between 3 and 5 on the Mohs' scale.

MARBLE

FROM ANCIENT SEAS TO KITCHEN COUNTERS

Marble countertops, statues, and columns dot the landscapes, filling our homes and museums. Every piece of the iconic stone, so common today, began in the fires and fissures of Earth's molten seams, or volcanic hot spots. Marble is a metamorphic rock. It begins as the crystallized calcium remnants of deep sea corals or other creatures. In the fiery seams of Earth's tectonic plates, or volcanic magma chambers, new crystals begin to form, and the metamorphosis begins. The more this crystallization spreads, the larger and stronger the marble becomes. Eventually vast marble beds form, containing millions of tons of the soft stone ready to be shaped. It comes in colors from pure white to pink, yellow, and black, depending on the mineral content.

IN ADDITION TO ITS FAMILIAR USES IN SCULPTING AND ARCHITECTURE, GROUND MARBLE IS SOMETIMES ADDED TO ANIMAL FEED AS A SOURCE OF CALCIUM.

Mohs' Mineral
HARDNESS SCALE

1 — **Easily scratched by fingernail, feels soapy or greasy** *Example: talc*

2 — **Can be scratched by fingernail** Gold, 2.5–3.0. *Example: gypsum*

3 — **Can be scratched by copper coin** Copper penny, 3.2. *Example: calcite*

4 — **Can be scratched by knife** Platinum, 4–4.5; iron, 4–5. *Example: fluorite*

5 — **Scratched by knife with difficulty** Pocketknife, 5.1; plate glass, 5.5. *Example: apatite*

6 — **Can be scratched by steel file but not knife; scratches glass with difficulty** Steel needle, 6.5. *Example: feldspar*

7 — **Scratches window glass** *Example: quartz*

8 — **Scratches glass very easily** Varieties of beryl, 7.5–8. *Example: topaz, cubic zirconia, emerald, aquamarine*

9 — **Cuts glass** *Example: corundum (ruby and sapphire)*

10 — **Cuts glass so easily that it is used as a glass cutter** *Example: diamond*

SAVING PRISTINE SEAS

THERE ARE PLACES IN THE WORLD WHERE MARINE LIFE ABOUNDS

National Geographic Explorer-in-Residence Enric Sala launched the Pristine Seas project in 2008 to explore and help save the last wild places in the ocean. Since then, thanks to this effort, 21 marine reserves have been created and more than two million square miles of ocean have been protected.

THE OCEAN COVERS 70 PERCENT OF THE PLANET, YET ONLY 5 PERCENT OF THE OCEAN IS PROTECTED.

Manta rays glide through the pristine waters of Palau, in the South Pacific.

RUSSIAN ARCTIC NATIONAL PARK

ARCTIC OCEAN

Last Ice Area
Canada, *Greenland*
(Denmark)

ASIA

PACIFIC OCEAN

NORTH AMERICA

EUROPE

Azores
Portugal

Selvagens Islands
Portugal

AFRICA

REVILLAGIGEDO NATIONAL PARK

SEAMOUNTS MARINE MANAGEMENT AREA

PACIFIC REMOTE ISLANDS MARINE NATIONAL MONUMENT

CLIPPERTON MARINE PROTECTED AREA

PALAU NATIONAL MARINE SANCTUARY

ATLANTIC OCEAN

MALPELO FAUNA AND FLORA SANCTUARY

GABON MARINE PROTECTED AREA NETWORK

INDIAN OCEAN

GALÁPAGOS MARINE RESERVE

SOUTHERN LINE ISLANDS PROTECTED AREA

Ascension
U.K.

SEYCHELLES MARINE PROTECTED AREA

NIUE MARINE PROTECTED AREA

PACIFIC OCEAN

MOTU MOTIRO HIVA MARINE PARK

SOUTH AMERICA

Southern Mozambique

AUSTRALIA

NATURAL PARK OF THE CORAL SEA

Rapa Iti
France

NAZCA-DESVENTURADAS MARINE PARK

Tristan da Cunha
U.K.

JUAN FERNÁNDEZ MARINE PARK

PITCAIRN ISLANDS MARINE RESERVE

DIEGO RAMÍREZ MARINE PARK

NAMUNCURÁ-BURDWOOD BANK II

ROSS SEA MARINE PROTECTED AREA

YAGANES

Antarctic Peninsula

ANTARCTICA

Pristine Seas

■ Protected area

● Other expedition

A WORD FROM

A Spiritual Experience We go to the pristine places in the ocean to try to understand the ecosystems, to try to measure or count fish and sharks and see how these places are different from the places we know. But the best feeling is this biophilia that E. O. Wilson talks about, where humans have this sense of awe and wonder in front of untamed nature ... If it were not for these places that show hope, I don't think I could continue doing this job.

—ENRIC SALA, *marine ecologist*

VOLCANIC ISLANDS

BORN FROM LAVA

Earth is constantly changing. Volcanic eruptions can reshape shorelines and create new islands, while ocean waves can erode and strip them away. In 2018, Hawaii briefly gained a new island as lava from the Kilauea volcano filled in over 700 acres of what used to be open ocean. Across the Pacific, the Polynesian island of Hunga Tonga-Hunga Ha'ipi, which erupted into existence in 2014, fought the slow erosion of the tides. NASA originally gave the island just six months to live before erosion stripped it below the waves, but new research estimates it may survive as long as 30 years.

The Kilauea eruption briefly formed a tiny islet in Hawaii.

The World's
VOLCANIC ISLANDS

■ HAWAII
Deep below the Pacific Ocean, submarine vents grew into volcanoes, building up the Hawaiian Islands over millions of years through continuous eruptions of lava. Today, the islands rise more than 10,000 feet above sea level.

■ TRISTAN DA CUNHA
This small island in the southern Atlantic Ocean measures just under 80 square miles; it may well be the most remote inhabited island in the world. The island is home to Queen Mary's Peak, which last erupted in 1961.

■ KRAKATAU
This massive volcano in Indonesia was the site of one of the largest and deadliest eruptions in recorded history in 1883. The sound of the eruption could be heard more than 2,800 miles away, and more than 34,000 people were killed.

■ SANTORINI
This well-known travel destination in the Aegean Sea is a volcanic lagoon, its rocky cliffs encircling a powerful shield volcano. The island's geological history is apparent in these cliffs, which show the layers of solidified lava built up over the course of many eruptions.

■ ICELAND
Located along a tectonic plate boundary, Iceland is one of the most active volcanic regions in the world. The island formed as the North American and Eurasian plates moved apart, and lava filled the gaps left between. The plates are still in motion, which means earthquakes and eruptions are common in Iceland today.

WINTER SKY

FINDING ORION

The winter sky hosts some of the brightest stars in the night sky, including the recognizable and popular constellation of Orion.

Orion: Hunter, Shepherd, Farmer

In the Northern Hemisphere, Orion is lord of the winter sky, his distinctive shape filled with bright stars and other astronomical sights. The constellation is named for a famed hunter of Greek mythology, but it is not the only story associated with this star pattern. Other cultures have seen the constellation as representing a shepherd or a harvesting scythe, because it first appears in the northern sky during harvest times.

Orion features two of the brightest stars in the sky. To the north, at the hunter's shoulder, is Betelgeuse, the ninth brightest star, with a diameter larger than the orbit of Earth and a mass of 20 suns. To the south Rigel, the sixth brightest, is also quite large (17 solar masses) and, thanks to its proximity to the Equator, was one of the "nautical stars" that sailors would use to locate themselves on the ocean. But the real action, astronomically speaking, is in Orion's belt and the "sword" that hangs from it. There you will find the Orion Nebula, one of the few easily seen with the naked eye.

STELLAR MAGNITUDES

● −0.5 and brighter	● 2.1 to 2.5
● −0.4 to 0.0	● 2.6 to 3.0
● 0.1 to 0.5	● 3.1 to 3.5
● 0.6 to 1.0	• 3.6 to 4.0
● 1.1 to 1.5	• 4.1 to 4.5
● 1.6 to 2.0	· 4.6 to 5.0
	⊛ Variable star

DEEP SKY OBJECTS

⊛ Open star cluster

⊕ Globular star cluster

▫ Bright nebula

✧ Planetary nebula

⬭ Galaxy

A WORD FRO

Stars Being Bor
below Orion's belt,
of fainter stars just
naked eye. This sp
in the sword is a co
nursery more than
years distant called the
Nebula . . . a glowing cloud in th
blooming flower made of dust an
hydrogen. It's amazing to think th
glowing from the light of dozens
stars inside.

—**ANDREW FAZEKAS,** *"The Night S*

SUMMER SKY

WARM WEATHER SKIES

When you're outside enjoying a pleasant summer evening, see how easy it is to find the Summer Triangle overhead.

The Bright Summer Triangle

Just because all of the officially recognized constellations were in place by the 18th century doesn't mean that people aren't finding new pictures and patterns in the sky. The Summer Triangle—an asterism (or group of stars) featuring three bright stars in three separate constellations—is an example of this: Although the asterism itself was first noted in the 19th century, the name Summer Triangle was not popularized until the 1950s, when British broadcaster and astronomer Sir Patrick Moore used it and astronomer H. A. Rey (creator of Curious George) included it in his guidebook, *Find the Constellations.*

The stars that create the Summer Triangle are three of the brightest in the northern sky: Vega, in Lyra, is the second brightest star in the summer sky and the first (apart from the sun) to be photographed. Deneb, in Cygnus, is estimated to be 60,000 times more luminous than the sun. Altair, in Aquila, is just 16.7 light-years away. The grouping is visible to most in the Northern Hemisphere.

> **" THE STARS AWAKEN A CERTAIN REVERENCE, BECAUSE THOUGH ALWAYS PRESENT, THEY ARE INACCESSIBLE."**
>
> —RALPH WALDO EMERSON, POET

STELLAR MAGNITUDES

- −0.5 and brighter
- −0.4 to 0.0
- 0.1 to 0.5
- 0.6 to 1.0
- 1.1 to 1.5
- 1.6 to 2.0
- 2.1 to 2.5
- 2.6 to 3.0
- 3.1 to 3.5
- 3.6 to 4.0
- 4.1 to 4.5
- 4.6 to 5.0
- Variable star

DEEP SKY OBJECTS

- Open star cluster
- Globular star cluster
- Bright nebula
- Planetary nebula
- Galaxy

EARTH DAY EVERY DAY

For Better Viewing
LIGHTS OUT

More than 80 percent of the planet's land areas—and 99 percent of the population of the United States and Europe—live under skies so blotted with man-made light that the Milky Way has become virtually invisible.

SHAPES IN THE STARS

Connecting the Dots Humans have an urge to order the heavens—whether for tracking seasons, navigating travel, or conveying history and myth. Here are 16 easily distinguished constellations in the Northern Hemisphere.

ANDROMEDA, the Chained Maiden
View in Oct.–Nov.;
contains galaxy visible to naked eye

AQUARIUS, the Water Bearer
Large constellation visible
in the SW U.S. during autumn

CANIS MAJOR, the Dog
Just southeast of Orion; contains
Sirius, brightest star in the night sky

CAPRICORNUS, the Sea Goat
Distinctive triangle of 12 faint stars;
visible in southern sky in late summer

CASSIOPEIA, the Queen
W-shape visible year-round
near North Pole

CYGNUS, the Swan
Shaped as if a bird, wings out, flying
south; also called the Northern Cross

DRACO, the Dragon
A long tail visible year-round
between Ursa Major and Ursa Minor

GEMINI, the Twins
From the twins originate
December's Geminid meteor showers

HYDRA, the Sea Serpent
Largest constellation of all; a serpentine
series of 17 stars visible in spring

ORION, the Hunter
Huge stars; famous Orion Nebula
easy to spot under belt

PERSEUS, the Hero
Double star cluster atop head; source
of August's Perseid meteor shower

SAGITTARIUS, the Archer
Prominent in midsummer; contains
eight high-magnitude stars

SCORPIO, the Scorpion
Bright star Antares known to the
Romans as the "heart of the scorpion"

URSA MAJOR, the Great Bear
Includes the well-known Big Dipper;
points to the North Star

URSA MINOR, the Little Bear
Also called the Little Dipper;
includes Polaris, the North Star

VIRGO, the Virgin
Second largest constellation in the
sky; visible in the SE in late spring

> " THE COSMOS IS ALSO WITHIN US. WE ARE MADE OF STAR STUFF. WE ARE A WAY FOR THE COSMOS TO KNOW ITSELF."
>
> **—CARL SAGAN,** AUTHOR AND COSMOLOGIST

The annual Perseid meteor shower

Skywatching Events
IN 2020

1 TOTAL SOLAR ECLIPSE, DECEMBER 14. Totality will be visible from southern Chile and Argentina.

2 SUPERMOONS. Full moons especially close to Earth will be visible on February 19, March 9, and April 7.

3 CONJUNCTION OF JUPITER AND SATURN, DECEMBER 21. For the first time since 2000, these two planets will appear at the same time.

4 MERCURY SIGHTINGS, FEBRUARY 10, JUNE 4, OCTOBER 1. On these dates, Mercury will show above the horizon in the evening.

5 MARS SIGHTING, OCTOBER 13. On this date, you may be able to pick out some surface details with a telescope.

6 JUPITER SIGHTING, JULY 14. Four moons may be visible with binoculars.

7 SATURN SIGHTING, JULY 20. The ringed gas giant will be at its closest and brightest.

8 GEMINIDS METEOR SHOWER, DECEMBER 7–17. The shower will peak on December 13 and 14, when a nearly new moon will ensure dark skies.

9 PERSEIDS METEOR SHOWER, JULY 17–AUGUST 24. Dozens of meteors an hour, with peak viewing on August 12 and 13

10 ETA AQUARIDS METEOR SHOWER, APRIL 19–MAY 28. A smaller shower produced from dust particles left behind by Halley's comet, peaking on May 4 and 5

PLANETARY CONJUNCTIONS

At the dawn of our solar system, a massive proto-planetary disk of gas and dust formed along the celestial equator. Virtually all the planets in our solar system formed along this invisible plane. As the planets orbit the sun, they will fall into natural alignments and oppositions along this plane. A planetary conjunction occurs when Earth, the sun, and a planet or planets occur in a straight line. Astrologers and mystics have often ascribed great importance to these alignments, because from Earth, the planets seem to group together in the sky. While the grouping is amazing to witness, it is an illusion, belying the immense distance between them.

SPACE SCIENCE
TIME LINE

14 BYA to 1 BC	AD 1 to 1600	1600 to 1700	1700 to 1800

14 BYA to 1 BC

■ 13.8 bya*
The universe forms
in the big bang.

■ 13.2 bya
Our home galaxy,
the Milky Way, forms.

■ 4.6 bya
Our solar system starts to
emerge around the sun.

■ 4.6 bya
Planet Earth forms.

■ 4.5 bya
Earth's moon forms
from debris.

■ 240 BC
Chinese astronomers
make the first record
of what becomes known
as Halley's comet.

* billion years ago

AD 1 to 1600

■ 46
Roman emperor Julius
Caesar introduces
the Julian calendar.

■ ca 150
Ptolemy writes the
Almagest, a standard
guide to astronomy for
over a thousand years.

■ 310
Chinese astronomers
produce a comprehensive
star map.

■ 1150
Astronomer
Solomon Jarchus
compiles the first
celestial almanac.

1600 to 1700

■ 1610
Galileo observes four
of Jupiter's moons.

■ 1645
Flemish cartographer
Michael Langrenus
publishes the first map
of the moon.

■ 1655
Dutch scientist Christiaan
Huygens confirms that
Saturn has rings.

■ 1664
English scientist Robert
Hooke describes Jupiter's
red spot.

■ 1676
Danish astronomer Ole
Romer makes the first
quantitative measure of
the speed of light.

1700 to 1800

■ 1725
Catalog of over 3,000 stars
compiled by England's first
Astronomer Royal, Rev. John
Flamsteed, is published.

■ 1731
English astronomer
John Bevis discovers
the Crab Nebula.

■ 1771
Charles Messier publishes
catalog of astronomical
objects including galaxies,
star clusters, and nebulae.

■ 1781
British astronomer
William Herschel
discovers the planet
Uranus.

■ 1783
English physicist
John Michell predicts
the existence of
black holes.

| 1800 to 1900 | 1900 to 1950 | 1950 to 1990 | 1990 to PRESENT |

1838
Friedrich Bessel uses stellar parallax to estimate the distance to the star 61 Cygni.

1846
German astronomer Johann Galle is first to observe Neptune.

1872
American astronomer Henry Draper first photographs the spectrum of a star (Vega).

1877
Two moons of Mars, Phobos and Deimos, discovered by American astronomer Asaph Hall.

1889
American astronomer Edward Barnard takes first pictures of the Milky Way.

1915
Scottish astronomer Robert Innes locates Proxima Centauri, the nearest star to the sun.

1916
Albert Einstein publishes his paper on the general theory of relativity.

1927
Georges Lemaître proposes the big bang theory.

1930
Clyde Tombaugh discovers Pluto.

1957
USSR launches Sputnik 1, first man-made satellite to orbit Earth.

1961
Russian astronaut Yuri Gagarin becomes first man in space.

1966
U.S.S.R. lands Luna 9, unmanned vehicle, on moon.

1969
U.S. Apollo 11 mission puts first men on moon.

1981
U.S. space shuttle *Columbia* completes maiden flight.

1990
Hubble Space Telescope launched into orbit.

2000
Two Russians and one American become the first crew to occupy the International Space Station.

2004
NASA lands two rovers, Spirit and Opportunity, on Mars.

2012
Mars Science Lab and Curiosity rover land on Mars.

2012
NASA's Voyager 1, launched in 1977, leaves the solar system and enters interstellar space.

2012
NASA's New Horizons probe passes close to Pluto and continues on to the Kuiper belt.

OUR
NEIGHBORHOOD

ONCE UPON A TIME

Many of us grew up with the idea of a static solar system, with well-behaved planets in their reliable orbits. But a more dramatic view has arisen among some scientists. Not only did the solar system go through a dramatic birth, but it also experienced a raucous adolescence: Hundreds of millions of years after they formed, the biggest planets were swept into new orbits, casting large rocks and comets every which way. The scarred surface of the moon is lingering testimony to a period of epic mayhem and gravitational instability.

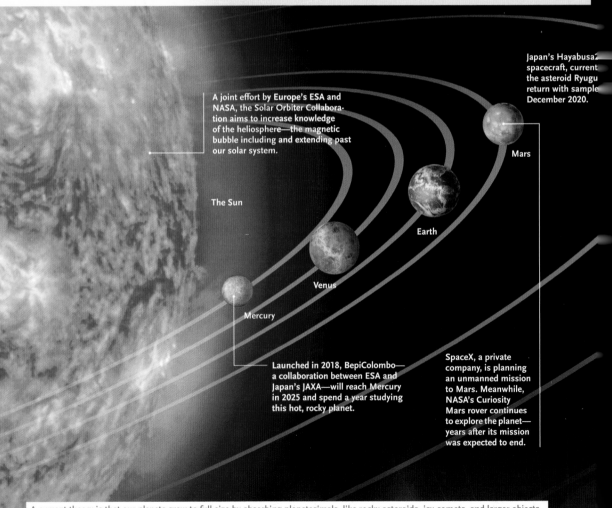

Japan's Hayabusa2 spacecraft, current the asteroid Ryugu return with sample December 2020.

A joint effort by Europe's ESA and NASA, the Solar Orbiter Collaboration aims to increase knowledge of the heliosphere—the magnetic bubble including and extending past our solar system.

The Sun

Mars

Earth

Venus

Mercury

Launched in 2018, BepiColombo—a collaboration between ESA and Japan's JAXA—will reach Mercury in 2025 and spend a year studying this hot, rocky planet.

SpaceX, a private company, is planning an unmanned mission to Mars. Meanwhile, NASA's Curiosity Mars rover continues to explore the planet—years after its mission was expected to end.

A current theory is that our planets grew to full size by absorbing planetesimals, like rocky asteroids, icy comets, and larger objects.

Neptune

Uranus

NASA's New Horizons probe, having
completed its investigation of Pluto, will
conduct a flyby of 2014 MU69, an object
in the Kuiper belt, about one billion miles
beyond Pluto.

Saturn

In 2017, NASA's Cassini spacecraft made
its planned crash landing into Saturn after
sending back years of valuable data about
the planet, its rings, and its moons.

Jupiter

NASA AND RUSSIA'S SPACE AGENCY, ROSCOSMOS,
ARE COLLABORATING ON A NEW SPACE STATION
THAT WILL BE A STAGING POINT FOR BOTH LUNAR
EXPLORATION AND DEEPER SPACE SCIENCE.

DWARF PLANETS

MEET THE NEW NEIGHBORS

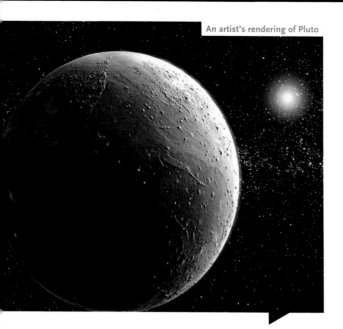

An artist's rendering of Pluto

PLANETARY RULES

PLANET OR DWARF?
In 2006, scientists at the International Astronomers Union conference created three rules for a planet: It orbits the sun, has enough mass that gravitational forces shape it nearly round, and has cleared its orbit of all other material. If a heavenly body meets only the first two categories, it is called a dwarf planet. It was a great advance for science but the death knell for Pluto, which was demoted to a dwarf. Our solar system lost one planet but gained dozens or even hundreds of dwarf planets in the exchange.

PLUTO

THE FORMER PLANET
Pluto may be the ninth largest body in our solar system, but it's not a planet. It sits in the crowded asteroid field known as the Kuiper belt, violating the rules of planethood. While it is only one and a half times the size of Earth's moon, Pluto has five smaller moons of its own. The rocky world was visited by NASA's New Horizons probe in 2015 and found to have blue skies and red snow.

ERIS

THE HIDDEN GIANT
Pluto once marked the edge of our solar system, but today that honor belongs to Eris. The dwarf planet's orbit is three times as far out as Pluto's, nearly 9.5 billion miles from the sun. Eris has an unusual orbit: It doesn't follow the parallel rings of the inner planets but instead follows its own path at a nearly 45-degree angle to the others.

OUR SOLAR SYSTEM MAY CONTAIN AS MANY AS 200 DWARF PLANETS, ACCORDING TO ASTRONOMERS' ESTIMATES.

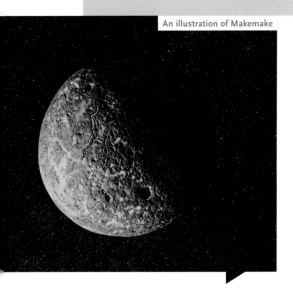
An illustration of Makemake

CERES

A ONCE WATERY WORLD

Although most dwarf planets lie beyond Pluto in the vast Kuiper belt, Ceres can be found in the asteroid belt between Mars and Jupiter. It used to have vast oceans, but today all that remain are salts such as sodium carbonate. How Ceres got to the asteroid belt is perhaps one of its most intriguing mysteries. Some scientists think Ceres may have been a planetary wanderer, moving into the inner asteroid belt from beyond the solar system.

MAKEMAKE

MINIATURE WORLD

Makemake (pronounced MAH-keh MAH-keh) is the second brightest object in the Kuiper belt after Pluto. It's a small world, just 888 miles across, with the same red-brown shading as Pluto. But this is an airless place, with no atmosphere at all. Little is known about its makeup and structure, but its discovery changed history. The discovery of Eris in 2003 and Makemake in 2005 led astronomers to redefine what makes a planet.

HAUMEA

BATTERED PLANET

At some point in its distant past, the dwarf planet Haumea slammed into another world at 7,000 miles per hour. The collision blasted huge chunks of Haumea into space and sent the celestial body spinning. Haumea spins so rapidly that a day there is equivalent to four hours on Earth. This super-speed of its rotation has even shaped the dwarf planet into an elongated football. Two moons and faint rings, also remnants of ancient disaster, circle the planet.

EARTH'S MOON

MAGNIFICENT DESOLATION

The topography of the moon is varied. Collisions with meteors over its 4.5-billion-year life have created a surface of pulverized rock, called regolith. Craters are as wide as 1,600 miles across, with mountainous walls as high as 4.8 miles. Its distinctive "seas" are actually areas given a smooth sheen by molten lava brought to the surface after major impacts that occurred around 3.8 to 3.9 billion years ago.

OCEANUS PROCELLARUM
This large, dark "ocean of storms," easily visible from Earth, is probably rift valleys formed by emerging magma. Apollo 12 landed here in 1969.

MONTES APENNINUS
Apollo 15 landed at the base of this mountain range in 1971. Formed by the impact of an asteroid, comet, or other object almost four billion years ago, it includes the tallest lunar mountain, Mons Huygens.

APOLLO 11 LANDING SITE
Neil Armstrong and Buzz Aldrin landed at Tranquility Base in Mare Tranquillitatis (the Sea of Tranquility). NASA hopes to preserve this and other landing sites.

North Pole

60°   60°

60°   30°W   0°   30°E   60°

MARE FRIGORIS

Endymion

Sinus Roris

30°   30°

Sinus Iridum

Plato

Chang'e 3 (China) ✳ Landed Dec. 14, 2013

Lacus Somniorum

Montes Caucasus

MARE

MARE IMBRIUM

MARE SERENITATIS

MARE

Apollo 17 (U.S.) ✳ Landed Dec. 11, 1972

MARE CRISIUM

Aristarchus

Montes Apenninus

Apollo 15 (U.S.) ✳ Landed July 30, 1971

MARE TRANQUILLITATIS

MARE VAPORUM

MARE INSULARUM

Copernicus

Apollo 12 (U.S.) Landed Nov. 19, 1969 ✳

EQUATOR

0°   0°

Grimaldi

✳ Apollo 14 (U.S.) Landed Feb. 5, 1971

Apollo 11 (U.S.) ✳ Tranquility Base Landed July 20, 1969

MARE SMYTHII

MARE COGNITUM

Apollo 16 (U.S.) ✳ Landed April 21, 1972

MARE FECUNDITATIS

Langrenus

MARE NUBIUM

MARE NECTARIS

MARE HUMORUM

Rupes Altai

Tycho

30°   30°

Clavius

60°   60°

South Pole

0 mi   500   1000

0 km   500   1000

✳ Spacecraft landing or impact site

OCEANUS PROCELLARUM

IN 2019 CHINA'S CHANG'E 4 BECAME THE FIRST CRAFT EVER TO LAND ON THE MOON'S FAR SIDE. IT BOUNCED IMAGES BACK TO EARTH VIA RELAY SATELLITE QUEQIAO.

GAGARIN CRATER
This feature is named for the first human in space, Yuri Gagarin, a Soviet cosmonaut who orbited Earth in 1961. On the moon, large craters tend to be older than small ones.

APOLLO LARGE IMPACT BASIN
This double-ring impact crater was not a landing site for any Apollo missions, though it is named in their honor. Because the impact that created it was at the edge of a basin, scientists hope it forced up materials from deep within the moon's surface.

Craters labeled in blue commemorate the seven space shuttle Challenger *astronauts.*

SOUTH POLE
NASA crashed a rocket and a satellite into a crater on the moon's south pole, looking for evidence of water. The crashes did find signatures associated with water ice.

ON TO MARS

WATER ON THE FOURTH PLANET

Astronomers using some of the world's most powerful telescopes have determined that an ocean at least a mile deep covered a significant fraction of the Martian surface four billion years ago. The research reinforces earlier evidence that water once existed on the surface of the red planet, leaving traces such as stream pebbles, ancient shorelines, river deltas, minerals that must have formed in a watery environment, and more.

OLYMPUS MONS
This enormous shield volcano, the tallest mountain on Mars, is nearly three times as high as Mount Everest. Its base is as wide as Arizona.

CHRYSE PLANITIA
Scientists debate the origin of this plain—the landing site for both the Viking 1 lander, the first American spacecraft to reach the planet's surface, and the Mars Pathfinder probe. Was it formed by lava or by large bodies of water?

VALLES MARINERIS
Largest known canyon in the solar system—almost four times longer, 20 times wider, and four times deeper than our Grand Canyon—this may have formed as the planet cooled.

✳ Spacecraft landing or impact site

CHEMICAL DISCOVERIES MADE IN 2019 BY NASA'S CURIOSITY ROVER SUGGEST THAT MICROSCOPIC LIFE MAY HAVE LIVED ON MARS—AND MAY LIVE THERE STILL.

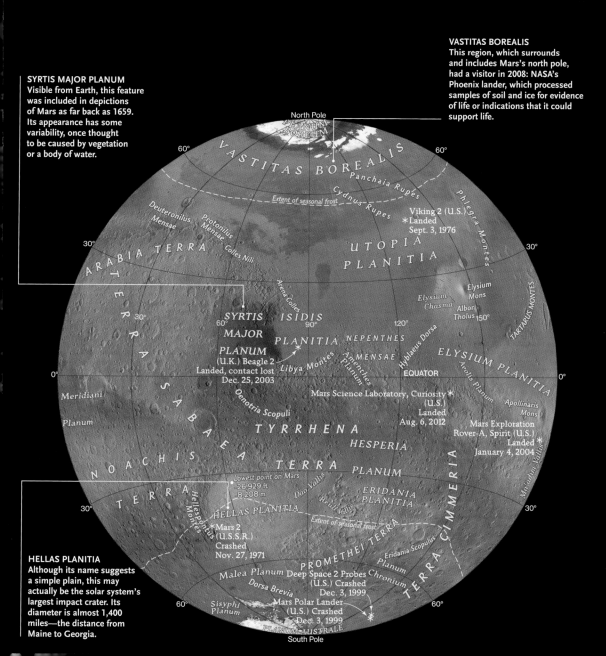

VASTITAS BOREALIS
This region, which surrounds and includes Mars's north pole, had a visitor in 2008: NASA's Phoenix lander, which processed samples of soil and ice for evidence of life or indications that it could support life.

SYRTIS MAJOR PLANUM
Visible from Earth, this feature was included in depictions of Mars as far back as 1659. Its appearance has some variability, once thought to be caused by vegetation or a body of water.

HELLAS PLANITIA
Although its name suggests a simple plain, this may actually be the solar system's largest impact crater. Its diameter is almost 1,400 miles—the distance from Maine to Georgia.

North Pole

PLANUM BOREUM

VASTITAS BOREALIS

Panchaia Rupes

Cydnus Rupes

Extent of seasonal frost

Deuteronilus Mensae

Protonilus Mensae

Colles Nili

ARABIA TERRA

Phlegra Montes

UTOPIA PLANITIA

Elysium Chasma

Elysium Mons

Albor Tholus

TARTARUS MONTES

SYRTIS MAJOR PLANUM
(U.K.) Beagle 2
Landed, contact lost
Dec. 25, 2003

ISIDIS PLANITIA

Arena Colles

Viking 2 (U.S.)
*Landed
Sept. 3, 1976

NEPENTHES

Libya Montes

Amenthes Planum

MENSAE

Hyblaeus Dorsa

ELYSIUM PLANITIA

Aeolis Planum

EQUATOR

Meridiani Planum

TERRA SABAEA

Oenotria Scopuli

Mars Science Laboratory, Curiosity *
(U.S.)
Landed
Aug. 6, 2012

Apollinaris Mons

Mars Exploration Rover-A, Spirit (U.S.)
Landed *
January 4, 2004

TYRRHENA TERRA

HESPERIA PLANUM

NOACHIS TERRA

Lowest point on Mars
-26,929 ft
-8,208 m

Dao Vallis

Reull Vallis

ERIDANIA PLANITIA

TERRA CIMMERIA

Masada Vallis

Hellespontus Montes

HELLAS PLANITIA

Extent of seasonal frost

Eridania Scopulus

PROMETHEI TERRA Planum

*Mars 2 (U.S.S.R.)
Crashed
Nov. 27, 1971

Malea Planum

Dorsa Brevia

Deep Space 2 Probes
(U.S.) Crashed
Dec. 3, 1999

Chronium Planum

Sisyphi Planum

Mars Polar Lander
(U.S.) Crashed
Dec. 3, 1999

PLANUM AUSTRALE

South Pole

MARTIAN
PROBES

MISSIONS TO MARS

Each line below is color-coded to represent one mission that reached Mars, or failed in the attempt, the type of mission, and the county of origin.

Flyby   Lander   Orbiter

HOW WE STUDY
THE RED PLANET

Even before humans landed on Earth's moon, we'd been sending spacecraft to our closest planetary neighbor, Mars. As these craft have flown past, orbited around, landed on, and driven over the surface of Mars, there have been utter failures and spectacular successes. As NASA sets its sights on a manned Mars mission in the 2030s, we look back on mission history.

1960   Marsnik 1 Launched 1960

          Mariner 4 1964

1970

          Mars 3 1971

          Mars 6 1973
          Viking 1, Viking 2 1975
1980
1990   Phobos 2 1988

          Mars Pathfinder 1996

2000   Mars Odyssey 2001
          Mars Express 2003
          Spirit, Opportunity 2003

2010   MSL Curiosity 2011
          Mars Orbiter Mission 2013
          ExoMars 2016
          43 TOTAL MISSIONS*

SUCCESS   FAILURE
          Russia/U.S.S.R.
          United States
          European Space Agency
          Japan
          China-Russia
          India

MARINER 4
U.S. 1964
This flyby provided the first close-up photos of Mars.

MARS 3
U.S.S.R. 1971
This was the first successful lander, though it stopped transmitting after 20 seconds.

VIKING 1 & 2
U.S. 1975
The first U.S. landers on Mars returned color images from the surface.

2001 MARS ODYSSEY
U.S. 2001
The orbiter is the longest
serving Mars spacecraft.

MARS EXPRESS
ESA 2003
The lander was lost,
but the orbiter keeps
making images.

MARS ORBITER MISSION
INDIA 2013
India's first Mars probe
carries imaging and
scientific instruments.

JUPITER & ITS MOONS

LEARNING FROM JUNO'S OBSERVATIONS

According to NASA, Jupiter is "a physics lab of sorts," and one of the phenomena under study is the Jovian magnetosphere, using data and images collected by the Juno spacecraft, which spent a few years in orbit around our largest planet. For example, scientists are working to understand Jupiter's radiation belts, in part because protecting spacecraft and astronauts from radiation is a constant concern. And unlike auroras in our atmosphere (triggered by extraplanetary particles), Jupiter's most intense auroras are the result of an as-yet unknown acceleration process.

POP!

TOP 10 SPACE FLICKS

- *Metropolis* (1927)
- *Star Wars, Episode IV: A New Hope* (1977)
- *Alien* (1979)
- *E.T. The Extra-Terrestrial* (1982)
- *Aliens* (1986)
- *WALL-E* (2008)
- *Star Trek* (2009)
- *Gravity* (2013)
- *Star Wars, Episode VII: The Force Awakens* (2015)
- *Arrival* (2016)

Jupiter's Great Red Spot is 1.3 times as wide as Earth.

Europa, one of Jupiter's 69 moons

OTHER MOON LANDINGS

For obvious reasons, investigating a gas giant needs to be done from some distance, but we may be able to get a vessel on or near Jupiter's four Galilean moons—the largest among its 69—instead. Here's why Europa seems to be the most likely destination.

Great Amenities and Quite a View

Although this moon has an outer crust of solid ice, cracks in its surface indicate that the crust sits on top of liquid water. Because little warmth from the sun reaches Europa, it's likely that its ocean is kept from freezing by hydrothermal vents. Hubble telescope images from 2013 show plumes of liquid water at Europa's south pole, too. All of this—water! heat! nutrients!—makes Europa a compelling candidate for life.

Because it will be years before a spacecraft (already being referred to as the Europa Clipper) reaches Europa, scientists are investigating life found in Earth's extreme environments to feed their imagination of what life on other planets might look like.

KEY DATES

Getting to Know
JUPITER

■ 1610: GALILEO SEES THE MOONS
When astronomer Galileo Galilei observed four satellites orbiting Jupiter through his improved telescope, he also identified the key to Copernicus's sun-centered model, displacing the Earth-centered Ptolemaic system.

■ 1831: RED SPOT SPOTTED
Although several stargazers had noted Jupiter's spotted appearance, Samuel Heinrich Schwabe, a German amateur astronomer studying sunspots, first described the planet's distinctive Great Red Spot (a cyclone).

■ 1955: JUPITER SPEAKS TO US
While collecting radio signals to map the spring sky, astronomers Bernard Burke and Kenneth Franklin captured interference eventually revealed as coming from Jupiter—and that helped find the planet's rotation speed.

■ 1979: PUT A COUPLE RINGS ON IT
Saturn's always been the one with flashy rings, but Jupiter's dusty, beautiful rings were photographed by the paparazzi known as Voyager 1 and 2 (and, later, Galileo).

■ 1995: AN EXTENDED STAY
When the Galileo spacecraft arrived in Jupiter's neighborhood for a four-year visit to the planet and its moons, it brought along a probe that entered the planet's atmosphere.

■ 2016: JUNO CALLING
Data from the Juno orbiter will be analyzed by pros and citizen scientists studying structure, composition, and magnetic and gravitational fields. Highlights include the stunning, mysterious auroras at the north pole.

■ 2018: DISCOVERY OF NEW MOONS
While searching for a hypothetical planet on the outskirts of the solar system, researchers found 12 small, previously unknown moons around Jupiter. They range in size from about one to three miles across, and their discovery brings the total number of Jupiter's moons to 79.

BEST OF @NATGEO

TOP PHOTOS OF THE NIGHT SKY

@renan_ozturk | RENAN OZTURK
ce and snow reflect the aurora borealis on the Vatnajökull glacier in Iceland.

@geosteinmetz | GEORGE STEINMETZ
Rock sculptures shaped by strong winds in Egypt's White Desert shine on a moonlit night.

@salvarezphoto | STEPHEN ALVAREZ
Petroglyphs on the Butler Wash panel in southeastern Utah date back to approximately 1500 BC.

@jimmy_chin | JIMMY CHIN
The Kamchatka Peninsula in Russia is home to the planet's highest concentration of active volcanoes.

> ## "WE ALL LIVE UNDER THE SAME SKY, BUT WE DON'T ALL HAVE THE SAME HORIZON."
> —KONRAD H. J. ADENAUER, GERMAN STATESMAN

@pedromcbride | PETE MCBRIDE
A six-hour exposure captures the movement of the stars in the Andean Altiplano in Argentina.

@lucalocatelliphoto | LUCA LOCATELLI
Telescopes at the Deimos Sky Survey in southern Spain collect about 50,000 images every night.

@renan_ozturk | RENAN OZTURK
Climbers scale an ice wall under the glow of the northern lights in Iceland.

@johnstanmeyer | JOHN STANMEYER
Explorer Paul Salopek stands under the Milky Way, visible in the darkness of the Kyzylkum Desert in Uzbekistan.

BIRTH OF THE UNIVERSE

A HISTORY SHAPED BY DARK FORCES

Cosmologists have determined that the universe was born 13.8 billion years ago. But they've also concluded that what we see in the sky makes up only 5 percent of the observable universe. The invisible majority consists of 27 percent dark matter and 68 percent dark energy.

What's Dark Matter?

We can't see dark matter, but we can see the effects of its gravity. And dark matter can't just be inconspicuous

normal matter—in no plausible scenario would it add up to five times the mass of the bright stuff—hence scientists think it must be made of more exotic materials.

What's Dark Energy?

Dark energy, even more mysterious, refers to whatever is accelerating the rate at which the cosmos expands. It has been called a "general label for what we do not know about the large-scale properties of our universe."

Dark matter

The big bang

13.8 billion years ago

Our universe blossoms from a hot, dense state smaller than an atom. Within milliseconds it inflates enormously.

Dark matter forms

First seconds of the universe

Dark matter also emerges in the first second. Interacting with particles of normal matter only through gravity, it begins to pull them together.

Stars light up

100 million years after the big bang

Clouds of hydrogen assembled by the gravity of dark matter collapse to form the first scattered stars. Nuclear fusion inside them creates heavier elements—and lights space.

Composition of the universe

Dark energy <1%	Dark matter <1%		86%	
<1%	Matter <1%	Radiation 99%*	<1% ·····	<1% 13%

A BELGIAN PRIEST NAMED GEORGES LEMAÎTRE FIRST SUGGESTED THE BIG BANG THEORY IN THE 1920S WHEN HE THEORIZED THAT THE UNIVERSE BEGAN FROM A SINGLE PRIMORDIAL ATOM.

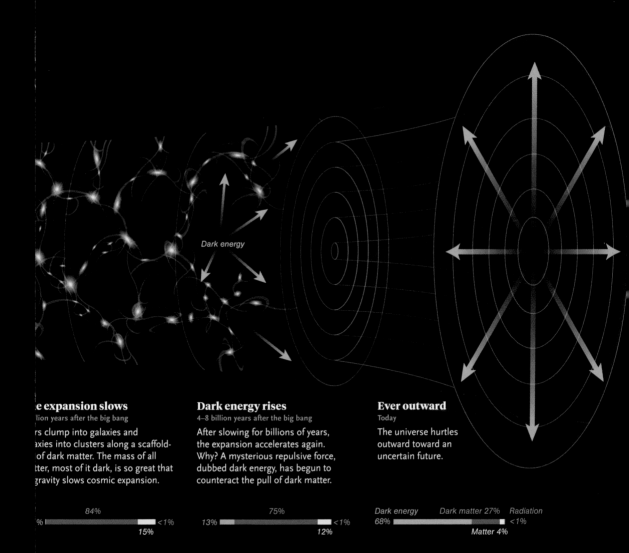

Dark energy

e expansion slows
lion years after the big bang

rs clump into galaxies and
axies into clusters along a scaffold-
of dark matter. The mass of all
tter, most of it dark, is so great that
gravity slows cosmic expansion.

Dark energy rises
4–8 billion years after the big bang

After slowing for billions of years,
the expansion accelerates again.
Why? A mysterious repulsive force,
dubbed dark energy, has begun to
counteract the pull of dark matter.

Ever outward
Today

The universe hurtles
outward toward an
uncertain future.

84%	
% ▮	▬ <1%
	15%

75%	
13% ▮	▬ <1%
	12%

Dark energy	Dark matter 27%	Radiation
68% ▬▬▬▬	▮	<1%
	Matter 4%	

* Percentages do not add up to 100 due to rounding.

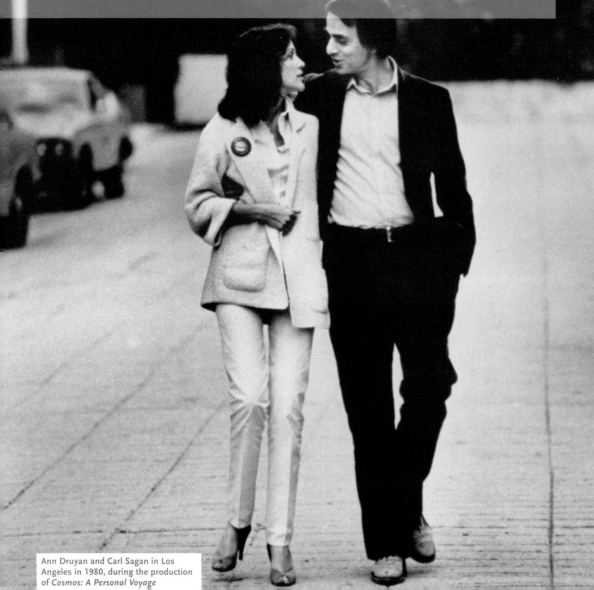

ANN DRUYAN
SCIENCE COMMUNICATOR

A LIFE OF WONDERMENT

The wonders of the cosmos have fascinated Ann Druyan since her childhood. Though girls were not encouraged to explore science in the 1950s, Druyan prevailed, finding ways to share her fascination with science.

Ann Druyan and Carl Sagan in Los Angeles in 1980, during the production of *Cosmos: A Personal Voyage*

In 1977, Ann was chosen by Carl Sagan to be the creative director of the iconic NASA Voyager Interstellar Message, better known as the Golden Record, a repository of 118 pictures, greetings in 54 languages and one dialect of humpback whales, 27 pieces of world music, and a sound essay with everything from the chirping of crickets to the brain waves of a young woman newly fallen in love. "We all looked upon it as something sacred," Druyan says of the Golden Record: "a cultural Noah's Ark of human culture with a shelf life of billions of years." The record was affixed to the two Voyagers, which launched in 1977 and have been traveling ever since—the most distant objects ever touched by human hands.

THE COSMOS PHENOMENON

Druyan and Sagan fell in love while working on Voyager, and they soon went on to create their legendary collaboration, *Cosmos*. Together with Steven Soter they wrote the television series that first aired on PBS in 1980, won two Emmys and a Peabody Award, and went on to be broadcast in 60 countries. The beloved companion book, dedicated to Druyan, became one of the top-selling science books of all time and paved the way for six more *New York Times* best sellers on the importance of scientific knowledge in our world and to our future, all co-written by Sagan and Druyan.

Druyan's work as author and television producer has continued beyond Carl Sagan's untimely death in 1996. She has been creating sequels to *Cosmos*. The first, *Cosmos: A Spacetime Odyssey*, aired in 2014 and won four Emmys and a Peabody. The second, *Cosmos: Possible Worlds*, will debut in 2020.

Ann Druyan today

KEY DATES

Anne Druyan's ACCOMPLISHMENTS

■ **1979**
With Carl Sagan, co-creates *Contact,* which became a movie starring Jodie Foster

■ **1980**
With Carl Sagan, writes the landmark TV series *Cosmos*

■ **2000**
Founds Cosmos Studios, dedicated to creating science-based entertainment

■ **2005**
Serves as program director of the deep space solar sail mission COSMOS 1

■ **2014**
Serves as executive producer, writer, and director of *Cosmos: A Spacetime Odyssey*

■ **2019**
Performs the same roles on her third series, *Cosmos: Possible Worlds*

WHEN A STAR EXPLODES

THE LIFE CYCLE OF A STAR

Every star begins as a collapsing cloud of interstellar dust. Stars stabilize when the temperature in the core is hot enough to begin nuclear fusion: turning hydrogen into helium. From there, a star grows and changes, using the hydrogen at its core as fuel along the way. Eventually, there's nothing left to burn, and some of the star's mass flows into its core. Once the core reaches critical mass—becoming too heavy to withstand its own gravitational force—the star collapses in on itself, producing massive shock waves and the giant explosion of a supernova.

A WORD FROM

The Cosmic Dawn The Giant Magellan Telescope will have 10 times the resolution of the Hubble Space Telescope. It will be 20 million times more sensitive than the human eye. And it may, for the first time ever, be capable of finding life on planets outside of our solar system. It's going to allow us to look back at the first light in the universe—literally, the dawn of the cosmos.

—WENDY FREEDMAN, *astronomer*

The next supernova visible from Earth—as bright as Polaris—will be in Cygnus around 2022 and will last a year.

IN THE SPACE OF JUST A FEW YEARS A SUPERNOVA, A SPECIAL KIND OF EXPLODED STAR, RADIATES MORE ENERGY THAN OUR SUN DOES IN ITS ENTIRE LIFETIME.

Distances Out Into
THE UNIVERSE

■ **ASTEROID: 26,000 MILES**
A tiny asteroid, just 50–100 feet long and known as 2012 TC4, flew very close to Earth on Oct. 12, 2017, just above the orbit of communications satellites.

■ **COMET: 1.4 MILLION MILES**
Appearing about four times as large as a full moon to the naked eye in July 1770, comet Lexell (aka D/1770 L1) was six times as far away as the moon.

■ **NEXT STAR: 4.25 LIGHT-YEARS (LY)**
Proxima Centauri, our second nearest star (the sun is closer, obviously), is in the constellation of Centaurus. It is part of a three-star system with Alpha Centauri A and B.

■ **HABITABLE EXOPLANET: 4.25 LY**
Our nearest star has in its orbit an exoplanet (Proxima Centauri B) that could, based on its size and location, have liquid water.

■ **SUPERNOVA CANDIDATE: 150 LY**
The most likely star to become a supernova is the smaller partner in a binary system known as IK Pegasi at a not insignificant distance from Earth—but by the time it explodes, millions of years from now, the distance will be much greater.

■ **PLANETARY NEBULA: 650 LY**
Not actually home to planets, this celestial object is the glowing remnants of a sunlike star. The Helix Nebula, in the constellation of Aquarius, is likely the closest to us.

■ **BLACK HOLE: 3,000 LY**
Almost every galaxy has a supermassive black hole in its center. Ours is 27,000 ly from Earth. A stellar-mass black hole, V616 Monocerotis, is about 3,000 ly away.

■ **GALAXY: 25,000 LY**
The Canis Major dwarf galaxy, closest to us and to the center of the Milky Way (42,000 ly), is being unraveled by our galaxy's gravity.

SPACE RADIATION

FOLLOWING COSMIC RAYS THROUGH THE UNIVERSE

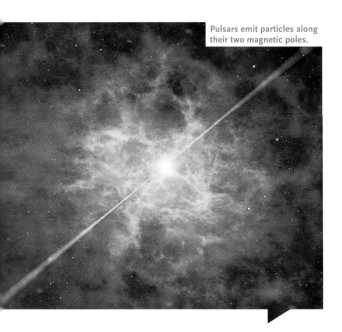

Pulsars emit particles along their two magnetic poles.

UNDER SIEGE

HIGH-ENERGY INVASION

Earth is pelted with high-energy particles from outer space every second. These high-energy projectiles are atomic particles born in distant stars, many traveling near the speed of light. Cosmic radiation is a danger for astronauts, but for scientists, these aren't threats but atomic ambassadors from across the universe. Cosmic radiation helped science unlock the world beyond the atom, and understanding it better can help astronomers radically advance our understanding of the cosmos.

TRACING A PATH

WHERE DO THEY COME FROM?

By the time most cosmic rays reach Earth, many have been traveling for thousands or millions of years across the cosmos. But even when traveling near the speed of light, the universe is a big place. For scientists, the distance is less of a problem than the direction. Most cosmic radiation carries an electrical charge, which can be significantly affected by magnetic fields. A cosmic ray passing too close to a sun or large planet can find its path altered by its magnetic field. By the time the particle gets to Earth, it could be coming from a completely different direction than it started from, which means scientists can't necessarily match a cosmic ray to its cosmic source. Generating the ability to follow these pathways would give scientists new tools to explore and understand the universe.

Particles of plasma lead to the aurora borealis.

Inside a Daya Bay neutrino detector

An illustration of Earth's radiation belts

NEUTRINOS

A PECULIAR PARTICLE

One type of subatomic particle, the neutrino, rarely interacts with matter. Neutrinos can fly through magnetic fields, asteroids, and even planets without ever altering course. To catch a neutrino, scientists have buried storage tanks deep beneath lead mines or the Antarctic ice sheets and waited for the brief flash when a neutrino interacts with their contents. If scientists can find a way to successfully trace neutrinos, they will open up a new way of searching the universe for supernovae, black holes, and other wonders of the cosmos.

A WORD FROM

The Human Body in Space On my previous flight to the space station, a mission of 159 days, I lost bone mass, my muscles atrophied, and my blood redistributed itself in my body, which strained and shrank the walls of my heart. More troubling, I experienced problems with my vision, as many other astronauts had. I had been exposed to more than 30 times the radiation of a person on Earth, equivalent to about 10 chest x-rays every day. This exposure would increase my risk of a fatal cancer for the rest of my life.

—SCOTT KELLY, *astronaut*

BLOCKING RADIATION

BEYOND THE SPHERE

Earth's magnetic field blocks 99.9 percent of space radiation , but humanity is safe only as long as we stay within our protective magnetic bubble. Beyond that layer, the radiation level rises, and so do health concerns for astronauts. High-energy cosmic rays can damage sensitive electronics, but even normal radiation could dramatically increase the risk of cancer. A single trip to Mars would be like undergoing an x-ray or MRI scan every week of the journey, and that covers only the voyage. Whether on the surface of Mars, the moon, or even the International Space Station, there is nowhere to hide from the cosmic storm. If humanity leaves the planet, understanding the cosmic storm will be vital.

EXOPLANETS
IS THERE LIFE?

IN SEARCH OF GOLDILOCKS

When astronomers discuss planets that might support life, they refer to Goldilocks: Conditions have to be just right for life to happen. Once an exoplanet (a planet outside our solar system) is identified, astronomers assess its distance from the star it orbits and determine whether it is too close or too far to keep surface water in a liquid state. Size also matters: A planet that's too small cannot maintain an atmosphere; one that's too large will have a crushing atmosphere. "Goldilocks" planets have the right atmospheric pressure and the right temperature.

POP!

PLANETARY PLAYLIST

- "Aquarius (Let the Sunshine In)," The 5th Dimension
- "Fly Me to the Moon," Frank Sinatra
- "From Here to the Moon and Back," Dolly Parton
- "Gagarin," Public Service Broadcasting
- "Here Comes the Sun," The Beatles
- "Kuiper Belt," Sufjan Stevens, Bryce Dessner, Nico Muhly & James McAlister
- "Man on the Moon," R.E.M.
- "Pluto," Clare & the Reasons
- "Rocket Man," Elton John
- "Space Oddity," David Bowie
- "Stars Align," Lindsey Stirling
- "Supermassive Black Hole," Muse
- "We Are All Made of Stars," Moby

Imagine a planet with two nearby moons, visible day and night.

ONE IN FIVE SUNLIKE STARS HARBORS AN EARTH-SIZE WORLD THAT ORBITS IN A "HABITABLE ZONE" FRIENDLY TO OCEANS AND PERHAPS LIFE.

Earth   Kepler-62e   Kepler-62f

IN SEARCH OF EARTHS

For nine years NASA's Kepler spacecraft stared from its perch in space toward a patch of sky studded with 156,000 stars. Its goal? To find the frequency of Earthlike planets in the habitable zones of stars. The spacecraft did this by watching for the periodic blips in starlight produced when a planet passed between its star and Kepler's unblinking eye. Of the 2,600 planets discovered, some are relatively nearby, which makes them obvious targets in the search for life.

DARK MATTER

A MYSTERY AS BIG AS THE UNIVERSE

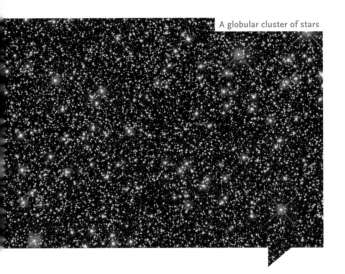

A globular cluster of stars

THE MISSING PIECE

A SEARCH FOR INVISIBLE MATTER

Astrophysics has a problem: The visible universe doesn't have enough stuff in it. Every star we see, every exoplanet and black hole we measure, every nebula we survey, is only 5 percent of what gravity tells us should be present in our universe. Hidden out in the vast reaches of space is a new type of matter—a new particle that neither emits nor reflects light but still makes up most of the universe. We can detect it only through its gravitational pushes and pulls on the visible universe we're familiar with. Scientists refer to it as the dark universe, a massive intergalactic web of dark matter and dark energy. A name is not an explanation, however, and scientists are still stumped for details.

DEFINING DARK MATTER

FILLING THE EMPTY SPACE

The idea of dark matter first appeared in the 1930s, when Swiss astronomer Fritz Zwicky focused on two galaxies orbiting each other in a distant stellar cluster. Without the galaxies containing much more mass than was seen, the galaxies should have spun away from each other. Zwicky theorized that galaxies must contain massive amounts of dark matter, many times greater than the visible matter we can detect. Other observations have only confirmed that hypothesis. In his planetary musings, Isaac Newton couldn't understand how gravity could pull Earth around the sun if the space between was totally empty. It turns out that empty space is far from empty. Our galaxy, and all the others, are filled with dark matter.

The Pinwheel galaxy

The Alpha Magnetic Spectrometer

SCIENTISTS HAVE OBSERVED A GALAXY ABOUT 65 MILLION LIGHT-YEARS AWAY. CALLED NGC 1052-DF2, IT APPEARS TO HAVE ALMOST NO DARK MATTER.

A computer simulation of dark matter

THEORETICAL PARTICLES

PICKING ON WIMPS

Scientists aren't certain what exactly dark matter is or where it comes from. Numerous theories have been formulated, but so far each one has been disputed. For decades scientists focused on a class of particles are known as WIMPs—weakly interacting massive particles. Some researchers are using ever more powerful colliders to search for these elusive entities; some seek evidence of dark matter collisions in sunken tanks containing various chemicals; a third approach is to study cosmic rays for evidence of dark matter. Some of the biggest and most expensive science experiments, both on and off the planet, are dedicated to searching out this mysterious form of matter. From the two-billion-dollar alpha magnetic spectrometer mounted on the International Space Station, to the Axion Dark Matter eXperiment (ADMX) in Seattle, Washington, the search is on.

SHINE A LIGHT

A NEW UNDERSTANDING

To reveal the secrets of dark matter would do more than unveil a new particle. It could rewrite our understanding of the universe. Dark matter is vital to create the universe around us; it is the soil where stars are born and the strings that connect galaxies. A simulated map of the dark universe we've identified reveals strands of the mystery material connecting stars, planets, and nebula in a vast intergalactic web. Some telescopes are able to study dark matter through its impact on light itself. Since dark matter affects gravity and gravity bends light, scientists have been able to literally "see" its effect. We can see it, but we do not know it. Not yet. So our universe is still literally held together by dark matter and mystery.

FURTHER

PATHWAY TO AN ICY FUTURE

We look to the icebound regions of the Poles—the lands above the Arctic Circle to the north and the frigid continent of Antarctica to the south—for signs that our human efforts to stave off global climate change might be making a difference. Cracks in the ice sheet and calving bergs cause concern. The Antarctic Peninsula, which stretches up toward South America, shows alarming signs of warming, despite eerily beautiful and frigid shades of aqua.

Sea-worn stones form a path to beached and broken sea ice on the Antarctic Peninsula.

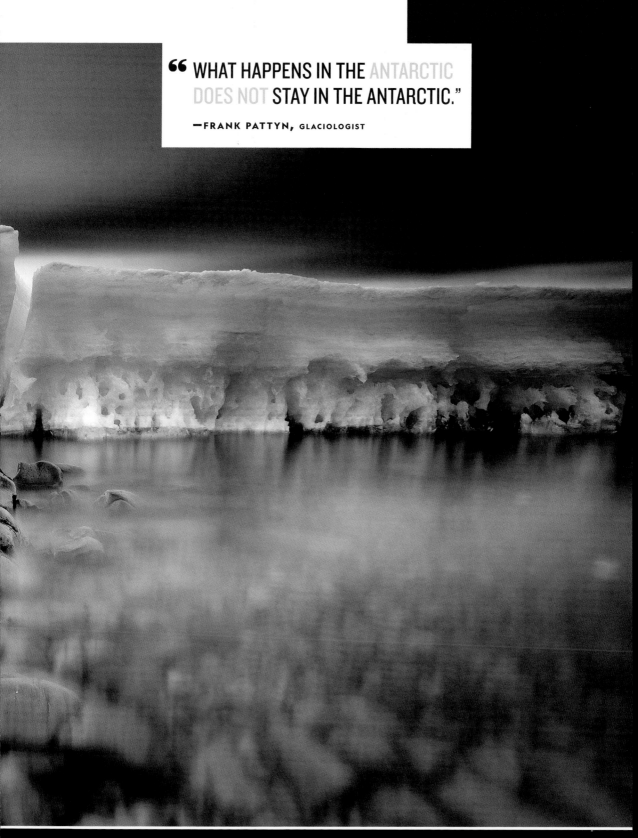

" WHAT HAPPENS IN THE ANTARCTIC DOES NOT STAY IN THE ANTARCTIC."

—FRANK PATTYN, GLACIOLOGIST

LIFE ON EARTH

ALL LIVING THINGS | OF THE EARTH

Endangered golden snub-nosed monkeys inhabit the Qinling Mountains in China.

OF THE SEA | OF THE SKY | CARE FOR ALL LIFE

QUIZ MASTER

Know Your Biosphere? Ever wonder what's the meaning of life? Start here for answers by exploring the many forms of life, from microbes to megafauna, from rarely seen life-forms to the plants and animals we know and love.

—**CARA SANTA MARIA,** *Our Favorite Nerd*

WHAT WAS THE **NAME** OF THE **SHEEP CLONED** IN 1996?
p161

WHAT IS THE ONLY GREAT APE NATIVE TO A COUNTRY OUTSIDE OF **AFRICA?**
p181

HOW MANY HEARTS DOES AN **OCTOPUS HAVE?**
p160

p192

IN WHAT YEAR DID NATURALIST CARL LINNAEUS INTRODUCE THE BINOMIAL NAMING SYSTEM FOR PLANTS AND ANIMALS?

IN WHICH CANADIAN PROVINCE WAS A WELL-PRESERVED SPECIMEN OF NODOSAUR FOUND?
p170

p162

NAME THE THREE **DOMAINS** OF LIFE.

WHICH SPECIES OF **BUTTERFLY** IS THE OFFICIAL STATE INSECT **OF SEVEN** U.S. STATES?

p203

AN ANCIENT CREATURE KNOWN AS PAKICETUS WAS AN ANCESTOR TO WHICH MODERN ANIMALS?

p189

p183

ABOUT HOW LONG AGO WERE DOGS FIRST DOMESTICATED?

p176

IN WHAT LANGUAGE DID KOKO THE GORILLA COMMUNICATE WITH HUMANS?

p174

HOW MANY KNOWN SPECIES OF HUMMINGBIRDS ARE THERE?

p198

WHAT TYPE OF INSECT IS OUR MOST VALUABLE POLLINATOR?

p204

ABOUT HOW FAR CAN A NORTHERN FLYING SQUIRREL GLIDE?

ON WHICH CONTINENT WILL YOU FIND A SMALL MARSUPIAL KNOWN AS A QUOLL?

p178

LIFE SCIENCE
TIME LINE

900 to 1 BC	AD 1 to 1100	1100 to 1600	1600 to 1800

ca 900 BC
Neolithic farmers use fertilizer and irrigation.

ca 800 BC
Egyptians use artificially heated incubators to hatch eggs.

ca 400 BC
Hippocrates of Kos describes human anatomy.

ca 350 BC
Aristotle draws up a classification scheme for plants and animals.

300 BC
Diocles of Carystus is credited with writing the first text on anatomy.

77
Roman scholar Pliny the Elder summarizes natural history as known to the Romans in his *Naturalis Historia*.

752
Chinese physician Wang Tao describes ailments including diabetes and malaria, along with remedies.

ca 900
Arab physician Rhazes distinguishes between measles and smallpox.

ca 1075
Female physician Trotula of Salerno writes about hygiene and women's disorders.

ca 1260
Arab physician Ibn al-Nafis describes the pulmonary circulation of the blood.

1276
Giles of Rome discusses the role of both parents in procreation in his work, *De Formatione Corporis*.

1410
Italian physician Benedetto Rinio catalogs more than 500 medicinal plants.

1517
Girolamo Fracastoro proposes that fossils are the petrified remains of once living organisms.

1583
Italian botanist Andrea Cesalpino devises a system of classifying plants by their structure.

1658
Dutch naturalist Jan Swammerdam describes red blood cells.

1665
Robert Hooke coins the word "cell" to describe individual units in plant tissues.

1677
Dutch scientist Antonie van Leeuwenhoek reports on his observations of bacteria.

1735
Swedish naturalist Carl Linnaeus introduces the binomial naming system.

1796
Georges Cuvier identifies "elephant" remains from Siberia as a separate and extinct species: "mammoth."

1800 to 1900	1900 to 1925	1925 to 1960	1960 to PRESENT

1822
Englishwoman Mary Ann Mantell discovers teeth from one of the first fossils to be recognized as a dinosaur.

1831–1836
Darwin completes a five-year voyage on the H.M.S. *Beagle*, during which he conducted studies that lead to his theory of evolution.

1860
The first fossil of *Archaeopteryx*, a birdlike prehistoric flying reptile, is found.

1865
Gregor Mendel presents his ideas on inheritance.

1876
Mitosis, the process of cell replication, is first described by Eduard Strasburger.

1900
Cuban-American physiologist Aristides Agramonte y Simoni discovers that yellow fever is transmitted through mosquitoes.

1901
Russian scientist Élie Metchnikoff determines the role of white blood cells in fighting infection.

1913
Alfred Sturtevant introduces the technique of chromosome mapping to record positions of genes.

1919
Karl von Frisch describes the "bee's dance," the way in which honeybees communicate.

1924
Fossils of human ancestor *Australopithecus* are discovered, helping establish Africa as the site of humankind's origins.

1926
Walter Cannon introduces the concept of homeostasis, in which the body's systems work together to maintain balance.

1944
Oswald Avery shows that nearly all organisms have DNA as their hereditary material.

1953
Francis Crick, James Watson, and Rosalind Franklin determine the double-helix structure of DNA.

1960
Jane Goodall begins her studies of chimpanzees in Gombe, Tanzania.

1969
The first human eggs are fertilized using in vitro fertilization.

1996
Scottish scientists clone a sheep named Dolly.

2000
The Human Genome Project produces a rough draft of the human genome sequence.

2006
Analysis of a 375-million-year-old fossil shows it to be a "missing link" between fish and four-legged vertebrates.

2010
Genetic evidence shows that interbreeding between humans and Neanderthals took place and that some modern humans have Neanderthal genes.

DOMAINS OF LIFE

AN INVISIBLE WORLD

We share this planet with more than eight million other species, and each of them falls into one of only three types: Archaea, the ancient line; bacteria, the microbial line; and Eukarya, which includes plants, animals, fungus, and others.

ARCHAEA

METHANOSARCINA SP.
A type of archaea
that produces methane

METHANOBREVIBACTER SP.
One of the archaea found
in the human gut

SULFOLOBUS SP.
Thrives in hot springs
>176°F (80°C)

ARCHAEA & BACTERIA

MILLIONS OF MICROORGANISMS

Archaea are so difficult to detect that they were unknown until the 1970s. They resemble bacteria in their simple shape and lack of complex cellular organs, but they are as genetically distinct from bacteria as humans are. Their ancient genetic markers suggest that life may have started in the hydrothermal vents of the deep ocean.

Despite their microscopic size, bacteria make up most of the mass of life on Earth. There are as many bacteria on your skin and inside your body as there are human cells making it up. Although the battle against bacterial infection has been common for centuries, this microbial world represents an ecosystem scientists are only starting to approach cohesively.

BACTERIA

MYCOBACTERIUM SP.
This bacterium
causes tuberculosis.

SALMONELLA SP.
Infected food causes
gastric disease.

FUNGI

POLYPORUS SP.
Shelf fungus, grows
on dead or dying trees

COOKEINA SP.
Tropical toadstool,
grows on trees

EUKARYA

FROM FUNGI TO PRIMATES

Eukarya, which contain every complex multicellular organism on the planet, are divided into four taxonomic kingdoms: Plants, Animals, Fungi, and Protoctista. Despite their seeming diversity, Eukarya share a single set of characteristics: multicellular organisms with clearly defined cellular structures, such as a nucleus, mitochondria, and other organelles.

ANIMALS

TANGARA SP.
Golden-hooded tanager,
from Costa Rica

CHAETODON SP.
Masked butterfly fish,
from Asia

ELEPHANT
Two species,
Indian and African

CHIMPANZEE
In African rainforests,
woods, and grasslands

PLANTS

MAMMILLARIA SP.
Twin-spined cactus,
from Mexico

COSMOS
Annual seed-
bearing flower

POACEAE SP.
One of 8,000 species
of grasses

QUERCUS SP.
Southern live oak,
North America

KEY DATES

Dates in the Evolution of LIFE ON EARTH

■ **CA 4 BILLION YEARS AGO**
Life begins on planet Earth.

■ **CA 2.4 BILLION YEARS AGO**
Great oxidation event occurs, giving Earth its oxygen.

■ **1.5 BILLION YEARS AGO**
Plants, animals, and fungus separate into distinct types.

■ **500 MILLION YEARS AGO**
Life moves onto land.

■ **65 MILLION YEARS AGO**
The Cretaceous–Tertiary extinction wipes out the dinosaurs.

■ **7 TO 8 MILLION YEARS AGO**
Hominids share last common ancestor with bonobos and chimpanzees.

PLANTS UP CLOSE

A WHOLE NEW LOOK AT ROSEMARY

When it comes to evolution, plants are anything but placid. At a microscopic scale, plants are dazzlingly varied and have astonishing structural complexity. Modern imaging reveals the incredible structures plants use to transform sunlight into energy and energy into everything else. Inside the cellular walls, chemical kitchens create oils, acids, and toxins that plants use to attract allies or keep away predators. If you've ever thought the kingdom of plants is boring, take a closer look. Here is a colorized microscopic look at a leaf of rosemary, a beloved kitchen herb.

A WORD FROM

Forests as Families In a single forest, a mother tree can be connected to hundreds of other trees. Using our isotope tracers, we have found that mother trees will send their excess carbon through the mycorrhizal network to the understory seedlings—and we've associated this with increased seedling survival.

—**SUZANNE SIMARD,** *ecologist*

A microscopic view of a rosemary leaf reveals a functional coat of hair.

THROUGH PHOTOSYNTHESIS, PLANTS TURN SUNLIGHT, WATER, AND CARBON DIOXIDE INTO OXYGEN AND SUGARS. THIS NATURAL TURNAROUND RETURNS 100 BILLION NET TONS OF CARBON ANNUALLY TO THE PLANETWIDE SYSTEM AND GENERATES 40% OF THE PRECIPITATION THAT FALLS ON LAND.

Tiny repositories of oily essences help to fend off predators and give rosemary its distinctive flavor.

Under a microscope, the slight furriness of a rosemary leaf looks like a tangle of uncombed hairs.

Plant cells are mostly green because chlorophyll, the pigment central to photosynthesis, reflects green light and absorbs red and blue.

Talking Trees

THE SECRETS WAYS OUR FORESTS ARE COMMUNICATING

Beneath a single patch of forest soil lies a vast interconnected web of life. Forest ecologist Suzanne Simard likens it to a kind of hidden intelligence. By tracking specific chemicals, she and other scientists observed how trees in the Douglas fir forests of Canada "talk," forming underground symbiotic relationships, called mycorrhizae, with fungi to relay stress signals and share resources.

Douglas fir
(hub tree)

Douglas fir
(younger tree)

Excess sugar from photosynthesis

Douglas fir
(seedling)

Understory nursery
Douglas fir trees use the network to identify and nurture related seedlings.

Symbiotic
fungal network

Resource pathways

→ Sugar from trees
→ Nutrients from soil
→ Mixed resources from network: nutrients and carbon (from sugar)
→ Chemical stress signals

Nitrogen, potassium, phosphorus, and other nutrients

Enlarged section
of tree root tip

Resource-
exchange
pathway

Fungal
thread

1.

Excess production

Taller, older trees, called hub trees, often have more access to sunlight and produce more sugar through photosynthesis than they need.

2.

Exchange of goods

A mass of fungal threads, or mycelium, envelops the root tips of a hub tree, feeding it nutrients from the soil in exchange for sugar, which the fungus lacks.

Tree
root cell

Western spruce budworm

Paper birch

Douglas fir (hub tree)

Chemical stress signals

Pine preparation
Fir trees infected with budworms send stress signals to nearby pines.

Ponderosa pine

In spring and fall, firs share sugar with leafless birches.

In summer, birches return the favor to shaded firs.

Symbiotic fungal network

▶ FOREST IN DISTRESS

3.

Deep connections
Weaker firs in the shaded understory tap into the network as it swells with resources. Firs can also share with other species, such as birch.

WARNING SIGNS
Through the network, trees under stress can transfer resources, such as water, and can send chemical signals that trigger defensive mechanisms in other trees. Threats like insect infestation and drought are expected to increase as the climate changes.

FOSSILS
PAST LIVES

LASTING IMPRESSIONS Fossils are the preserved remains or imprints of ancient living things. They offer clues about past life-forms and environments and are keys to understanding the evolution of life on Earth.

> " I WANT YOU TO SEE THE WORLD THROUGH THE EYES OF TRILOBITES ... MAKE A JOURNEY BACK THROUGH HUNDREDS OF MILLIONS OF YEARS. "
>
> —RICHARD FORTEY, PALEONTOLOGIST

PLANT PARTS
Leaves, spores, pollen from as far back as 450 mya

PETRIFIED WOOD
Preserved when minerals fill pores in organic material

GRAPTOLITES
Wormlike marine animals from 500–315 mya

BRYOZOANS
Aquatic colonies in shallow limestone formations

CORALS
Main component of reefs; some date to 500 mya

TRILOBITES
Extinct animals that once dominated Earth's oceans

BRACHIOPODS
Tens of thousands of species of these once flourished.

BIVALVES
Ancestors of today's clams, mussels, oysters, and scallops

GASTROPODS
Remains of ancient snails and sea slugs

AMMONITES
Spiral-shelled creatures once prolific, extinct about 65 mya

ECHINODERMS
Five-point symmetry, like sand dollars of today

CRINOIDS
Marine animals: flexible stalk, head of waving filaments

FISH
First vertebrates in fossil record, starting 500 mya

SHARK TEETH
One ancient species left behind teeth 7 inches long.

INSECTS
Amber, fossilized tree resin, has preserved whole bodies.

A fossil from the Burgess Shale in Canada shows a trilobite's flattened, segmented shape.

TRILOBITES

ANCESTORS OF THE HORSESHOE CRAB

In Earth's early seas, trilobites roamed, only known to us now through their distinctive shapes in the fossil record. Though paleontologists have identified more than 20,000 species of trilobite, we know very little about their behavior, diet, or even how they moved. A particularly well-preserved specimen found in Morocco in 2017 gave scientists some insight into their diets, which likely consisted of a mix of sediment feeding and scavenging.

TRILOBITES FIRST APPEARED MORE THAN 500 MILLION YEARS AGO DURING THE CAMBRIAN PERIOD.

NODOSAUR

AN ARMORED WONDER

This astonishing creature is a nodosaur, an armored dinosaur we know now better than ever thanks to fossils found in Alberta, Canada, in 2017. Traces of red pigment found on its body and the armor plates that scattered during decomposition remain preserved, though the fossil is around 110 million years old. The process of fossilization often distorts the core shape of living things, but this nodosaur was well preserved. Paleobiologist Jakob Vinther noted the specimen was so complete that it "might have been walking around a couple of weeks ago." The new discovery could reveal how dinosaur armor functioned and provide new windows into dinosaur evolution and behavior.

Fossilized remains were so complete, illustrators and sculptors could envision the nodosaur in all its detail.

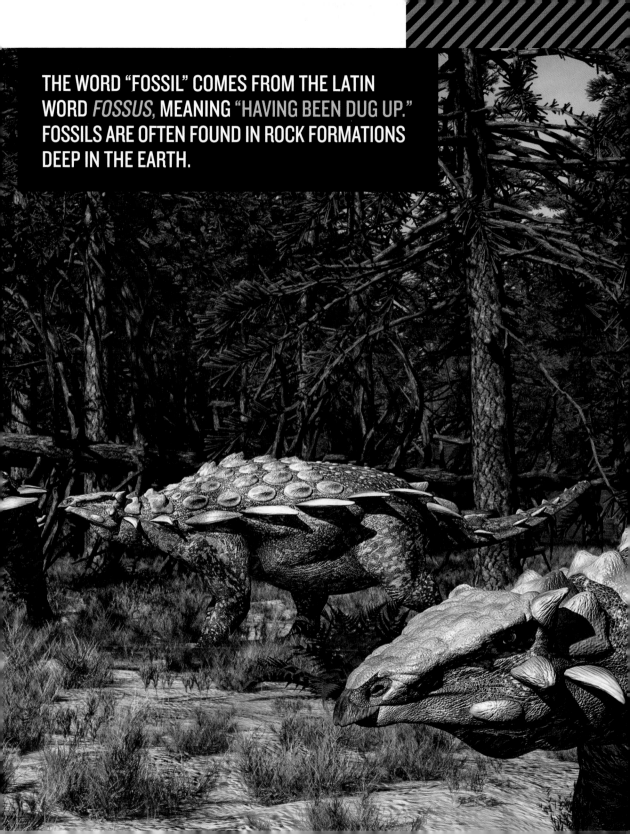

THE WORD "FOSSIL" COMES FROM THE LATIN WORD *FOSSUS*, MEANING "HAVING BEEN DUG UP." FOSSILS ARE OFTEN FOUND IN ROCK FORMATIONS DEEP IN THE EARTH.

BEST OF @NATGEO

TOP PHOTOS OF LIFE ON LAND

@ronandonovan | RONAN DONOVAN
Mr. Blue, a well-known wolf in Yellowstone National Park, stands alert over a drowned bison.

@franslanting | FRANS LANTING
This tiny primate is a tarsier. Found in the rainforests of Borneo, they're about the size of a mouse.

@kengeiger | KEN GEIGER
With distinct spots called rosettes helping it blend in, a leopard rests in the shade at Kenya's Maasai Mara National Reserve.

@argonautphoto | AARON HUEY
A herd of African elephants drink from their trunks, which are actually long noses used for smelling, breathing, and grabbing things.

> ## " THE GREATEST REALIZATION IS THAT ALL LIFE IS ONE."
>
> —CARL SAFINA, AUTHOR AND ECOLOGIST

@stefanounterthiner | STEFANO UNTERTHINER
A crested black macaque cradles her baby while grooming another macaque, a way of maintaining relationships within their groups.

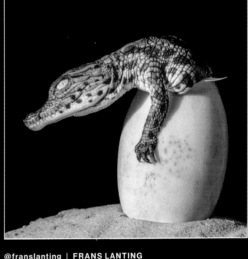

@franslanting | FRANS LANTING
Yet to become a fierce predator, a baby crocodile emerges from its egg in the Okavango Delta, Botswana.

@amivitale | AMI VITALE
A 16-year-old giant panda finds a perch in the Wolong Nature Reserve's panda center in China.

@florianschulzvisuals | FLORIAN SCHULZ
A mother polar bear nurses her cubs on an ice floe in the Arctic Circle, keeping them close for warmth.

TELLTALE TRACKS

Who Goes There? There is a hidden world all around you: Animals you do not see may still leave traces of their lives behind. By studying animal tracks, scientists and guides can estimate population size, ages, and even what the animal was doing as it left the marks.

VIRGINIA OPOSSUM
North America's only marsupial

BLACK-TAILED PRAIRIE DOG
Complex tunnel town dwellers

NORTHERN FLYING SQUIRREL
Can glide up to 300 feet

EASTERN GRAY SQUIRREL
Tail serves as umbrella or wrap.

GROUNDHOG
Also called woodchuck

EASTERN CHIPMUNK
Caches food underground for winter

AMERICAN BEAVER
Incisors fell trees to build dams.

NORTH AMERICAN PORCUPINE
Sharp quills fend off predators.

MUSKRAT
Still trapped for fur

NORTH AMERICAN DEER MOUSE
Huddles together in cold weather

HOUSE MOUSE
Can have up to 14 litters a year

NORWAY RAT
Prefers to live near humans

ANTELOPE JACKRABBIT
Huge ears help cool off.

EASTERN COTTONTAIL
Named for its powder-puff tail

NORTHERN SHORT-TAILED SHREW
Preys with poisonous bite

EASTERN MOLE
Flat, clawed forefeet dig tunnels

BOBCAT
Most widespread cat in North America

MOUNTAIN LION
Solitary unless mating

COYOTE
So adaptable, now in cities

RED FOX
Imported from Europe for sport

AMERICAN BLACK BEAR
Males weigh up to 900 pounds.

NORTH AMERICAN RIVER OTTER
Playful swimmer

BLACK FOOTED FERRET
Nearly extinct; takes over prairie dog dens

STRIPED SKUNK
Spray can be smelled half mile away.

RACCOON
Handy thanks to dexterous fingers

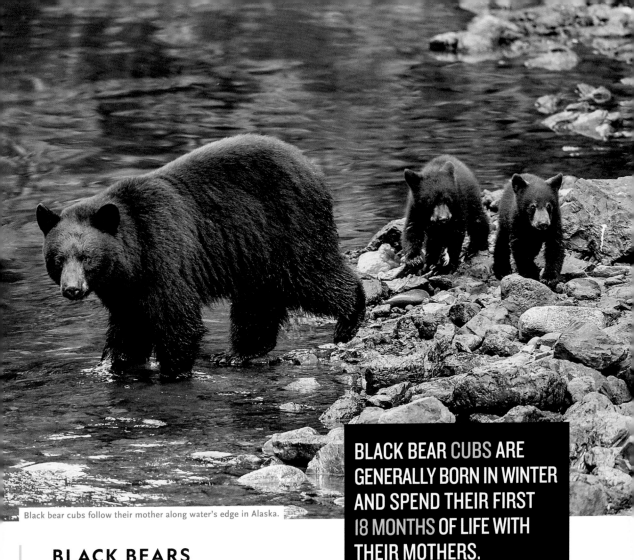

Black bear cubs follow their mother along water's edge in Alaska.

BLACK BEAR CUBS ARE GENERALLY BORN IN WINTER AND SPEND THEIR FIRST 18 MONTHS OF LIFE WITH THEIR MOTHERS.

BLACK BEARS

MAMMAL MODEL OF ADAPTABILITY

You can find the American black bear in forests across North America. As the smallest of the three American bears, the black bear may lack the massive size of polar bears or brown bears (better known as grizzlies), but it makes up for it in adaptability. There are estimated to be as many as 950,000 black bears living in North America—in Mexico, Canada, and 40 of the 50 states. They also aren't all black. Black bears' coats can come in red, brown, blond, and, rarely, blue and white. The secret to their success is adaptability. Black bears happily eat berries, insects, fish, mammals—almost anything they can get their paws on, even human trash.

A WORD FROM

Among the Bears There's only so much you can learn by measuring a tranquilized bear and putting dots on a map . . . Because if you want to learn about their habitat use, social organization, language—everything that makes a bear a bear—you have to at least see the animal that you're studying, and it can't be tranquilized. I knew I had to get close, and do more of a Jane Goodall kind of research.

—**LYNN ROGERS,** *biologist*

DOMESTICATION
TRANSFORMATION

ONCE WILD, NOW OUR FAITHFUL COMPANIONS

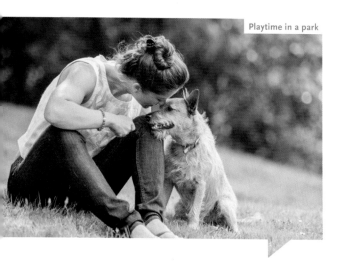

Playtime in a park

SHAPING EVOLUTION

MAKING OUR BEST FRIENDS

Today they're our best friends, but we are still unraveling the process that transformed wild cats into house cats and wolves into springer spaniels. Domestication isn't just about behavior or tameness; the friendliest wild animal is still wild in ways our pets can never be again. As humans worked with animals, our domesticated friends underwent a remarkable transformation, human-led evolution that changed behavior, size, and coloration. Cats and dogs, cows and mice—dozens of species have undergone domestication, each one with a suite of physical changes. A puppy's floppy ears and curly tail, a cow's white spots and massive size, and the orange coat of a tabby cat are all physical manifestations of this transformation.

SHAPING DOGS

FROM WOLF TO WOOF

The process of domesticating dogs began at least 10,000 years ago, and it may have happened simultaneously in different parts of the world. It likely began by accident, as wolves followed human hunters, scavenging their kills or eating scraps. While no one is certain exactly what the early relationship looked like, the transformation from fearful antagonist to companion and guardian happened remarkably quickly. Social transformation led to genetic change as humans began selecting for preferential traits. Some dogs were bred for strength, others for speed, but virtually all of them were chosen based on their behavior toward humans—survival of the friendliest. It was a genetic experiment that we're now seeing in the DNA and behavior of modern dogs around the world.

A wolf and a Maltese

Loving foxes

HOW TO MAKE A PET

EFFORTS TO REENACT EVOLUTION

In 1959, Russian geneticist Dmitry Belyaev began to study 130 silver foxes, breeding together the tamest individuals and those most responsive to humans. The goal was to re-create in miniature the long journey from wolves to dogs.

After six generations, the foxes were eager for human contact and attention. Physical changes also occurred. The foxes' tails shrank, the pups' ears stayed floppy, their tails began to wag, they began to lick their humans' faces, and they acted more like trusting young kits than wary adult foxes: a suite of genetic changes that have become known as the domestication phenotype.

EARTH DAY EVERY DAY

House Cats and
WILD BIRDS

According to the American Bird Conservancy, domesticated cats allowed to roam outdoors kill some 2.4 billion birds each year. The World Conservation Union (IUCN) includes house cats on their list of the world's 100 worst invasive species. By keeping pet cats indoors, you can help save biodiversity and beloved songbird species.

STUDIES HAVE FOUND THAT MANY DOGS CAN RECOGNIZE DIFFERENT EMOTIONS, AND MAY EVEN MIMIC THE EMOTIONAL STATE OF HUMANS THAT THEY'RE CLOSE TO.

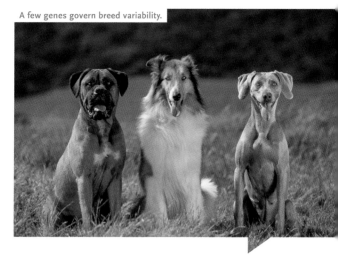

A few genes govern breed variability.

PET GENETICS

UNRAVELING THE DNA

When Belyaev's experiment began, genetic sequencing was a distant dream. But he believed that genetic changes could contain the answers he sought. Because dog breeds have almost always been governed by human selection, the deliberate creation and cultivation of traits has left clues in the genome that can be traced. Just a single gene can change a dog's size from Dachshund scale to Rottweiler scale. Hair length, ear shape, coat color, even fur type are all controlled by about 50 genetic switches. The diversity of dogs and their domestication is not a natural wonder. We have shaped our animal companions to be as amazing as they are. They are our perfect companions because we made them that way.

MEET THE
QUOLL

A MARSUPIAL ON THE MEND

This cat-size marsupial is a quoll, once native to Australia. Depleted habitat and introduced predators including cats drove them to the edge of extinction. Three subspecies survive in Australia, but one, the eastern quoll, persisted only in Tasmania. In 2017, 20 eastern quolls were released into southeastern Australia in the hope that these creatures will reestablish themselves in their original homeland.

TOXIC CANE TOADS, UNWITTINGLY INTRODUCED TO AUSTRALIA IN 1935, ACCOUNT FOR RECENT QUOLL DEATHS, BUT CARETAKERS HAVE BEEN TRAINING TASTE AVERSION IN SOME OF THE QUOLLS BEFORE REINTRODUCING THEM INTO THE WILD.

Quolls usually spend daytime in their dens, but sometimes they venture out to forage.

Wildlife Found Only in
AUSTRALIA

■ SOUTHERN CASSOWARY
Cassowaries are large, flightless birds—relatives to emus, ostriches, and kiwis. The southern cassowary is the largest of three species, standing up to six feet tall and weighing up to 160 pounds.

■ TASMANIAN DEVIL
These feisty mammals have one of the most powerful bites relative to their size in the animal kingdom. They were once common across the continent of Australia, but now their range is limited to the island of Tasmania.

■ KOALA
Though they're often called koala bears, these small gray animals are actually marsupials. Their diet is almost exclusively made of leaves from eucalyptus trees—a single koala can eat up to three pounds of leaves in a single day.

■ RED KANGAROO
One of the most recognizable Australian species, the red kangaroo is the largest marsupial in the world. With their powerful hind legs, they can jump up to six feet high and cover 25 feet in a single leap.

■ PLATYPUS
One of the few egg-laying mammals in the world, platypuses look like a mixture of a duck and a beaver. They're amphibious creatures that feed on frogs and fish and burrow into muddy riverbanks.

■ LAUGHING KOOKABURRA
Found in the eastern forests, the laughing kookaburra has a distinctive call that sounds a bit like manic laughter. Their long, distinctive beaks help them catch the small lizards, snakes, and insects that their diet comprises.

PRIMATE FAMILY TREE

OUR DISTANT COUSINS

Humans have many characteristics that make each of us unique, but biologically, we're not a class unto ourselves. Among the more than 500 different species of primate, we humans are just one. And these days, our family could use some help: Most of our cousins live in the shrinking tropical rainforest, and two-thirds of us are at risk of extinction.

SPECTRAL TARSIER

One of the smallest primates in the world is a scant three and a half inches in length. Although they may look adorable, tarsiers are the only truly carnivorous primates, grabbing beetles, bats, and even snakes—often in midair—before devouring them.

GOLDEN LION TAMARIN

These iconic creatures live in the forests of Brazil. Tamarin juveniles, which are raised by the entire community, are sometimes twins—rare among primates. Once on the edge of extinction, tamarins have been saved by intensive conservation efforts.

HAMADRYAS BABOON

These amazingly social creatures can often be seen in troops numbering in the hundreds. Though found across northeast Africa and the Arabian Peninsula, they are locally extinct in Egypt, where they were once revered as favorites of Thoth, the ancient Egyptian god of learning.

ORANGUTAN

Orangutans are the only great apes found outside of Africa: They live in the forests of Borneo and Sumatra, where they spend almost all of their time aloft. Like many primates, they have been seen creating and using simple tools when hunting and are chimpanzees' closest genetic relatives.

GORILLA

The largest of the primates, gorillas may look intimidating, but these herbivorous apes are more Curious George than King Kong. They spend most of their day wandering about, eating plants, and building new nests every night. A group of gorillas, called a "troop," can be as large as 30 individuals.

CHIMPANZEE

One of our closest genetic relatives, chimps live in tightly bonded families, use tools, and even eat medicinal plants when injured. Generally fruit and plant eaters, they also consume insects, eggs, and meat, including carrion. With such a varied diet, they can habituate themselves to African rainforests, woodlands, and grasslands. They are known to make weapons, commit murder, and even coordinate attacks on other tribes.

"WE ARE, INDEED, UNIQUE PRIMATES, WE HUMANS, BUT WE'RE SIMPLY NOT AS DIFFERENT FROM THE REST OF THE ANIMAL KINGDOM AS WE USED TO THINK."

—JANE GOODALL, PRIMATOLOGIST

A WORD FROM

Compassionate Conservation
Working with the gorillas taught me how readily our emotions, our sense of compassion, and our humanity influence conservation decisions. I finally understood that conservation is more than a science. I realized it was time to shift gears in my career and start teaching. I no longer wanted to work to save the last of a species or focus just on the science of veterinary medicine. I wanted to help inspire the next generation of conservationists.

—LUCY SPELMAN, *wildlife biologist*

KOKO
THE SIGNING GORILLA

ANIMAL AMBASSADOR

By the time of her death in 2018, Koko knew over 2,000 words in American Sign Language and held extended conversations with journalists, scientists, and entertainers. Her gentleness, playfulness, and humor led to a new imagining of animals' mental and emotional lives.

As Koko signals "eat" by moving her fingertips to her mouth, Francine Patterson rewards her with a treat.

Koko was born on July 4, 1971, at the San Francisco Zoo. When she was just one year old, she started working with Francine Patterson, then a graduate student in psychology at Stanford University. Earlier experiments had focused on primates' mimicking human speech, but Project Koko focused instead on sign language. The outcome seemed incredible. Koko made tremendous progress "talking" about her world. She showed interest in books, painting, and small animals, especially kittens, picking them up to pet or nurture. Her ability and seeming willingness to talk captured public attention.

Koko appeared in numerous documentaries and television shows, and twice on the cover of *National Geographic*. She became a celebrity in her own right, appearing with Mister Rogers and Robin Williams. Her adoption of the kitten All Ball became an image for animal empathy and inspired multiple children's books. She was an icon and ambassador but, despite many attempts, never a parent.

A LASTING LEGACY

Some scientists are skeptical of Koko's abilities. They see trained behaviors and anthropomorphism rather than independent speech, and some argue that her trainers and the public saw in Koko what they wanted to see. While Koko's fame has lasted, the idea of primate-speech studies has not, and few are ongoing. Even after her death in 2018, Koko offers hope for the possibility of interspecies communication.

> " UNCONTAMINATED BY HUMANS, [GORILLAS] ARE DEFINITELY CLOSER TO LIVING IN THE NOW . . . THEY ARE SO MUCH IN HARMONY WITH NATURE, WE SURELY COULD USE THEM AS A MODEL."
>
> —FRANCINE PATTERSON, PSYCHOLOGIST AND KOKO'S TEACHER

A western lowland gorilla, Koko lived to age 46.

KEY FACTS

Other Famous
TALKING ANIMALS

ALEX, GRAY PARROT In 1977, Irene Pepperberg bought an African gray parrot from a pet shop. Over the next 30 years Alex learned over 100 English words and simple math skills.

HECTOR AND HAN, BOTTLENOSE DOLPHINS These two young male dolphins seem to understand a request to innovate, responding by not performing the same trick twice in a given session.

CHANTEK, ORANGUTAN While living with anthropologist Lyn Miles, Chantek learned to communicate using American Sign Language, clean his room, and use a toilet.

BEST OF @NATGEO

TOP PHOTOS OF SEA LIFE

@brianskerry | BRIAN SKERRY
Green sea turtles mate off the coast of St. Croix in the U.S. Virgin Islands. These endangered turtles can weigh up to 700 pounds.

@cristinamittermeier | CRISTINA MITTERMEIER
With its tail fin poised, a humpback whale dives into ocean off the Antarctic Peninsula.

@brianskerry | BRIAN SKERRY
A spinner dolphin—known for its aerial maneuvers—jumps from calm waters after a morning storm in Oahu, Hawaii.

@carltonward | CARLTON WARD
Manatees breathe air above surface, but this mother and calf dip underwater during a rain shower in King's Bay, Florida.

> **" WE KNOW THAT WHEN WE** PROTECT **OUR** OCEANS, **WE'RE PROTECTING** OUR FUTURE."
>
> **—BILL CLINTON,** FORMER U.S. PRESIDENT

@mattiasklumofficial | **MATTIAS KLUM**
Clownfish have a symbiotic relationship with a stinging anemone; in exchange for safe shelter, the fish cleans and defends the anemone.

@timlaman | **TIM LAMAN**
Up close, the bright colors and intricate details of a sea star's skin are revealed.

@enricsala | **ENRIC SALA**
A Galápagos sea lion searches for its next meal in a large school of salema fish off the coast of Isabela Island.

@justinhofman | **JUSTIN HOFMAN**
Using its tail like a finger, a seahorse snatches trash caught in the current around the Indonesian islands.

SAVE THE REEFS

PARADISE ALMOST LOST

Coral reefs may seem like an explosion of color, but coral them-selves are translucent. Reefs get their radiant hues by hosting billions of colorful algae, which they use for food. Unfortunately, when waters warm, reefs expel these algae, leaving the reefs bleached and damaged. Back-to-back bleaching events in 2016 and 2017 damaged or destroyed over half of the Great Barrier Reef. A quarter of all marine species live on the reefs and rely on these algae. Without them, the whole ecosystem crumbles.

Color abounds at the Great Detached Reef on the Northern Great Barrier Reef.

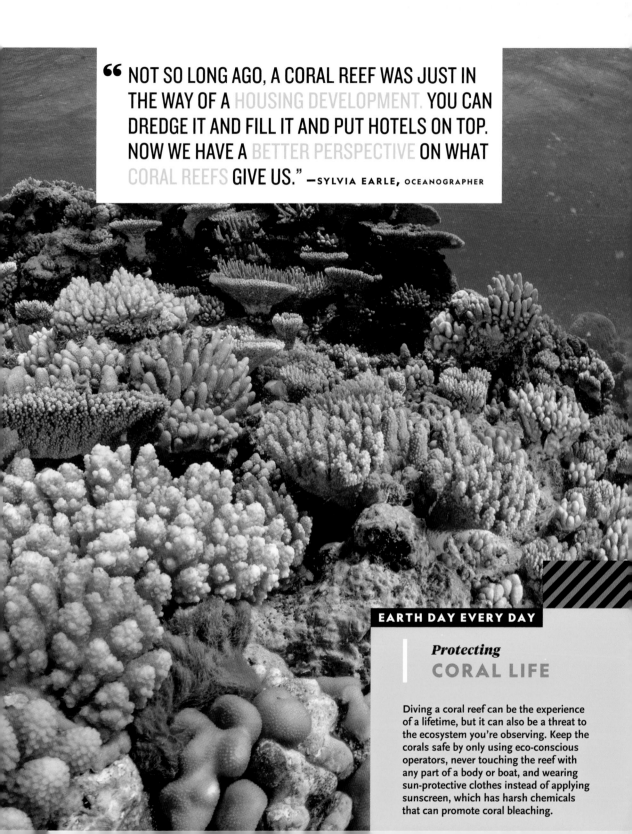

> **" NOT SO LONG AGO, A CORAL REEF WAS JUST IN THE WAY OF A HOUSING DEVELOPMENT. YOU CAN DREDGE IT AND FILL IT AND PUT HOTELS ON TOP. NOW WE HAVE A BETTER PERSPECTIVE ON WHAT CORAL REEFS GIVE US. "** —SYLVIA EARLE, OCEANOGRAPHER

EARTH DAY EVERY DAY

Protecting
CORAL LIFE

Diving a coral reef can be the experience of a lifetime, but it can also be a threat to the ecosystem you're observing. Keep the corals safe by only using eco-conscious operators, never touching the reef with any part of a body or boat, and wearing sun-protective clothes instead of applying sunscreen, which has harsh chemicals that can promote coral bleaching.

WHALES

LEARNING FROM THESE GIANTS OF THE SEA

A sperm whale tail

WHALE SONG

SOUNDS OF THE SEA

In the deep sound channel of the open ocean, the clicks and songs of whales filter in from thousands of miles away. For many, it is the song of the sea, and all whales are part of its chorus. These animals, including the blue whale, the largest mammal on Earth, fill the ocean with their haunting melody.

Like bats or dolphins, some whales can echolocate, using their calls to "see" objects through reflected soundwaves. Other whale songs are used to show off for mates or rivals, while mothers and calves whisper to each other to avoid aquatic eavesdroppers. Sometimes whale pods sing in something near conversation across hundreds of miles. Still, evolutionarily, this is a recent soundtrack, and the song of the whales wasn't always aquatic.

OCEAN ELDERS

A SPECTACLE OF SIZE AND LONGEVITY

Whales are some of the largest animals in the history of Earth, and some of the most graceful. Blue whales, which can weigh up to 150 tons and measure as long as the boats sent to watch them, glide with seemingly no effort. They leap from the water, spin, and dive with casual elegance.

Some whales can dive more than 10,000 feet into the darkest depths, going hours between breaths. The rewards for these astonishing dives are squid, krill, and crustaceans. The whale's massive size comes with a long life span. Baby whales can take a decade to reach adulthood, and even the shortest lived whales can live for 40 years, the longest for more than 200.

A humpback whale calf

A mother blue whale and her calf

SPERM WHALES HAVE THE LARGEST BRAINS EVER KNOWN TO EXIST ON EARTH, MEASURING NEARLY 500 CUBIC INCHES. A HUMAN BRAIN IS ABOUT 80 CUBIC INCHES.

A pod of sperm whales

EVOLUTIONARY HISTORY

THE EARLIEST WHALES

Pakicetus was an ancient ancestor of the massive blue whales and all other cetaceans, a group of marine mammals that includes dolphins and porpoises. With a hairy coat, four legs, a long tail, and a long, narrow mouth, this distant relative looked more like a German shepherd than a cetacean. It lived alongside the ocean, not in it, but over millions of years it evolved into more and more of an ocean dweller. Archaeologists have reconstructed the story piece by piece, watching the slow transformation of ankles to fins, and long snouts to massive mouths.

PROTECTING WHALES

KEEPING MARINE MAMMALS SAFE

They may be titans in the sea, but whales are under threat. Commercial whaling continues in countries like Iceland, Norway, and Japan, and traditional indigenous spear hunting continues as well. Whales often meet with accidental threats as well—entanglement in fishing lines or nets, strikes by oceangoing vessels. Changes in the temperature and water quality of the ocean affect their survival as well.

Climate change, the threat for most animals, hits some species harder than others. Some whales like the vaquita live in specialized climates, with no escape, while global wanderers like the gray whales are thriving in warmer waters and venturing into new regions.

A WORD FROM

Creating Crittercam I conceived of Crittercam as a scientific tool, a way of studying animal behavior in places people access. What I didn't expect was the tremendous attraction the resulting images hold for people. Every time we deploy, Crittercam brings home the animal's point of view . . . a perspective that allows people to connect with the animal and its struggles to survive. It's this empathic experience that I didn't necessarily expect when I invented Crittercam.

—**GREG MARSHALL,** *biologist and cinematographer*

SEA SHELLS

A Home in the Sea Creatures started building shells around 500 million years ago. Since then, they have evolved spirals, spines, and ridges, but the purpose is still the same: to protect the delicate animal living inside it.

FLORIDA FIGHTING CONCH
Spurred foot for defense, burrowing

FRILLED DOGWINKLE
Preys with tongue and poison

KNOBBED WHELK
Like conch, can be made into a horn

LETTERED OLIVE
Used by Native Americans for jewelry

ATLANTIC PLATE LIMPET
Attaches to rocks by suction

ATLANTIC SLIPPER SHELL
Shells stack for reproduction

BAY SCALLOP
Senses predators with 18 pairs of eyes

PACIFIC LITTLENECK CLAM
Abundant in U.S. West Coast shallows

EASTERN OYSTER
Must attach to hard surface to mature

PACIFIC RAZOR CLAM
Meaty edible bivalve

ATLANTIC JACKKNIFE CLAM
Digs itself down into sand or mud

ATLANTIC AUGER
Stuns prey with poisonous barb

PACIFIC GEODUCK
Can age to more than 150 years

NORTHERN QUAHOG
Harvested for clam chowder

MARINE MUSSEL
One of many edible mussel species

BLACK TURBAN SNAIL
Feeds on algae, has many predators

COMMON MARSH SNAIL
Breathes air, feeds on marsh grasses

COMMON PERIWINKLE
Two antennae, one foot

RED ABALONE
Long valued for pearlescent colors

VIOLET SEA SNAIL
Churns bubbles and floats to survive

> " **NATURE IS THE MOST BEAUTIFUL ENGINEER AND IT ALWAYS HAS A REASON FOR CHOOSING ANY SHAPE.**"
>
> —**DR. CHANDRA TIWARY,** INDIAN INSTITUTE OF SCIENCE

A man wades through a bed of giant clams in Kiribati, Polynesia.

CLAMMING UP

MARINE MARVELS

Clams, snails, and giant squids all are mollusks, one of the most diverse groups of life on Earth. There are more than 100,000 known species, but the number may be twice that, found in every aquatic environment from freshwater lakes to deep-sea trenches. Mollusks are invertebrates, with a mantle covering the soft body. Some possess a biological glue stronger than any other substance in nature, and some can survive briefly outside their aquatic environment. Their abundance and versatility has made them desirable food. In fact, early American waters had so many oysters, they were considered peasant food. Today they are an expensive gourmet treat.

THE AMAZING
OCTOPUS

UNDERWATER GENIUSES

The octopus is a strange animal. Its three hearts pump blue blood through a bone-less frame. Some can compress their bodies from three feet across to the size of a quarter. Other species mimic textures and shapes like ridges, bumps, or spines. It takes a common octopus approximately two seconds to fully camouflage itself with its surroundings. Octopuses may have been the first intelligent creature on Earth, yet of their 500 million neurons, two-thirds are located in their arms, not their heads.

The common octopus's pigment cells and special muscles give it unique camouflage abilities.

THE LARGEST OCTOPUS EVER RECORDED WAS A GIANT PACIFIC OCTOPUS THAT MEASURED 30 FEET ACROSS AND WEIGHED MORE THAN 600 POUNDS.

BEST OF @NATGEO

TOP PHOTOS OF LIFE ON THE WING

@franslanting | FRANS LANTING
n addition to their large, colorful bills, toucans have bright
blue and orange skin surrounding their eyes.

@timlaman | TIM LAMAN
A male red bird-of-paradise begins an elaborate courtship dis
play. The species is found only in the West Papuan Islands.

@carltonward | CARLTON WARD
Common in eastern North America, barred owls make a
range of calls and are more likely to be heard during the day
han other owls.

@joelsartore | JOEL SARTORE
These bright colors actually help the red-winged parrot
blend into its native rainforest environment.

@jasperdoest | JASPER DOEST
Flamingos are often seen in flocks gathered on mudflats, but his arthritic Caribbean flamingo favors water.

@stephenwilkes | STEPHEN WILKES
A group of migrating sandhill cranes take wing in Nebraska against the setting sun.

@brianskerry | BRIAN SKERRY
A mother gentoo penguin and her chick stick close together. Hatchling gentoos stay in the nest for up to a month.

@argonautphoto | AARON HUEY
A lone bird soars above the roofline in the old city of Kabul, Afghanistan.

BACKYARD
BIRDS

Flights of Fascination Birds wing their way through everyone's landscape, on every continent, whether hot or cold, rural or urban. Birding is about more than checking lists: Birders turn their love of these avians into real science.

AMERICAN GOLDFINCH
One of the few vegan birds

HOUSE FINCH
Males have rose-colored breast.

BALTIMORE ORIOLE
Weaves hanging nest of fibers

AMERICAN ROBIN
Traditional sign of spring

BLACK-CAPPED CHICKADEE
Chirps its own name

WESTERN BLUEBIRD
Nests in knotholes or birdhouses

EASTERN BLUEBIRD
Eats primarily insects and grubs

SONG SPARROW
May raise two or more broods a year

TUFTED TITMOUSE
Hoards food for winter

WARBLING VIREO
Melodious, recognizable song

NORTHERN CARDINAL
Males bright red, females olive

HOUSE SPARROW
Prefers to live near to humans

NORTHERN FLICKER
Digs in soil for ants and beetles

HOUSE WREN
Wide range, Canada through S. America

RED-WINGED BLACKBIRD
Winter flocks in the millions

RUBY-THROATED HUMMINGBIRD
Sips from red and orange flowers

GREAT HORNED OWL
Head swivels to look in all directions.

EASTERN PHOEBE
Perching, tail wags up and down

EUROPEAN STARLING
Mimics calls of other birds

CLIFF SWALLOW
Creates gourd-shaped nest of mud

AMERICAN CROW
Crafts tools to get at food

PURPLE MARTIN
Will move into erected nesting boxes

NORTHERN MOCKINGBIRD
May learn 200 different songs

WHITE-BREASTED NUTHATCH
Creeps along tree trunks, often head down

BLUE JAY
Throat pouch can hold 2–3 acorns.

Common ravens are the largest perching birds in North America.

CORVIDS

A family that includes ravens, crows, and magpies, corvids are often recognized as some of the most intelligent birds in the world. Their abilities run the gamut from mimicking other animal sounds to using tools and other problem-solving skills. Researchers studying animal cognition have found that ravens are able to preplan tasks, a skill once thought to be unique to humans and great apes. The Eurasian magpie, with its distinct black and white plumage, recognizes its own reflection in a mirror. Some species of crow recognize human faces, and sometimes they are more comfortable with humans they have interacted with before than with strangers.

MYTHICAL BIRDS

Corvids feature prominently in folklore across cultures and religions. In the Old Testament, it is said that Noah sent out both a raven and a dove to see if floodwaters had receded. In some Native American traditions, a raven swallowed the sun out of jealousy. The Norse God Odin had two ravens, named Huginn and Muninn—thought and memory.

> **"IF YOU TAKE CARE OF BIRDS, YOU TAKE CARE OF MOST OF THE ENVIRONMENTAL PROBLEMS IN THE WORLD."**
>
> **—THOMAS E. LOVEJOY,**
> **CONSERVATION BIOLOGIST**

A WORD FROM

Better Together [Crows] have this family unit, but they also have a neighborhood that they have some allegiance to as well. You keep your territory and you don't let the neighbors in, but if a predator is attacking them, you go help. They all know everybody in the neighborhood; they know what's happening by what everybody else is saying.

—KEVIN MCGOWAN, *ornithologist*

HUMMINGBIRDS
WINGED WONDERS

FIREWORKS IN FLIGHT

Hummingbirds fly like magical fairies and shimmer like jewels in the sky, but scientists have never fully understood these glorious birds. The hummingbird can fly backward, hover, and even fly sideways—all at incredible speed. But how? The answer comes in unique biological adaptations only recently discovered: larger brains to process information, symmetrical wing strokes, and longer "hands" for greater flexibility and movement. Despite their diminutive size—the smallest of 340 species weighs less than two grams—their brain represents 4.2 percent of their body weight, making it proportionally one of the largest in the animal kingdom.

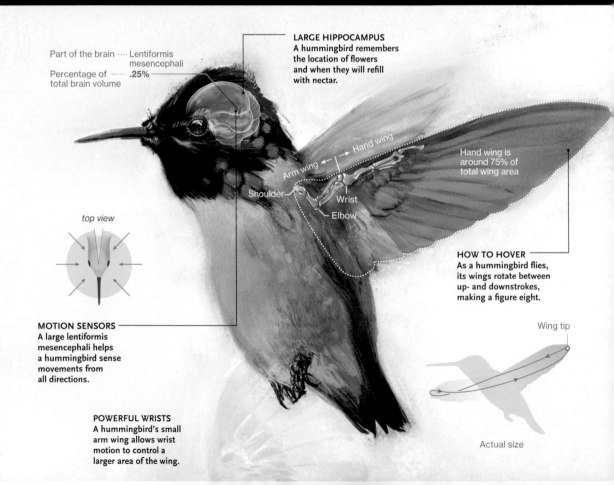

Part of the brain···· Lentiformis mesencephali

Percentage of ········ .25%
total brain volume

LARGE HIPPOCAMPUS
A hummingbird remembers the location of flowers and when they will refill with nectar.

Hand wing

Arm wing

Shoulder

Wrist

Elbow

Hand wing is around 75% of total wing area

top view

MOTION SENSORS
A large lentiformis mesencephali helps a hummingbird sense movements from all directions.

HOW TO HOVER
As a hummingbird flies, its wings rotate between up- and downstrokes, making a figure eight.

Wing tip

POWERFUL WRISTS
A hummingbird's small arm wing allows wrist motion to control a larger area of the wing.

Actual size

Lift

Airflow

Downstroke
75% of the lift

Upstroke
25% of the lift

Downstroke
100% of the lift

Upstroke
0% of the lift

DOWNSTROKE
Hummingbirds produce lift with both upward and downward wing strokes.

UPSTROKE
They can beat their wings up to 100 times a second.

PROPULSION
In larger birds, all the propulsion comes from downward wing strokes.

FORWARD
Larger birds tend to fly forward rather than hovering.

> ## " THE HUMMINGBIRD IN FLIGHT IS A WATER-SPARK, AN INCANDESCENT DRIP OF AMERICAN FIRE."
>
> **—PABLO NERUDA, POET**

SEEING EVERY MOVE

FLIGHT OF HANDS

By using super-high-speed cameras to slow down time, scientists are finally unlocking the secrets of the world's smallest bird. Hummingbirds have, proportionally, the longest hands and shortest arms of any bird. Arm wings are often used for gliding, while hand wings provide the lift. With a larger hand wing, hummingbirds can rotate the shape of their wing on every stroke, generating precise and constant lift, at the cost of constant flapping. Moving at this speed and control takes massive brainpower. Here too, the hummingbird is unique, having proportionally the second largest brain in the animal kingdom. Speed, smarts, and control are vital for the birds to access the nectar they so desperately need.

TOP FIVE

Best Flowers for
HUMMINGBIRDS

1 **SCARLET BEE BALM** Hummingbirds love this hardy perennial. Its red, pink, or lavender petals catch a wandering bird's eye.

2 **CARDINAL FLOWER** This 48-inch-tall flower is loaded with long-lasting deep-red blossoms providing nectar and height to any garden.

3 **TRUMPET VINE** The bright orange flowers on this creeping vine delight hummingbirds and other avians but can take over small areas.

4 **LUPINE** This early blooming flower attracts the first hummingbirds of the season.

5 **BUTTERFLY BUSH** True to its name, the thick clusters of flowers on this bountiful bush attract insects as well as hummingbirds.

PARROTS

MORE THAN JUST POLLY AND HER CRACKER

A row of macaws

SUCH DIVERSITY

A PLETHORA OF PARROTS

From the streets of San Francisco to the tip of South Africa, the Peruvian Amazon to the jungles of New Guinea, you can find parrots on five of the seven continents. The extensive range of these birds has led to incredible biodiversity. There are over 350 kinds of parrot scattered across the globe, appearing in all sizes: A tiny pygmy parrot measures just three inches across, while the hyacinth macaw's wingspan stretches more than three feet when fully spread.

Most are a riot of colors—pale greens and teal blues, deep blacks and violent reds—though others, like the African grays, are more muted. These birds aren't just beautiful flashes in the wilderness. Some of the larger species of parrots can live for over 80 years.

SOCIAL CREATURES

FLOCKING TOGETHER

At night in the tropics, the oldest, tallest trees in the forest resound with the singsong conversation of flocks of parrots. Tree canopies form the heart of a parrot's social life, and parrot parents often nest in the hollowed-out core of the tree below. Lorikeets, lovebirds, and cockatoos gather in flocks of hundreds or even thousands.

Unfortunately, this socialization has made them a prime target of trappers, who often gather numerous birds at once. In Mexico alone, up to 75,000 birds were harvested in a single year, and more than 75 percent of the birds harvested die before they even make it into trade. In the pet market, they often face a life of stress and isolation and develop symptoms of anxiety and depression.

Scarlet macaws

A crimson-fronted parakeet

PARROTS HAVE TASTE BUDS ON THE INSIDE OF THEIR BEAKS AS WELL AS ON THEIR TONGUES.

Australian king parrots

LANGUAGE LEARNERS

AN INSTINCT FOR IMITATION

While many birdcalls are biologically hardwired, parrots learn language from their flock. Some flocks develop unique accents and dialects. Certain calls can act as passwords, with parrot calls identifying outsiders to the flock. While parrots are famous for their mimicry—several species can accurately mimic other birdcalls, fire alarms, and even human speech—it's not limited to copying. Parrots have shown complex reasoning skills on the same scale as chimpanzees or small children.

WILDLIFE TRADE

A WILDLIFE DISASTER

No order of birds has been more exploited in the wild than the parrot, and no individual bird more than the African gray parrot. More than 1.3 million African grays were removed from the continent legally, and it's unknown how many others were smuggled out or died in transit. In Ghana, the population of African grays has been reduced by 99 percent, and a bird once as common as a pigeon is now exceedingly rare. Australian palm cockatoos can fetch up to $30,000 per bird and have attracted the types of organized crime usually associated with elephant and rhino poaching. The international pet trade means we may be loving these animals to death.

A WORD FROM

Bird Brain He [the African gray parrot Alex] was not supposed to be able to name objects and categories, understand "bigger" and "smaller," "same" and "different," because his was a bird brain. But, of course, Alex did do such things. I knew that Alex was proving a profound truth: Brains may look different, and there may be a spectrum of ability that is determined by anatomical details, but brains and intelligence are a universally shared trait in nature—the capacity varies, but the building blocks are the same.

—IRENE PEPPERBERG, *animal behaviorist and psychologist*

WHOSE CATERPILLAR?

MIRACULOUS TRANSFORMATION

The famous transformation from caterpillar to butterfly looks a little different to scientists studying the creatures than to poets writing about them. To change their structure so completely, caterpillars almost completely dissolve themselves into a stem cell soup inside the cocoon. They rebuild themselves from scratch using pockets of specialized imaginal cells before emerging in their new form.

GREAT PURPLE HAIRSTREAK
Seeks mistletoe, eats leaves and male flowers

PIPEVINE SWALLOWTAIL
Eats leaves of pipevine

WESTERN TIGER SWALLOWTAIL
Spins silk for shelter

BLACK SWALLOWTAIL
When threatened, forked gland spews odor

CABBAGE WHITE
Hatches from eggs laid on garden greens

GRAY HAIRSTREAK
Tended and defended by ants

GULF FRITILLARY
Eats only passionflower plants

MOURNING CLOAK
Eats leaves of hardwood trees and shrubs

RED ADMIRAL
Eats tender inside stem of nettles

AMERICAN LADY
Seeks sunflowers to eat

COMMON BUCKEYE
Metallic-blue branching spines

MONARCH
Turns distasteful to predators by eating milkweed

VICEROY
Mottled body resembles bird dropping

REGAL MOTH
Called hickory-horned devils, but harmless

IO MOTH
Prickly green spines that can sting

LUNA MOTH
Spins papery brown cocoon

BUTTERFLIES SIP WATER, NECTAR, AND EVEN ANIMAL BLOOD USING A LONG, THIN **PROBOSCIS**. ALTHOUGH IT LOOKS LIKE A STRAW, BUTTERFLIES DO NOT SUCK THROUGH IT. INSTEAD, THE ORGAN SOAKS UP FLUID BY **CAPILLARY ACTION**, AS IF IT WERE A TUBE MADE OUT OF PAPER TOWEL.

GREAT PURPLE HAIRSTREAK
Brilliant blue on upper wing

PIPEVINE SWALLOWTAIL
Poisons from pipevine deter predators.

WESTERN TIGER SWALLOWTAIL
Clusters in mud puddles

BLACK SWALLOWTAIL
Courting pairs flutter before landing.

CABBAGE WHITE
One of spring's first butterflies

GRAY HAIRSTREAK
3–4 generations a year in the southern U.S.

GULF FRITILLARY
Migrates south to escape cold

MOURNING CLOAK
Long life span of 11–12 months

RED ADMIRAL
Prefers dung and carrion to nectar

AMERICAN LADY
Males are territorial.

COMMON BUCKEYE
Wing eyespots may scare predators.

MONARCH
State insect or butterfly in seven U.S. states

VICEROY
Mirrors bitter-tasting monarch as defense

REGAL MOTH
Adults do not eat at all.

IO MOTH
When disturbed, spreads wings to show eyespots

LUNA MOTH
Wing tails distract bats from preying on body.

PLIGHT OF THE HONEYBEE

POLLINATOR IN PERIL

One of tens of thousands of pollinating species, honeybees do more than their share: It's estimated that one out of eight nonagricultural plants around the world was pollinated by honeybees. But honeybees face many threats: habitat loss, monoculture farming, pesticides, and parasitic mites, to name several. Since wild bees often don't produce honey, commercial honeybees are imported, but these nonnative bees can spread disease to wild populations or turn invasive. Wild bees are suffering as a result, some seeing population drops of 70 percent and others going completely extinct. The humble workers of the bee world can't seem to catch a break.

Worker bees forage for pollen and nectar; they are the only bees that most people see.

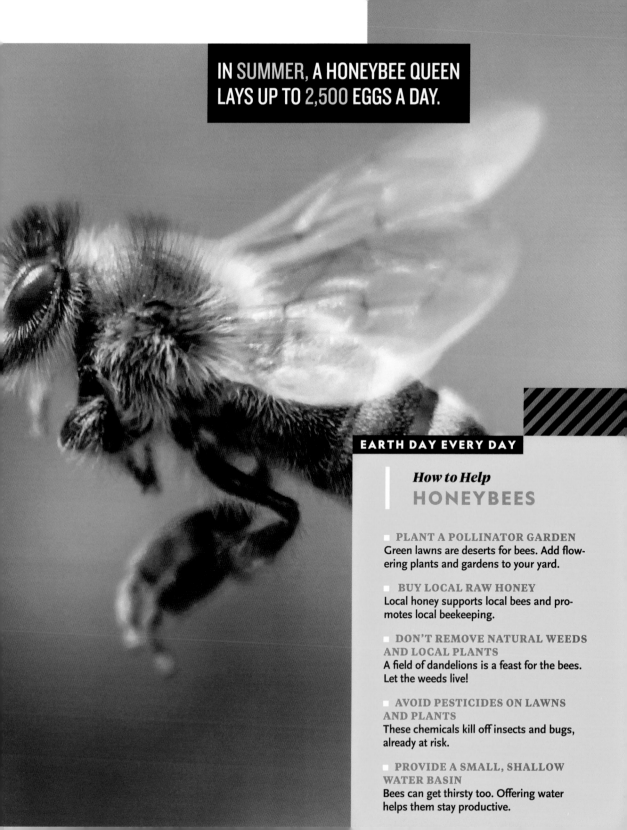

IN SUMMER, A HONEYBEE QUEEN LAYS UP TO 2,500 EGGS A DAY.

How to Help
HONEYBEES

■ **PLANT A POLLINATOR GARDEN**
Green lawns are deserts for bees. Add flowering plants and gardens to your yard.

■ **BUY LOCAL RAW HONEY**
Local honey supports local bees and promotes local beekeeping.

■ **DON'T REMOVE NATURAL WEEDS AND LOCAL PLANTS**
A field of dandelions is a feast for the bees. Let the weeds live!

■ **AVOID PESTICIDES ON LAWNS AND PLANTS**
These chemicals kill off insects and bugs, already at risk.

■ **PROVIDE A SMALL, SHALLOW WATER BASIN**
Bees can get thirsty too. Offering water helps them stay productive.

CONSERVATION
TIME LINE

8000 to 1 BC	AD 1 to 1850	1850 to 1900	1900 to 1950

8000 BC
Organized agriculture begins: cultivated plants and herded animals.

6000 BC
Animal manure is used as fertilizer.

6000 BC
Maize is domesticated in the Americas.

ca 1500 BC
Aztecs build chinampas, floating gardens, on edges of Mexican lakes.

1661
London's Vauxhall Gardens open to the public.

1701–1731
Jethro Tull invents seed drill, improves plow, and makes other farming innovations.

1730
British statesman-farmer Charles Townshend develops four-year crop rotation.

1789
Englischer Garten opens in Munich, Germany.

1849
The U.S. Department of Interior is established.

1854
Henry David Thoreau's *Walden* is published.

1858
Construction of New York City's Central Park, the first major urban park in the U.S., is under way.

1863
Britain's Alkali Act curbs acid gas emissions.

1872
Yellowstone National Park, the first legislated national park, is established.

1892
The Sierra Club is founded, with John Muir as its first president.

1913
German People's Park Association (Deutscher Volksparkbund) is founded in Germany.

1916
U.S. and Canada sign Migratory Birds Treaty, first international conservation effort.

1916
The U.S. National Park Service is established.

1918
Fritz Haber receives Nobel Prize for synthesizing ammonia, used for fertilizer.

1940s
High-yield wheat is introduced in Mexico, starting "green revolution."

1950 to 1970	1970 to 1980	1980 to 2000	2000 to PRESENT

1950 to 1970

■ **1962**
Rachel Carson's *Silent Spring* is published.

■ **1964**
U.S. legislates Wilderness Act, protecting lands from development.

■ **1968**
Apollo 8 astronauts create "Earthrise" photo.

■ **1968**
First edition of the *Whole Earth Catalog* is published.

■ **1968**
Paul R. Ehrlich's *The Population Bomb* is published.

1970 to 1980

■ **1970**
About 20 million participate in first Earth Day, April 22.

■ **1970**
The U.S. Environmental Protection Agency is established.

■ **1970**
Monsanto develops glyphosate herbicide, soon known as Roundup.

■ **1971**
Greenpeace begins as protest against nuclear testing in Alaska.

■ **1972**
Apollo 17 astronauts create "Blue Marble" photo.

■ **1973**
U.S. Congress approves Endangered Species Act.

■ **1979**
An accident occurs at Three Mile Island nuclear power plant.

1980 to 2000

■ **1980**
Green Party is established in West Germany.

■ **1987**
Montreal Protocol, which reduces emissions that deplete the ozone layer, is signed by 140 nations.

■ **1988**
First GMO crops, Roundup-resistant soybeans, developed.

■ **1992**
United Nations convenes Earth Summit in Rio de Janeiro, Brazil.

2000 to PRESENT

■ **2000**
In U.S., Green Party presidential candidate Ralph Nader receives 2.7% of vote.

■ **2008**
Svalbard Global Seed Vault is established in Norwegian Arctic.

■ **2011**
The population of humans on Earth reaches 7 billion, according to estimates from the United Nations.

■ **2016**
Paris Agreement is ratified, joining nations in combating climate change.

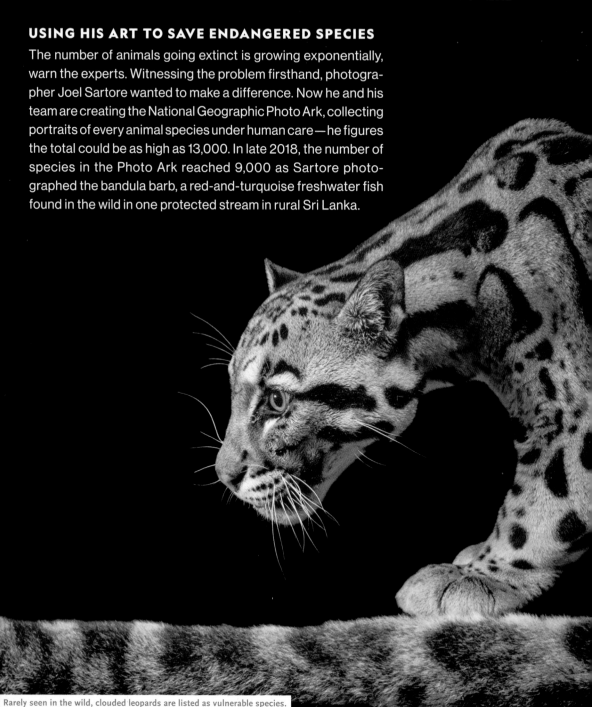

PHOTO ARK

USING HIS ART TO SAVE ENDANGERED SPECIES

The number of animals going extinct is growing exponentially, warn the experts. Witnessing the problem firsthand, photographer Joel Sartore wanted to make a difference. Now he and his team are creating the National Geographic Photo Ark, collecting portraits of every animal species under human care—he figures the total could be as high as 13,000. In late 2018, the number of species in the Photo Ark reached 9,000 as Sartore photographed the bandula barb, a red-and-turquoise freshwater fish found in the wild in one protected stream in rural Sri Lanka.

Rarely seen in the wild, clouded leopards are listed as vulnerable species.

> **" WITH EVERY** PHOTO ARK **TRIP, I MEET PEOPLE WHO ARE** TRUE **CONSERVATION** HEROES ... **THEY'RE DOING ALL THEY CAN, RIGHT THIS MINUTE, TO ENSURE** BIODIVERSITY **SURVIVES."**
>
> **—JOEL SARTORE,** PHOTOGRAPHER AND CREATOR OF THE PHOTO ARK

Joel Sartore meets black flying foxes at the Australian Bat Clinic.

KEY NUMBERS

Species and Subspecies
PHOTOGRAPHED

■ **AMPHIBIANS**
807 species

■ **BIRDS**
2,464 species

■ **FISH**
1,243 species

■ **INVERTEBRATES**
(TERRESTRIAL AND AQUATIC)
2,312 species

■ **MAMMALS**
1,177 species

■ **REPTILES**
1,582 species

■ **TOTAL**
9,585 species and subspecies
photographed as of April 2019

BIODIVERSITY

THE WORLD'S CREATURES ARE UNDER SIEGE

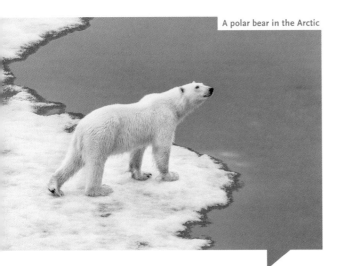

A polar bear in the Arctic

SIXTH EXTINCTION?

THE NEXT APOCALYPSE

There have been five mass extinction events in the history of Earth, when over half of all the species present on the planet died off. Today, we may be in the middle of a new extinction. Earth may have as many as two billion species, from bacteria to elephants, but that number is falling rapidly. Past extinctions resulted from volcanic eruptions and asteroid impacts, but the current extinction is caused by humans.

Since the agricultural revolution 12,000 years ago, humanity has reshaped the planet for farms and food. So many creatures have died that it would take an estimated three million to five million years to restore what has already been lost. From the mastodons hunted during the last ice age to massive coral fields bleaching in warming seas, the planet's life is under threat—but it is not too late to turn the tide.

KEYSTONE SPECIES

WHY BIODIVERSITY MATTERS

Like any other complex mechanism, the life of eco-systems depends on every element within them. Certain species can help protect or even enhance biodiversity. Sharks and otters are keystone species representing thriving and healthy ecosystems. Beavers, wolves, and kelp act as ecosystem engineers, creating specialized climates for other animals.

Coral reefs support billions of people, dependent on fishing for food and livelihood, as well as global populations of sharks and other animals. Our oxygen is generated by phytoplankton and plants, our water filtered through natural purification in swamps, and dunes and mangroves protect our cities from storms. Respecting these processes is part of the solution.

A wolf pack

The Atlantic Forest in Brazil

MORE THAN 26,000 SPECIES OF PLANTS AND ANIMALS ARE CURRENTLY AT RISK OF EXTINCTION, ACCORDING TO THE INTERNATIONAL UNION FOR CONSERVATION OF NATURE.

ESSENTIAL FORESTS

CHANGING CLIMATE, CHANGING WORLD
Tropical rainforests contain about 80 percent of the world's documented species: a riotous diversity of plants, insects, birds, and other animals. A changing climate, clear-cutting for agriculture, and timber harvesting all threaten this lush ecosystem and its biodiversity.

Halting biodiversity loss in the tropics requires a mix of solutions, from small to global. Improving and increasing protected areas can renew habitat and rescue fragile ecosystems. International actions such as the Paris Climate Agreement and zero deforestation commitments by multinationals can influence progress on a larger scale. At home, here's one thing you can do: Eat less meat, which reduces the demand to clear forests for grazing.

A WORD FROM

Marketplace of Life Extinction is not evolution's driver; survival is . . . Competition among living species drives proliferation into diversified specialties . . . We can think of this as a marketplace of life, where little competition necessitates little specialization, thus little proliferation. An area with many types of trees, for instance, directly causes the evolution of many types of highly specialized pollinating insects, hummingbirds, and pollinating bats, who visit only the "right" trees. Many flowering plants are pollinated by just one specialized species.

—**CARL SAFINA,** *ecologist*

Clouds over the Amazon Basin

UNITED EFFORT

A WORLD PROTECTED
In 2010, the United Nations passed a Strategic Plan for Biodiversity, 2011-2020, with ambitious goals including halving the rate of habitat loss and increasing protection of wild places by at least 17 percent on land and 10 percent in the ocean and along coastlines. So how have we done? "Despite numerous efforts on countless fronts in practically all the corners of the world," says Cristiana Paşca Palmer, executive secretary of the UN Convention on Biological Diversity, "we are losing too many ecosystems, too many species, too many genes and their combinations far too quickly." She invites people and nations around the world to seek to live "in harmony with nature," so that "by 2050, biodiversity is valued, conserved, restored, and wisely used, . . . sustaining a healthy planet and delivering benefits essential for all people."

PLASTIC IN OUR WORLD

AN ENDURING THREAT

Since it was first mass-produced in the 1940s, plastic has made its way into every corner of life, from soda bottles and IV bags, to car parts and insulation, and even soaps and shampoos. It has revolutionized our society—but at a cost. Plastic takes more than 400 years to degrade, so most of it still exists in some form. Only 12 percent has been incinerated, and only 9 percent has been recycled. Of the 8.3 billion metric tons produced to date, 6.3 billion has become plastic waste.

The vast majority of plastic waste—79 percent—is accumulating in landfills or sloughing off in the natural environment as litter.

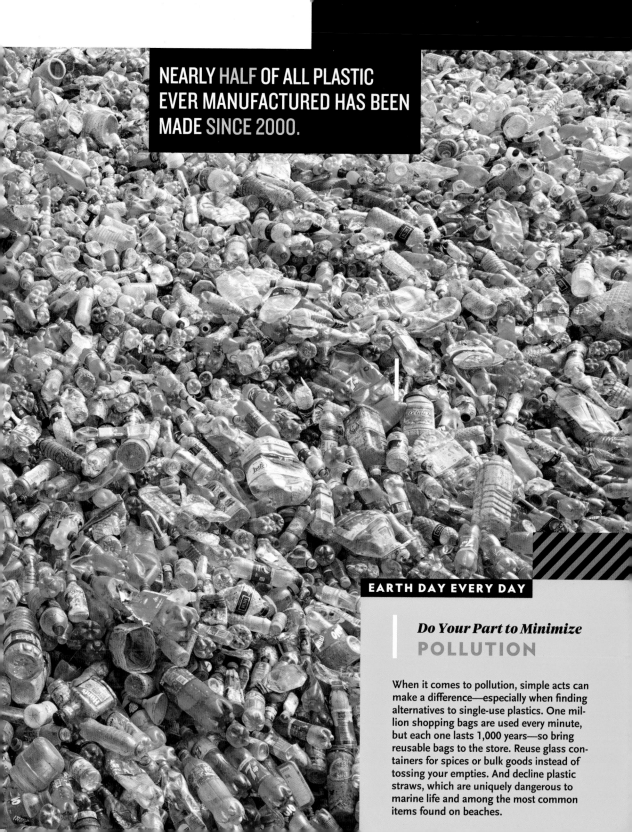

NEARLY HALF OF ALL PLASTIC EVER MANUFACTURED HAS BEEN MADE SINCE 2000.

Do Your Part to Minimize
POLLUTION

When it comes to pollution, simple acts can make a difference—especially when finding alternatives to single-use plastics. One million shopping bags are used every minute, but each one lasts 1,000 years—so bring reusable bags to the store. Reuse glass containers for spices or bulk goods instead of tossing your empties. And decline plastic straws, which are uniquely dangerous to marine life and among the most common items found on beaches.

HEATHER KOLDEWEY
MARINE BIOLOGIST

THE GHOST NET BUSTER

Originally a research scientist, now Heather Koldewey has turned activist, finding ways to help communities balance conservation with their own human needs. In one of her many projects, she hunts ghosts—deadly, virtually invisible, abandoned fishing nets that are threatening species around the world. "Ghost nets" account for almost 10 percent of all plastic in the ocean and have killed millions of creatures, from whales, sea lions, and seals to shorebirds and smaller fish. Koldewey works with fishing villages to remove these nets from the ocean, and transform them into something useful.

Heather Koldewey wants to see the end of single-use plastic water bottles as part of a more ocean-friendly society.

The Philippines' Danajon Bank was Koldewey's proving ground. A rare double barrier reef, where a second reef formed over subsiding shoals, Danajon Bank once teemed with fish. Overfishing devastated the area. As catch rates declined, fisheries used more nets, caught fewer and smaller fish, and often left remnants of their efforts behind. Ghost nets still haunt the reef, devastating the ecosystem.

Today, these fisheries, part of Net-Works, hunt down and gather the very nets they once used. The nets represent massive amounts of recyclable plastics and a new economy for the local villages. Now these communities have an incentive to remove these harmful waste nets. The nets are locally gathered and bailed and then shipped into the global market for recycled plastic, protecting the livelihood of the community and the lives in the marine environment at the same time.

SEARCHING FOR A SAFER OCEAN

Globally, nearly 650,000 tons of fishing nets are lost every year, part of the eight million tons of plastic pollution that enter our oceans annually, creating a sea filled with deadly traps. Whether broken, lost, or abandoned, ghost nets kill until they are trapped on the ocean floor. So far, Koldewey and the Net-Works team have pulled out more than 200 metric tons of plastic. The program's success is even changing the minds of local fishers, who now track and recycle their old nets rather than abandoning them. This slow exorcism of the seas will take time, but Koldewey envisions an ocean where fish swim free, unhaunted by these ghosts.

" WE NEED TO RETHINK PLASTIC, VALUE IT AND THE WAY WE USE IT, AND ENSURE IT NEVER GETS INTO THE OCEAN IN THE FIRST PLACE."

Heather Koldewey looks for conservation solutions that benefit both people and the planet.

KEY DATES

Milestones in
OCEAN PLASTIC

■ **1907**
The first fully artificial plastic created.

■ **1960s**
First plastic debris observed in ocean.

■ **1979**
Plastic grocery bags introduced in the U.S.

■ **1990s**
Plastic microbeads now used in cosmetics.

■ **1997**
The Great Pacific Garbage Patch discovered.

■ **2007**
San Francisco bans plastic bags.

■ **2014**
The Netherlands bans microbeads.

■ **2015**
Some 448 million tons of plastic produced globally.

EARTH DAY
50 YEARS LATER

KEEPING THE PROMISE

"Why haven't we seen a picture of the whole earth yet?" Stewart Brand scribbled in his notebook. "There it would be for all to see, the earth complete, tiny, adrift, and no one would ever perceive things the same way." That was 1966. In 1968, Apollo 8 astronauts circled the moon and sent back the famous photo of "Earthrise." In 1969, Brand and friends began publishing the era-defining *Whole Earth Catalog*. In 1970, the first Earth Day was celebrated. Fifty years later, it's worth seeing how far we have come.

The famed Earthrise photo taken from the Apollo 8 mission in 1968 changed the way we see our planet.

EARTH DAY EVERY DAY

In 1970, Earth Day was a grassroots explosion across the United States, driven by Wisconsin senator Gaylord Nelson. The celebration and environmental teach-in spread across 12,000 schools, colleges, and universities. Twenty million people—nearly 10 percent of the U.S. population at that time—took part. The success drove immediate legislative and political actions, and the years following that first Earth Day led to the creation of the Environmental Protection Agency, the National Oceanic and Atmospheric Administration, the Clean Air and Clean Water Acts, and a new spirit of environmental awareness.

Today, Earth Day is an annual reminder for us to renew our commitment to protecting the planet's environment. Particularly as we celebrate the 50th anniversary of Earth Day, it's time to revive the determination, vision, and joy that was felt in its first celebration. Let's make a promise from now on that every day is Earth Day!

Crowds gather outside the U.S. Capitol on Earth Day.

EARTH DAY EVERY DAY

> **"EARTH DAY WORKED BECAUSE OF THE SPONTANEOUS RESPONSE AT THE GRASSROOTS LEVEL . . . THAT WAS THE REMARKABLE THING ABOUT EARTH DAY. IT ORGANIZED ITSELF."**
>
> **—GAYLORD NELSON, GOVERNOR, SENATOR, AND FOUNDER OF EARTH DAY**

Contributing to a
HEALTHIER PLANET

1 **CALL YOUR LEGISLATORS**
Make your voice heard on environmental issues.

2 **COMMUNITY CLEANUPS**
Pollution starts at home; cleaning it up does too.

3 **TAKE THE PLASTICS PLEDGE**
Single-use plastics take centuries to dissolve. Using less reduces waste and protects the ocean.

4 **REDUCE WASTE**
Hundreds of millions of tons of waste end up in landfills where it cannot be recycled. Use less, waste less.

5 **RETHINK TRAVEL**
Use human-powered methods (e.g., biking, walking) where possible.

FURTHER

THE SECRET TO LIFE EVERLASTING

Throbbing through Earth's oceans for hundreds of millions of years, dating back to way before the dinosaurs, jellyfish must have some secret formula for prevailing. Today there are about 2,000 known species, every one of them surviving without bones, brains, eyes, or hearts. This golden jellyfish *(Mastigias papua etpisonii)* lives in one saltwater lake on an uninhabited island of Palau, closed for a while to protect the species but now reopened to divers, who must take special precautions: no sunscreen, no scuba tanks, no kicks, no touching.

Jellyfish throng a saltwater lake on Palau's Mecherchar, or Eil Malk.

"I HAVE VISITED SOME OF THE MOST REMOTE PLACES IN THE OCEAN, FULL OF SHARKS AND HUGE FISH SCHOOLS, BUT THESE LITTLE ANIMALS, VIRTUALLY WATER INSIDE A LIVING BAG, MADE ME FEEL CLOSER TO NATURE THAN ANYTHING EVER HAD BEFORE."

—ENRIC SALA, MARINE ECOLOGIST, ON SWIMMING IN JELLYFISH LAKE, PALAU

THE SCIENCE
OF US

ORIGINS | THE HUMAN JOURNEY

Marcia and Millie, fraternal twins, share a mother from England and a father of Jamaican descent.

BODY & BRAIN | HEALTH & MEDICINE

QUIZ MASTER

Expert on You and Me? There's a lot to know about the world of us humans, from our earliest ancestors to our cities today, from the microbes in our gut to the neurons in our brain. And you don't have to leave home to do the exploring!

—**CARA SANTA MARIA,** *Our Favorite Nerd*

SCIENTISTS USED A SPINACH LEAF **TO BUILD A MUSCLE** FOR WHAT **HUMAN ORGAN?**

p272

IN WHAT YEAR DID THE FIRST SUCCESSFUL HEART TRANSPLANT TAKE PLACE?

p267

FOR WHAT PURPOSE DID **ANCIENT** EGYPTIANS CHEW ON CARDAMOM **PODS?**

p277

WHAT IS THE **LARGEST CITY** IN SOUTH AMERICA?

p244

ABOUT HOW MANY **YEARS AGO** DID ANIMALS START WALKING UPRIGHT **AND ON** TWO LEGS?

p224

WHO INVENTED THE VACCINE FOR POLIO?

p267

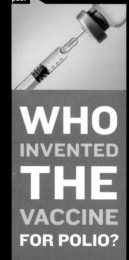

WHAT **IS THE** LEADING **CAUSE OF BLINDNESS** IN THE WORLD?

p269

p249

WHICH ENGLISH NATURALIST PUT FORTH HIS THEORY OF EVOLUTION IN A BOOK CALLED *ON THE ORIGIN OF SPECIES*?

p225

IN WHAT COUNTRY DO CELEBRATIONS OF DÍA DE LOS MUERTOS ORIGINATE?

p235

WHICH RIVER IN INDIA IS SACRED TO THE HINDU RELIGION?

IN WHAT REGION OF THE WORLD ARE QUECHUA-SPEAKING PEOPLE FOUND?

p234

ON AVERAGE, HOW MANY SPECIES OF BACTERIA LIVE ON THE HUMAN FOREARM?

p276

WHAT HERB IS A TRADITIONAL REMEDY TO SOOTHE AN UPSET STOMACH?

APPROXIMATELY HOW MANY PEOPLE ON EARTH ARE BLIND?

HUMAN EVOLUTION
TIME LINE

4 MYA to 80,000 YA	80,000 YA to 8000 BC	8000 to 1500 BC	1500 to 1 BC

4 MYA to 80,000 YA

■ **3.5 mya***
Upright bipedalism—walking on two legs—evolves.

■ **ca 1.75 mya**
Homo erectus, an early ancestor of modern humans, uses stone tools.

■ **ca 400,000 ya****
Neanderthals use fire as a tool in some areas.

■ **ca 160,000 ya**
Homo sapiens, the modern human race, first appears.

■ **ca 120,000 ya**
Neanderthals live in modern-day Europe.

■ **ca 80,000 ya**
Early humans begin moving out of Africa onto other continents.

* *million years ago*
** *years ago*

80,000 YA to 8000 BC

■ **ca 80,000 ya**
Modern humans move into Europe and live alongside Neanderthals.

■ **ca 65,000 ya**
Modern humans reach the Australian continent.

■ **ca 40,000 ya**
Neanderthals die out.

■ **ca 25,000 ya**
A small figurine called the Venus of Willendorf is crafted. It is the oldest known art in Europe.

■ **ca 15,000 ya**
The first human settlements appear in North America.

■ **ca 11,000 ya**
Agricultural systems begin to emerge in the Middle East, as humans cultivate plants and domesticate animals.

8000 to 1500 BC

■ **ca 6500 BC**
Farming begins in the Indus Valley in modern-day Pakistan and western India.

■ **ca 5000 BC**
Rice is cultivated as a crop in central and eastern China.

■ **ca 3500 BC**
First wheels appear in Mesopotamia, used for pottery and later for vehicular use.

■ **2630 BC**
The Egyptians begin building pyramids.

■ **ca 2300 BC**
The earliest known maps are produced in Mesopotamia.

■ **ca 2000 BC**
Austronesians settle on islands in the South Pacific.

1500 to 1 BC

■ **ca 1550 BC**
The Mesopotamian empire begins to grow from the city of Mittani.

■ **ca 1050 BC**
Ironworking is introduced to Greece.

■ **1000 BC**
The Phoenicians develop an alphabet.

■ **ca 600 BC**
The Maya use cacao to make a chocolate drink.

■ **ca 400 BC**
Hippocrates of Kos describes human anatomy and various diseases.

■ **ca 300 BC**
The Maya build pyramids in modern-day Mexico.

| **AD 1 to 1850** | **1850 to 1900** | **1900 to 1975** | **1975 to PRESENT** |

AD 1 to 1850

■ **1677**
Dutch scientist Antonie van Leeuwenhoek observes and describes both bacteria and human sperm cells.

■ **1691**
John Ray suggests that fossils are the remains of creatures from the distant past.

■ **1735**
Swedish naturalist Carolus Linnaeus introduces the binomial naming system.

■ **1836**
English naturalist Charles Darwin completes his five-year voyage on the H.M.S. *Beagle*.

1850 to 1900

■ **1856**
Workmen digging in the valley of the Neander River near Düsseldorf, Germany, discover remains of Neanderthal man.

■ **1859**
Charles Darwin publishes *On the Origin of Species*, the book in which he puts forward his theory of evolution.

■ **1865**
Austrian monk Gregor Mendel presents his research on inheritance.

■ **1868**
French paleontologist Louis Lartet excavates fossils of Cro-Magnon man in southwestern France.

■ **1891**
Dutch anthropologist Eugene Dubois discovers fossils of the human ancestor "Java man," now known as *Homo erectus*.

1900 to 1975

■ **1924**
Raymond Dart discovers the first fossils of human ancestor *Australopithecus* in Africa.

■ **1933**
Anthropologists discover a 92,000-year-old fossil of *Homo sapiens* in Israel.

■ **1948**
English anthropologist Mary Leakey discovers fossils of possible ape ancestor *Proconsul africanus* in Africa.

■ **1960**
Anthropologist Jonathan Leakey discovers the remains of *Homo habilis* in Tanzania.

■ **1972**
Anthropologist Richard Leakey finds an intact skull of *Homo habilis*.

1975 to PRESENT

■ **1974**
Donald Johanson unearths "Lucy," a fossil of *Australopithecus afarensis*, in Ethiopia.

■ **1993**
Anthropologists from Berkeley discover remains of oldest known hominoid, *Ardipithecus ramidus*.

■ **2004**
An 80,000-year-old skeleton of a small humanoid called *Homo floresiensis* is found in Indonesia.

■ **2008**
Fossil of a new hominid, *Australopithecus sediba*, is discovered by Lee Berger in South Africa.

■ **2013**
Multiple remains of a newly discovered species, *Homo naledi*, are found in a cave in South Africa.

MEET OUR HUMAN ANCESTORS

HOW WE GOT TO WHERE WE ARE NOW

Scientists no longer use a family tree to depict relationships among early humans. It is now understood that several lines of early humans evolved at the same time. We also know that chimpanzees (or other apes) didn't evolve into humans. Instead, both lineages descended from a common ancestor and went their separate ways.

ARDIPITHECUS RAMIDUS (4.4 MYA)

Found in northeastern Ethiopia in 1992–1994, the partial skeleton of a female *Ar. ramidus* (nicknamed "Ardi") is more like a human—and less like a chimpanzee—than was expected in the human-ape record. For example, some believe foot and pelvis characteristics indicate that *Ar. ramidus* walked upright when on the ground. It is not clear yet whether it is an ancestor of *H. sapiens*.

AUSTRALOPITHECUS AFARENSIS (3.85–2.95 MYA)

"Lucy" *(Au. afarensis),* the most famous of our fossilized ancestors, was discovered in 1974 in eastern Africa. Scientists have concluded that *Au. afarensis* climbed trees, though it was mostly bipedal. Despite having a brain about one-third of modern humans', this tenacious species lived for over 900,000 years.

PARANTHROPUS BOISEI (2.3–1.2 MYA)

P. boisei, discovered in 1955, was immediately distinctive, because of its large jaw. This indicates a diet that required heavy chewing, though other evidence that it consumed hard substances (like nuts) is lacking. A recent report identified another exceptional characteristic: It may have carried HSV2, the virus causing genital herpes.

HOMO HABILIS (2.4–1.4 MYA)

H. habilis (aka "handy man") was discovered in 1960 at Tanzania's Olduvai Gorge at the same site and by the same team that found *P. boisei*. Its appearance reoriented the search for human origins from Asia, where *H. erectus* had been found, to Africa. A prominent researcher recently argued that it is different enough from other *Australopithecus* and *Homo* specimens to merit its own genus.

HOMO ERECTUS (1.89 MYA–143,000 YA)

H. erectus has proportions similar to modern humans', including shorter arms and longer legs in relation to the torso. Tools such as hand axes have been found near to and in the same sediment layers as *H. erectus,* marking an important moment in evolution. *H. erectus* was also migratory. In fact, it was first discovered in Indonesia in 1891.

HOMO SAPIENS IS NOW THE ONLY SPECIES OF HUMAN ON EARTH. BUT THAT'S BEEN TRUE FOR LESS THAN 30,000 YEARS.

POP!

PREHISTORY ON-SCREEN

- *One Million Years B.C.* (1966)
- *The Land That Time Forgot* (1974)
- *At the Earth's Core* (1976)
- *Quest for Fire* (1981)
- *Iceman* (1984)
- *The Clan of the Cave Bear* (1986)
- *Encino Man* (1992)
- *10,000 B.C.* (2008)
- *The Croods* (2013)
- *Early Man* (2018)

SHARED TIME ON EARTH?

These hand bones are among thousands recently found by paleoanthropologist Lee Berger and his team in South Africa. They belong to an all-new hominid species, *Homo naledi*, which likely lived alongside *Homo sapiens* less than 500,000 years ago.

PAUL SALOPEK
IMMERSIVE JOURNALIST

FOLLOWING ANCIENT PATHS

Over the course of several years, Pulitzer Prize–winning journalist and National Geographic Fellow Paul Salopek is retracing the path, as best we know it, taken by our *Homo sapiens* ancestors over millennia: from the Rift Valley in Ethiopia, through the Holy Lands of the Middle East, onto the Silk Road, into Pakistan and India, north to the Russian Far East, over the Bering Sea into North America, and down to the tip of South America—ETA 2023.

Paul Salopek waits for water to boil at his campsite in the Kyzylkum Desert, Uzbekistan, during his years-long trek.

Paul Salopek's 21,000-mile odyssey is a decade-long experiment in slow journalism. Along the way he is covering modern stories—from climate change to technological innovation, from mass migration to cultural survival—by giving voice to the people who inhabit them every day. His words, as well as his photographs, video, and audio, create a global record of human life at the start of a new millennium as told by villagers, nomads, traders, farmers, soldiers, and artists who rarely make the news.

He has walked alongside Syrian refugees and was detained by security forces in Pakistan. He is joined by local walking partners, including nature photographer Arati Kumar-Rao and environmentalist Siddharth Agarwal while in India. A cargo animal—sometimes a camel, sometimes a donkey—is also a constant companion.

GROUND-LEVEL INSIGHT

In his second dispatch of 2019, Salopek shared two impressions from his journey so far. First, he witnesses migration everywhere. "Even at the utterest ends of the Earth," he wrote, "I've found myself walking among striving people on the move." Second, he sees the world orienting toward China: "I have seen societies transformed by Chinese economic power: new highways, pipelines, communications grids, railroads."

"All roads may yet lead to Rome. But there are new Romes now," he writes. "Whatever the case, there is no need for fear. The key is to stop and talk, and then to keep moving. To cross the next river. To look around the next mountain. Humankind's ancestors did this, and they gave us the world."

> " BREAKING BREAD IS THE UNIVERSAL BONDING MECHANISM OF HUMANITY. AT A TABLE, OVER FOOD, ONE HAS NO ENEMIES. AT LEAST NOT FOR THE DURATION OF THAT MEAL. WARS TAUGHT ME THIS."

Paul Salopek enjoys a cup of Arabian coffee in the desert of Jericho, West Bank.

KEY DATES

Salopek's Out of Eden
MILESTONES

JAN. 21, 2013
Day 1, mile 0, elev. 1,809 ft.
Began walk in Ethiopia

NOV. 23, 2015
Day 1,049, mile 3,000, elev. 2,566 ft.
Gabala, Azerbaijan

SEPT. 7, 2017
Day 1,703, mile 5,000, elev. 10,217 ft.
Chapursan Valley, Pakistan

FEB. 28, 2019
Day 2,160, mile 6,200, elev. 252 ft.
Near Varanasi, Uttar Pradesh, India

2023
Projected to complete the 21,000-mile journey

OUR DEEP ANCESTRY

STAGES OF HUMAN MIGRATION

The character of a person's mitochondrial DNA (passed down intact from mother to child) and, in each male, of the Y chromosome (passed intact from father to son) are only two threads in the vast tapestry of genetic information in any individual's genome. Studies like the years-long National Geographic Genographic Project now allow us to map human migration over tens of thousands of years by comparing the mtDNA and Y chromosomes of people from various populations.

What Stories Do Our Genes Tell?

Between 70,000 and 50,000 years ago, a small group of *Homo sapiens*—perhaps as few as 1,000, to whom all modern non-Africans are related—emigrated from Africa. One group continued along the coast to southern Asia, reaching a super-continent made up of Tasmania, Australia, and New Guinea. Recent DNA research confirms that Aboriginal civilization is one of the longest continuous human occupations outside Africa.

EARLY HUMAN MIGRATIONS

ARCTIC OCEAN

EUROPE

ASIA

NORTH AMERICA

ATLANTIC OCEAN

AFRICA

PACIFIC OCEAN

INDIAN OCEAN

SOUTH AMERICA

ATLANTIC OCEAN

AUSTRALIA

0 mi   2,000   4,000
0 km 2,000 4,000

MAP KEY

Postulated area of human origin

60,000 years ago
50,000 years ago
40,000 years ago
30,000 years ago
20,000 years ago
10,000 years ago

FINDING YOUR ROOTS

TRACKING THE HUMAN JOURNEY

These days it's possible to learn more about your own deep ancestry through projects like National Geographic Genographic Project or commercial offerings from companies like Ancestry.com or 23andMe. A swab of cells from inside your cheek provides enough to learn what your genetic makeup tells about the path your long-ago ancestors took in the massive human migrations over tens of thousands of years. You may find your ancestors coming from one of several directions.

AFRICA

The diversity of genetic markers is greatest in the African continent, the earliest home of modern humans. "The genetic makeup of the rest of the world is a subset of what's in Africa," says Yale geneticist Kenneth Kidd.

ASIA

As some modern humans pushed into Central Asia, others traveled through Southeast Asia and China, eventually reaching Japan and Siberia. Humans in northern Asia eventually migrated to the Americas.

EUROPE

Genetic data show that the DNA of today's western Eurasians resembles that of people in India. It's possible that an inland migration from Asia seeded Europe between 40,000 and 30,000 years ago.

THE AMERICAS

When sea levels were low and the first humans crossed the land bridge between Siberia and Alaska, ice sheets covered the interior of North America, forcing the new arrivals to travel down the west coast.

> **" I THINK [EARLY HUMANS] WERE MAINLY MOTIVATED BY CURIOSITY AND THE DESIRE FOR EXPLORATION."**
>
> —ELENI PANAGOPOULOU, ARCHAEOLOGIST

Immigrants gather at a Sikh festival in Barcelona.

KEY FACTS

Natural Reasons for
MIGRATION

CLIMATE CHANGE Modern humans' departure from Africa around 60,000 years ago was likely in response to a deteriorating climate, growing cooler and drier and less hospitable to human life.

LAND BRIDGES Climate changes can determine access between regions, such as the sea-level drop about 40,000 years ago that exposed a lowland area connecting Australia to Tasmania.

COMPETITION Despite arriving in Europe hundreds of thousands of years before their modern relatives, Neanderthals went extinct not long after modern humans' arrival.

SEAFARING Axes found on Crete in 2010 may be evidence that early humans had the knowledge and technology to sail across the Mediterranean to the island.

AGRICULTURE Farming and herding developed around 12,000 years ago in the Near East and then, as farmers migrated to Europe and elsewhere, quickly replaced the hunter-gatherer lifestyle.

NEANDERTHALS
JOIN THE FAMILY

NOT-SO-DISTANT RELATIVES

When our ancestors emerged from Africa into Eurasia around 45,000 years ago, they found the landscape already inhabited. Neanderthals were 99.5 percent genetically identical to modern humans *(Homo sapiens)* but had evolved distinctive anatomy—such as wide bodies to conserve heat—during hundreds of thousands of years in the cold Eurasian climate.

NEANDERTHAL FEATURES

A form of the gene *MC1R* would have endowed its carriers with red hair and pale skin.

Large browridges combined with a receding forehead gave Neanderthals a beetle-browed look.

Neanderthal skulls were long and low, but they held brains slightly larger than those of living humans.

Neanderthal faces projected farther forward in the middle than do those of modern humans.

Large, conical rib cages housed big lungs needed for high levels of activity.

Neanderthals carried a version of the *FOXP2* gene, associated with language ability.

Neanderthal mandibles lacked chins.

DIVERGENT LINES REUNITE

Neanderthals, our closest prehistoric relatives, dominated Eurasia for the better part of 200,000 years. During that time, they poked their famously large and protruding noses into every corner of Europe and beyond. But climate swings and competition with newcomers may have combined to push Neanderthals into a few outposts before they went extinct, mysteriously dying out about 30,000 years ago.

Friend or Foe?

Scientists posit that the lineages of Neanderthals and their European successors diverged long before modern humans migrated out of Africa, as far back as 370,000 years ago. But until recently, questions lingered: Did modern humans replace Neanderthals, or did they interbreed with them?

Then, in 2010, scientists uncovered the first solid genetic evidence that "modern" humans interbred with their Neanderthal neighbors. Today, we know that genomes of people currently living outside Africa are composed of 1.8 to 2.6 percent Neanderthal DNA. Some parts of non-African genomes are totally devoid of Neanderthal DNA, but other regions abound with it, including those containing genes that affect our skin and hair. This hints that those Neanderthal gene versions conferred some benefit and were retained during evolution. Other genes, however, match segments now closely associated with various health concerns, including blood cholesterol levels and rheumatoid arthritis.

250,000–45,000 YEARS AGO
Neanderthals before the arrival of modern humans in Eurasia

Neanderthal range

0 mi 800
0 km 800

45,000–28,000 YEARS AGO
Period of Neanderthal and modern human overlap in Eurasia

Neanderthal range
Modern human range

Extent of ice (30,000 years ago)

0 mi 800
0 km 800

Mediterranean Sea

Modern humans move out of Africa

DIGGING DEEPER

At-Home
DNA TESTING

Today it is possible to collect a DNA sample, send it in, and have it analyzed for ancestry markers. Some organizations will link you up with other contemporary individuals who are a match and have a good probability of being related to you. National Geographic's Genographic Project, which has more than 800,000 participants, probes further, providing regional and deep ancestry going back hundreds of generations—even identifying two hominin species, Neanderthals and Denisovans. The project has found that most non-Africans are about 2 percent Neanderthal and slightly less than 2 percent Denisovan.

INTANGIBLE CULTURE

MORE THAN MONUMENTS AND ARTIFACTS

Communities worldwide are working to identify and preserve practices, events, skills, and knowledge—intangibles—passed down by ancestors.

Dancers perform the *Ramayana*.

PERFORMING ARTS

THE RAMLILA, INDIA

An epic poem recounting the eventful life of Rama, an important Hindu god, the *Ramayana* is reenacted each fall in northern India. During Ramlila ("Rama's play"), which can last up to a month, seasoned storytellers are joined on stage by audience members—who also help create masks, costumes, and sets.

SHADOW PUPPETS, SYRIA

In these performances, a puppeteer voices characters in traditional stories and situations depicting current social issues with humor, satire, and music. Shadows of two-dimensional handmade puppets enact scenarios starring two characters—one clever, the other naive. As of 2018, only one puppeteer remained active in the country.

CULTURAL PRACTICES

SACRED KAYA FORESTS, KENYA

The Mijikenda of coastal Kenya believe that their ancestors reside in sacred forest *kayas*—village sites that date back to the 16th century, uninhabited but still tended and protected. Stories and ritual ceremonies honor and maintain the forest even as urban development encroaches.

Q'ESWACHAKA ROPE BRIDGE, PERU

Beyond facilitating transportation, the Q'eswachaka bridge serves as a sacred connection for Quechua-speaking people in the southern Andes. They congregate to restore the rope suspension bridge over a three-day gathering that includes ritual ceremonies and a festival. Families make ropes that bridge builders attach to ancient stone pillars.

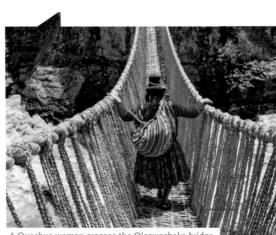

A Quechua woman crosses the Q'eswachaka bridge.

Celebrants dress up for Día de los Muertos.

TO SAFEGUARD THE WORLD'S INTANGIBLE HERITAGE, UNESCO CURRENTLY RECOGNIZES 508 PRACTICES, ARTS, AND CULTURAL EXPRESSIONS FROM 122 COUNTRIES.

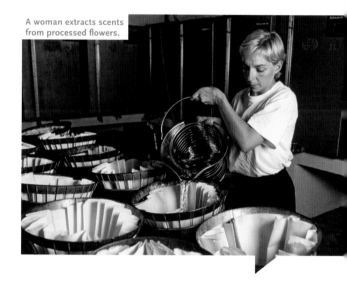

A woman extracts scents from processed flowers.

CELEBRATIONS

DÍA DE LOS MUERTOS, MEXICO

Flower petals strewn from homes to cemeteries, ancestors' favorite foods placed at tombs—these are part of Day of the Dead celebrations, combining precolonial religious rites and Catholic practices.

CATALAN HUMAN TOWERS, SPAIN

Costumed men and young children—surrounded by a base of tightly packed adults (the *pinya*)—rise up into human towers. Music featuring the *gralla,* a traditional Catalonian reed instrument, tells *castellers* how far a tower has progressed.

ARTS & CRAFTS

PERFUME, FRANCE

For over 400 years, the community of Pays de Grasse in southern France has cultivated plants and created fragrances. This artisanal, community-based approach stands in contrast to more commercial enterprises, which import oils and create synthetic perfumes.

WASHI PAPER, JAPAN

Just three communities produce authentic washi—paper used as stationery and in iconic Japanese room dividers, doors, and screens. Washi is made by hand using fibers from mulberry plants, clear river water, and bamboo screens. Members of the community participate at every stage, strengthening community bonds.

EARTH DAY EVERY DAY

The Ancient Arts of PLANTS

Ethnobotanists are trying to preserve the indigenous knowledge about medicinal plants that is disappearing along with plant species and habitats. They interview practitioners to learn their treatments for everything from infections and heart disease to mental illness and cancer.

SEEKING REFUGE

ON THE MOVE TO SAFETY AND A BETTER LIFE

In 2010, the United Nations identified more than 15 million refugees; 2017 saw more than 25 million. In that same time period, the number of asylum seekers more than tripled. The United Nations estimates that in 2017, 44,000 people per day were forcibly displaced from their homes.

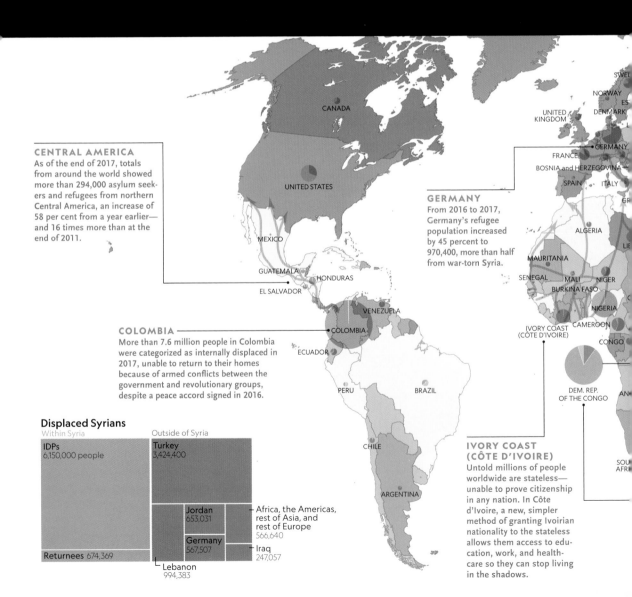

CENTRAL AMERICA
As of the end of 2017, totals from around the world showed more than 294,000 asylum seekers and refugees from northern Central America, an increase of 58 per cent from a year earlier—and 16 times more than at the end of 2011.

GERMANY
From 2016 to 2017, Germany's refugee population increased by 45 percent to 970,400, more than half from war-torn Syria.

COLOMBIA
More than 7.6 million people in Colombia were categorized as internally displaced in 2017, unable to return to their homes because of armed conflicts between the government and revolutionary groups, despite a peace accord signed in 2016.

IVORY COAST (CÔTE D'IVOIRE)
Untold millions of people worldwide are stateless—unable to prove citizenship in any nation. In Côte d'Ivoire, a new, simpler method of granting Ivoirian nationality to the stateless allows them access to education, work, and healthcare so they can stop living in the shadows.

Displaced Syrians

Within Syria
- IDPs 6,150,000 people
- Returnees 674,369

Outside of Syria
- Turkey 3,424,400
- Jordan 653,031
- Germany 567,507
- Lebanon 994,383
- Africa, the Americas, rest of Asia, and rest of Europe 566,640
- Iraq 247,057

IN 2018 UN MEMBER STATES AGREED TO A GLOBAL COMPACT FOR SAFE, ORDERLY, AND REGULAR MIGRATION IN ORDER TO BETTER MANAGE INTERNATIONAL MIGRATION AND STRENGTHEN MIGRANT RIGHTS.

MYANMAR

More than half a million stateless Rohingya Muslims have fled brutal persecution in Myanmar, making dangerous treks through forests and by sea to reach refugee camps in Bangladesh. More than 40% were under age 12.

FORCED TO FLEE

The United Nations counted 68.5 million people of concern in 2017 who were fleeing their homes because of conflict, violence, or natural disaster. This includes internally displaced people (IDPs) migrating within their own countries and refugees and asylum seekers who have crossed national borders.

International Migrants, 2017
Percent of total population
- More than 40
- 20–40
- 10–19.99
- 3–9.99
- 1–2.99
- Less than 1
- No data
- Main migration routes

People of Concern to UNHCR by Country of Asylum, 2017
- 10 million
- 5 million
- 1 million
- 50,000

Some values include estimates.
Values for Serbia include Kosovo.

- Refugees or people in refugee-like situations
- Asylum seekers
- Internally displaced people (IDPs)
- Returnees, both refugees and IDPs
- Stateless persons
- Others under protection of UNHCR

SOMALIA

Decades of conflict combined with natural disasters have created an extreme refugee crisis for Somalians. In 2017, more than two million were displaced within the country, while another 986,000 sought refuge beyond the borders.

DEMOCRATIC REPUBLIC OF THE CONGO

Despite being of the world's poorest countries, in 2017 the Democratic Republic of the Congo hosted more than 500,000 refugees fleeing violence in neighboring countries, while 4.4 million native Congolese were internally displaced.

BEST OF @NATGEO

TOP PHOTOS OF WORLD TRADITIONS

@cristinamittermeier | CRISTINA MITTERMEIER
A tribeswoman in Papua New Guinea gazes from beneath a generations-old headdress.

@johnstanmeyer | JOHN STANMEYER
A group of boys watch as pilgrims at the Ganges make their offerings to the sacred river.

@irablockphoto | IRA BLOCK
An irresistible salesgirl wears and sells peanuts on the Maeklong train in Thailand.

@amivitale | AMI VITALE
A woman roasts coffee in her home in the village of Choche, Ethiopia, where the drink is a cultural mainstay.

@ciriljazbec | **CIRIL JAZBEC**
Samburu warriors in customarily bright adornments pose on the Samburu Reserve in Kenya.

@chancellordavid | **DAVID CHANCELLOR**
A gamekeeper at Scotland's Cairngorms National Park gives his tired companion a lift.

@kitracahana | **KITRA CAHANA**
A young girl in traditional Mexican dress celebrates the Day of the Virgin of Guadalupe in Tijuana.

@paleyphoto | **MATTHIEU PALEY**
Honoring a centuries-old practice, Kazakh eagle hunters ride to a festival in western Mongolia.

DISAPPEARING
LANGUAGES

WE MAY LOSE OVER HALF OF OUR 7,000 LANGUAGES BY 2100

Language defines a culture, through the people who speak it and what it allows speakers to say. Words that describe a particular cultural practice or idea may not translate precisely into another language. To lose those words is to lose those treasures.

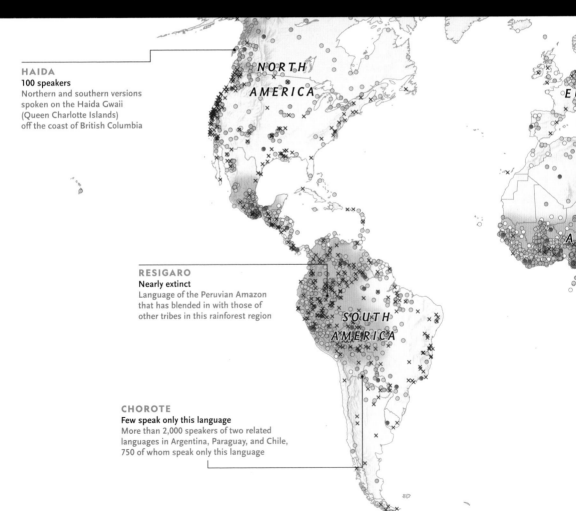

HAIDA
100 speakers
Northern and southern versions
spoken on the Haida Gwaii
(Queen Charlotte Islands)
off the coast of British Columbia

NORTH
AMERICA

EU

RESIGARO
Nearly extinct
Language of the Peruvian Amazon
that has blended in with those of
other tribes in this rainforest region

SOUTH
AMERICA

A

CHOROTE
Few speak only this language
More than 2,000 speakers of two related
languages in Argentina, Paraguay, and Chile,
750 of whom speak only this language

> ## " EVERY TIME A LANGUAGE DIES, WE LOSE PART OF THE PICTURE OF WHAT OUR BRAINS CAN DO."
> **—K. DAVID HARRISON,** LINGUIST AND ANTHROPOLOGIST

DOLGAN
About 1,000 speakers
Spoken in the far north of Central Russia; few speak it, although those who do still teach this language to their children.

BOBOT
Threatened with extinction
In 1989, about 4,500 spoke Bobot, linguistically related to three other Indonesian languages. Bobot is purely oral; it is not a written language.

ASIA

AUSTRALIA

THAYORE
May have disappeared
Indigenous to Australia's Cape York Peninsula, only 29 speakers in 2006, although some children were learning it in 2011

Language Location and Endangerment Level
× Extinct
● High
◐ Medium
◉ Low
○ Minimal
▬ Language hot spot
(Regions with high linguistic density, severe endangerment, and lack of documentation)

KATE ORFF
LANDSCAPE ARCHITECT

RESTORATION AND ADAPTATION

Making places beautiful is not enough for Kate Orff. The landscape architect also wants to make them adaptable to climate change and its extreme effects. "Every square inch of the planet has been impacted, intentionally or not, by human agency," she says. "My goal is to translate that into something positive."

Kate Orff approaches landscape design with an eye to the challenges of climate change and social issues.

As director of Columbia University's Urban Design Program, Orff approaches landscape design from what she calls "a stance of activism." One of her current efforts is the Living Breakwaters project along the south shore of Staten Island, which was pummeled by Hurricane Sandy in 2012. Breakwaters protect the coastline from storm damage and erosion, help restore marine habitat, and provide places along the shore for residents to learn about the ecosystem and to engage with it. Behind it, throughout the harbor, dozens of artificial reefs built from stone, rope, and wood pilings will be seeded with oysters and other shellfish.

NATURAL BREAKWATERS

Living Breakwaters is part of the vision cast by Orff and SCAPE (her landscape architecture and urban design studio), which is informed by New York's past—before islands and shallows were demolished by harbor-dredging and landfill projects to add new real estate. It conceives of a living reef that would grow as sea levels rose, helping to buffer storm waves; resident shellfish, being filter feeders, would also help clean the harbor.

Along with her colleagues, Orff—the first MacArthur Fellow in landscape architecture—works to both restore shorelines' original profiles and make them responsive to rising sea levels, warmer temperatures, and escalating carbon levels. Other adaptive SCAPE projects include the Gowanus Lowlands in Brooklyn; Town Branch Commons in Lexington, Kentucky; and Alameda Creek in the San Francisco Bay Area—all of which also provide recreation space and opportunities for education and activism.

> ## "THERE IS A WAY THAT DESIGN AND PLANNING CAN PLAY A ROLE TO PRESERVE AND PROTECT ECOSYSTEMS AND ECOLOGIES, BUT ALSO A WAY THAT HUMAN SETTLEMENT CAN PERSIST AND STILL BE STRONGLY CONNECTED TO THE COAST."

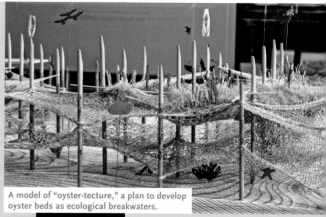

A model of "oyster-tecture," a plan to develop oyster beds as ecological breakwaters.

KEY DATES

Orff's
ACCOMPLISHMENTS

2010
Gives TED Talk, "Reviving New York's Rivers—With Oysters!"

2011
Co-edits *Gateway: Visions for an Urban National Park*

2012
Publishes, with photographer Richard Misrach, *Petrochemical America*

2016
Publishes *Toward an Urban Ecology*

2018
Named director of the Center for Resilient Cities and Landscapes at Columbia University's Graduate School of Architecture, Planning, and Preservation

URBANIZATION

MOVING TO THE CITY

By 2050, almost 70 percent of the global population will live in cities. As recently as 1950, these figures were reversed, and 70 percent lived in rural areas. The number of people living in rural areas has changed little, however, indicating that cities have been absorbing the world's exponential population growth since the mid-20th century—from 2.5 billion in 1950 to almost eight billion today.

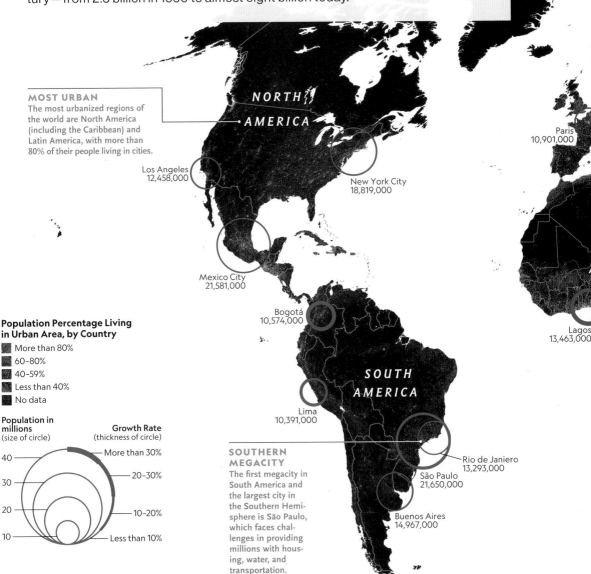

MOST URBAN
The most urbanized regions of the world are North America (including the Caribbean) and Latin America, with more than 80% of their people living in cities.

NORTH AMERICA

Paris
10,901,000

Los Angeles
12,458,000

New York City
18,819,000

Mexico City
21,581,000

Bogotá
10,574,000

Lagos
13,463,000

Population Percentage Living in Urban Area, by Country
- More than 80%
- 60–80%
- 40–59%
- Less than 40%
- No data

SOUTH AMERICA

Lima
10,391,000

Population in millions
(size of circle)

Growth Rate
(thickness of circle)

- 40
- 30
- 20
- 10

- More than 30%
- 20–30%
- 10–20%
- Less than 10%

SOUTHERN MEGACITY
The first megacity in South America and the largest city in the Southern Hemisphere is São Paulo, which faces challenges in providing millions with housing, water, and transportation.

Rio de Janiero
13,293,000

São Paulo
21,650,000

Buenos Aires
14,967,000

IN 2000, THE WORLD COUNTED 19 CITIES OVER 10 MILLION, 10 OF WHICH WERE IN ASIA. BY 2018, THERE WERE 33 MEGACITIES—HOME TO ONE IN EIGHT PEOPLE ON THE PLANET.

WHERE WE LIVE

The world's urban population passed 55% in 2018, but the size and location of population centers varies. North Americans and Europeans tend to spread out among small and medium-size cities, with relatively few migrating to megacities of more than 10 million people. Nations as diverse as Iceland, Kuwait, and Uruguay are more than 90% urban, while Liechtenstein, Burundi, and Papua New Guinea are among the most rural.

Moscow 12,410,000

ASIA

ROPE

Tianjin 13,215,000

Beijing 19,618,000

Lahore 11,738,000
Delhi 28,514,000

Istanbul 14,751,000

Chongqing 14,838,000

Kolkata 14,681,000

Tokyo 37,468,000

Osaka 19,281,000

Karachi 15,400,000

Cairo 20,076,000

CA

Dhaka 19,578,000

Shenzhen 11,908,000

Shanghai 25,582,000

SHRINKING CITIES
Japan's low population growth affects its cities: Osaka is the only megacity with a declining population, and Delhi will displace Tokyo as the world's largest by 2030.

Mumbai 19,980,000

Manila 13,482,000

Bangalore 11,440,000

Bangkok 10,156,000

Chennai 10,456,000

Guangzhou 12,638,000

Kinshasa 13,171,000

RURAL-URBAN BALANCE
India has the world's largest rural population—at almost 900 million—and the most rapidly growing urban population, adding over 400 million city dwellers by 2050.

Jakarta 10,517,000

AUSTRALIA

URBAN ISLANDS
Indonesia is urbanizing at lightning speed, and it expects to see over 60% of its people living in cities by 2025—including the new megacity of Jakarta.

MOST RURAL
In 2018, 57% of Africa's population was still rural, but some cities are growing rapidly, including Kinshasa, which may be the most populous African city by 2030.

URBAN NATURE

MAKING METRO MEAN HEALTHY

Cities around the world are striving to improve air quality and provide better transit options to their citizens by embracing environmentally friendly practices such as creating bike lanes, using alternative fuels, and offering incentives for electric vehicles. A recent survey of a hundred international cities ranks how well municipal governments are doing at helping people get where they need to go while also making cities more livable and attractive—and sustainable.

A jogger and a bike rider enjoy Manhattan's Central Park in the fall.

TOWARD GREENER CITIES

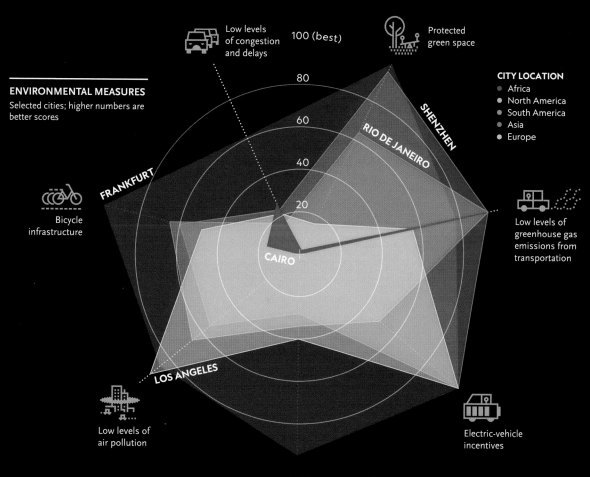

ENVIRONMENTAL MEASURES
Selected cities; higher numbers are better scores

Low levels of congestion and delays

100 (best)

Protected green space

CITY LOCATION
- Africa
- North America
- South America
- Asia
- Europe

80

60

40

20

SHENZHEN

RIO DE JANEIRO

FRANKFURT

CAIRO

Bicycle infrastructure

Low levels of greenhouse gas emissions from transportation

LOS ANGELES

Low levels of air pollution

Electric-vehicle incentives

Legislative efforts to lower transportation emissions

HOW THE CITIES RANK

Munich, Berlin,
Germany Germany
(#2) (#3)

Edinburgh,
U.K. (#22)

Baltimore,
U.S. (#25)

Boston,
U.S. (#43)

Sydney,
Australia
(#61)

Johannesburg,
South Africa
(#72)

Mumbai,
India
(#84)

Seoul,
South Korea
(#11)

1 FRANKFURT

German cities score high due to advanced bike infrastructure, plentiful green spaces, and low greenhouse gas emissions.

28 SHENZHEN

Despite its rapid growth from fishing village to megalopolis of over 10 million people, the Chinese city has developed sustainable transit.

52 RIO DE JANEIRO

To combat major pollution, the Brazilian city launched a 50-year strategy in 2015 to improve air quality and local ecosystems by using cleaner fuels.

67 LOS ANGELES

Electric-vehicle incentives and investments in public transit are improving mobility in the U.S. city, which is known for its epic traffic jams.

97 CAIRO

The densely populated Egyptian city struggles to meet demand for public transit. Offering a wider variety of transit options could help.

RELIGION
AROUND THE WORLD

CULTURE AND MEANING

Religion's great power comes from its ability to speak to the heart and longings of individuals and societies. In time, an untold number of local religious practices yielded to just a few widespread traditions.

CHACO CANYON
A ceremonial site for the Pueblo peoples between AD 850 and 1250, the complex remains here are protected as a U.S. National Historical Park and a UNESCO World Heritage site.

NORTH AMERICA

MEXICO CITY
The Basilica of Our Lady of Guadalupe in Mexico City is the most visited Catholic pilgrimage site in the world. Accounts state that a vision of the Virgin Mary appeared there in 1531.

SOUTH AMERICA

GUYANA
Although most of South America is predominantly Christian, Guyana is predominantly Hindu; nearby Suriname includes both Christian and Hindu adherents, yet neither represents the majority religion.

EARTH DAY EVERY DAY

When Beliefs Drive
ACTION

Many find their religious faith fueling conservation efforts. For example, A Rocha is an international network of environmental projects—from freshwater filtration in Africa to bird-watching tours in Australia, meadow assessment in Switzerland to tree planting in Lebanon—consciously linked to principles of Christianity.

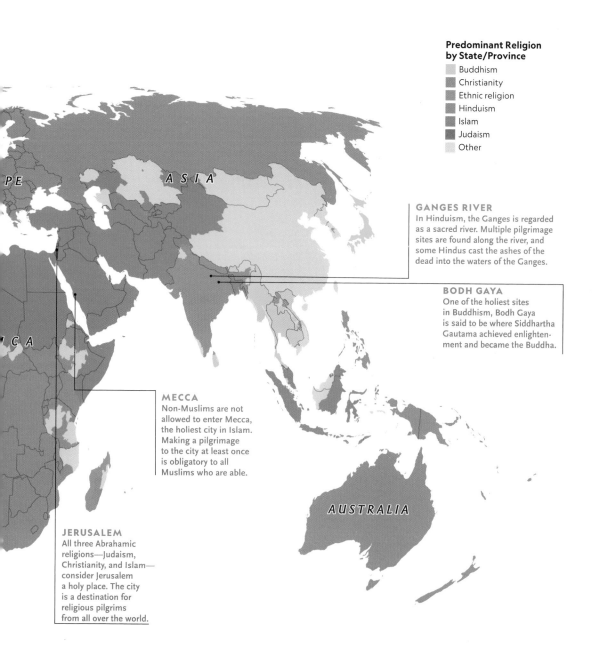

Predominant Religion by State/Province

- Buddhism
- Christianity
- Ethnic religion
- Hinduism
- Islam
- Judaism
- Other

GANGES RIVER
In Hinduism, the Ganges is regarded as a sacred river. Multiple pilgrimage sites are found along the river, and some Hindus cast the ashes of the dead into the waters of the Ganges.

BODH GAYA
One of the holiest sites in Buddhism, Bodh Gaya is said to be where Siddhartha Gautama achieved enlightenment and became the Buddha.

MECCA
Non-Muslims are not allowed to enter Mecca, the holiest city in Islam. Making a pilgrimage to the city at least once is obligatory to all Muslims who are able.

JERUSALEM
All three Abrahamic religions—Judaism, Christianity, and Islam—consider Jerusalem a holy place. The city is a destination for religious pilgrims from all over the world.

ASIA

AUSTRALIA

PE

CA

Religious Holidays

SOMEWHERE IN THE WORLD, a meal, ritual, or offering is being prepared in religious observance – most likely by the busy adherents of Roman Catholicism or Hinduism. If Catholics celebrated every saint's day or Hindus commemorated each deity's birthday, nearly the entire year would be accounted for.

WHO CELEBRATES THE MOST?
With feasts, fasts, and prayers, the world's nine largest religions can collectively observe more than a hundred holidays in a year.

HINDUS LEAD THE FESTIVITIES
Hinduism recognizes the birthdays and milestones of hundreds of deities. It also commemorates the changing of the seasons, the harvest, and lunar phases.

New Year celebration

Holidays
17
8
5
1 1   2 2   2 1
J F M A M J J A S O N D

HINDUISM
1 billion followers

39 days per year

Size of the square represents the number of holidays

2   3 2 2 2 4 1 4 3 3
J F M A M J J A S O N D

SIKHISM
25.3 million

26 days

9
2   1   2   8
J F M A M J J A S O N D

JUDAISM
14.7 million

33 days

The Jewish calendar has dozens of holidays — but the Torah only mandates strict observance of the five holiest. Muslims, too, are holiday minimalists. In Islam the biggest celebrations are saved for the last days of its two major holidays: Id al-Fitr for Ramadan and Id al-Adha to end the hajj pilgrimage.

Compiling a schedule of the holidays most widely observed by the world's nine largest religions is no simple task. Different countries and regions, as well as denominations, celebrate their own versions of the holidays, and some religions follow a unique calendar.

China's lunar calendar runs on a 60-year cycle; India uses several types of calendars.

The establishment of the international date line in 1884 pushed holidays that used to begin at sunset to the next day in many countries. Today holiday scheduling can be influenced by things like economic productivity, which is the reason some celebrations move around each year to bookend a weekend.

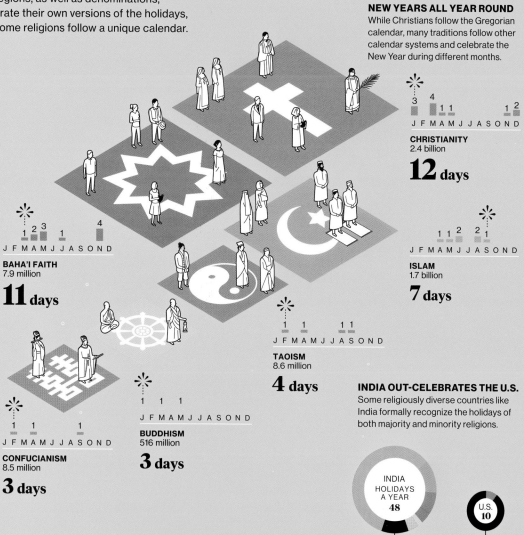

NEW YEARS ALL YEAR ROUND
While Christians follow the Gregorian calendar, many traditions follow other calendar systems and celebrate the New Year during different months.

3 4 1 1   1 2
J F M A M J J A S O N D

CHRISTIANITY
2.4 billion

12 days

1 2 3 1   4
J F M A M J J A S O N D

BAHA'I FAITH
7.9 million

11 days

1 1 2 2 1
J F M A M J J A S O N D

ISLAM
1.7 billion

7 days

1 1   1 1
J F M A M J J A S O N D

TAOISM
8.6 million

4 days

1 1 1
J F M A M J J A S O N D

BUDDHISM
516 million

3 days

1 1   1
J F M A M J J A S O N D

CONFUCIANISM
8.5 million

3 days

INDIA OUT-CELEBRATES THE U.S.
Some religiously diverse countries like India formally recognize the holidays of both majority and minority religions.

INDIA
HOLIDAYS
A YEAR
48

U.S.
10

SECULAR
5

SECULAR
9

BEST OF @NATGEO

TOP PHOTOS OF PEOPLE

@renan_ozturk | RENAN OZTURK
A village elder from the shamanistic Kulung culture in Nepal draws wisdom from the forest.

@cristinamittermeier | CRISTINA MITTERMEIER
Feathers of Amazonian parrots and macaws make a beautiful headdress for a Kayapó man.

@brianfinke | BRIAN FINKE
A competitor eyes the open water in a nearly 3,000-mile rowing race from the Canary Islands to Barbados.

@salvarezphoto | STEPHEN ALVAREZ
Wearing bright woven textiles, a young Peruvian woman honors the Andean weaving tradition.

> ## " CULTURE DOES NOT MAKE PEOPLE. PEOPLE MAKE CULTURE."
>
> —CHIMAMANDA NGOZI ADICHIE, WRITER

@mmuheisen | MUHAMMED MUHEISEN
A nine-year-old Afghan girl adapts to life as a refugee at a camp north of Athens, Greece.

@stephsinclairpix | STEPHANIE SINCLAIR
American trapeze artist Kristin Finley prepares to fly in a circus performance.

@paleyphoto | MATTHIEU PALEY
A mother and son pose in front of a mud wall in their home in Afghanistan.

@chamiltonjames | CHARLIE HAMILTON JAMES
A boy in the Amazon gives a capuchin monkey a ride on his head.

THE SCIENCE
OF SLEEP

Listeners relax during a performance by the Philharmonie de Paris designed to ease its audience into rest.

THE NECESSITY OF SLEEP

Everything we've learned about sleep has emphasized its importance to our mental and physical health. Our sleep-wake pattern is a central feature of human biology—an adaptation to life on a spinning planet, with its endless wheel of day and night. The 2017 Nobel Prize in medicine was awarded to three scientists who, in the 1980s and 1990s, identified the molecular clock inside our cells that aims to keep us in sync with the sun. When this circadian rhythm breaks down, recent research has shown, we are at increased risk for illnesses such as diabetes, heart disease, and dementia.

There is evidence that sleep is essential for maintaining a healthy immune system, body temperature, and blood pressure. Without enough of it, we can't regulate our moods well or recover swiftly from injuries. Sleep may be more essential to us than food. Animals will die of sleep deprivation before starvation.

Good sleep likely also reduces one's risk of developing dementia. It appears that while we're awake, our neurons are packed tightly together, but when we're asleep, some brain cells deflate by up to 60 percent, widening the spaces between them. These intercellular spaces are dumping grounds for the cells' metabolic waste—notably a substance called beta-amyloid, which disrupts communication between neurons and is closely linked to Alzheimer's. Only during sleep can spinal fluid slosh like detergent through these broader hallways of our brain, washing beta-amyloid away.

HOW LIGHT AFFECTS US

How perky we're feeling at any moment depends on the interaction of two processes: "sleep pressure," which is thought to be created by sleep-promoting substances that accumulate in the brain during waking hours, and our circadian rhythm, the internal clock that keeps brain and body in sync with the sun. The clock can be set backward or forward by light. We're particularly sensitive to blue (short-wavelength) light, the kind that brightens midday sunlight and our computer screens, but can disrupt our cycle—especially at night, when we need the dark to cue us to sleep.

A seven-year-old falls asleep watching cartoons on his iPad.

SLEEP LITERALLY MAKES CONNECTIONS YOU MIGHT NEVER HAVE CONSCIOUSLY FORMED, AN IDEA WE'VE ALL INTUITIVELY REALIZED. NO ONE SAYS, "I'M GOING TO EAT ON A PROBLEM." WE ALWAYS SLEEP ON IT.

Eating Insects

As incomes rise in developing countries, so too does the demand for meat. But raising livestock uses a lot of resources. Eating insects—already common in many tropical countries—could be an alternative. Beetles and crickets, for example, are packed with nutrients and provide protein at a low environmental cost.

Palatability poses a problem. "People have an emotional response to bugs—it's the yuck factor," says Arnold van Huis of Wageningen University in the Netherlands. To disguise their form, insects can be processed into powders or pastes. What's next? Protein-rich "bug flours" that are part flour and part ground insect are starting to appear on the market.

ON THE MENU

2 billion

MORE THAN A FOURTH OF THE WORLD'S PEOPLE EAT INSECTS.
The popularity of Western diets is reducing insect consumption in developing countries.

2,000

NUMBER OF KNOWN EDIBLE SPECIES

EFFICIENT PROTEIN

Edible insects provide a sustainable alternative to meat. They are a healthy food source with a high protein and fat content, but their nutritional value varies by species.

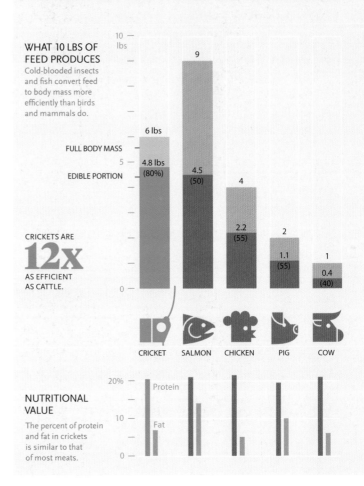

WHAT 10 LBS OF FEED PRODUCES
Cold-blooded insects and fish convert feed to body mass more efficiently than birds and mammals do.

FULL BODY MASS
EDIBLE PORTION

CRICKETS ARE

12x

AS EFFICIENT AS CATTLE.

CRICKET — 6 lbs / 4.8 lbs (80%)
SALMON — 9 / 4.5 (50)
CHICKEN — 4 / 2.2 (55)
PIG — 2 / 1.1 (55)
COW — 1 / 0.4 (40)

NUTRITIONAL VALUE
The percent of protein and fat in crickets is similar to that of most meats.

Protein
Fat

MOST COMMONLY CONSUMED
Beetles are the most consumed species; mealworms are beetle larvae.

BEETLES	CATERPILLARS		OTHER	
31%	18%	15%	13%	23%
		ANTS, BEES, WASPS	CRICKETS, GRASS-HOPPERS, LOCUSTS	DRAGONFLIES, FLIES, TERMITES

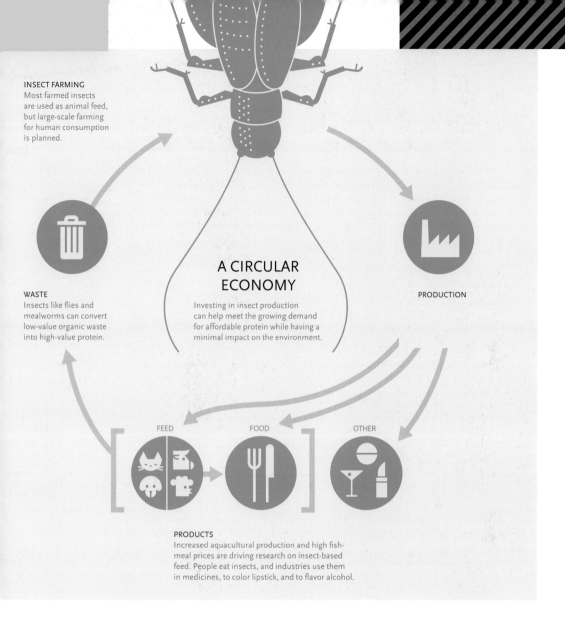

INSECT FARMING
Most farmed insects are used as animal feed, but large-scale farming for human consumption is planned.

A CIRCULAR ECONOMY

Investing in insect production can help meet the growing demand for affordable protein while having a minimal impact on the environment.

PRODUCTION

WASTE
Insects like flies and mealworms can convert low-value organic waste into high-value protein.

FEED

FOOD

OTHER

PRODUCTS
Increased aquacultural production and high fish-meal prices are driving research on insect-based feed. People eat insects, and industries use them in medicines, to color lipstick, and to flavor alcohol.

ENVIRONMENTAL IMPACT

Insects emit fewer greenhouse gases and require less land to produce than livestock such as pigs and cattle.

GREENHOUSE GAS PRODUCTION
Pounds of CO_2-eq* generated from producing a pound of protein

14
MEALWORM

38
PIG

LAND USE
Square feet needed to produce a pound of protein

88
MEALWORM

269
PIG

A DELICACY

IN UGANDA A POUND OF GRASSHOPPERS COSTS

40%

MORE THAN
A POUND OF BEEF

* CO_2-equivalents: the sum of carbon dioxide, methane, and nitrous oxide emissions

How the World Gives Birth

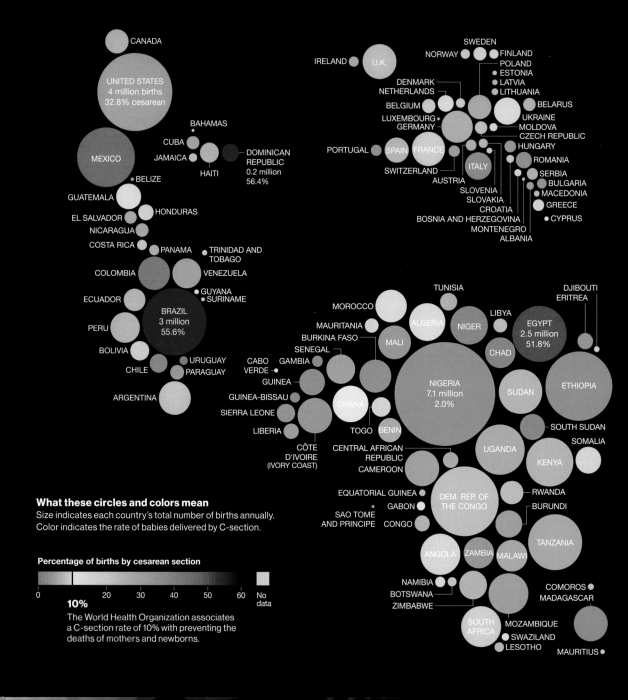

CANADA

UNITED STATES
4 million births
32.8% cesarean

BAHAMAS
CUBA
JAMAICA
MEXICO
BELIZE
HAITI
DOMINICAN REPUBLIC
0.2 million
56.4%

GUATEMALA
HONDURAS
EL SALVADOR
NICARAGUA
COSTA RICA
PANAMA
TRINIDAD AND TOBAGO
COLOMBIA
VENEZUELA
ECUADOR
GUYANA
SURINAME
BRAZIL
3 million
55.6%
PERU
BOLIVIA
URUGUAY
CHILE
PARAGUAY
ARGENTINA

SWEDEN
NORWAY
IRELAND
U.K.
FINLAND
POLAND
ESTONIA
LATVIA
LITHUANIA
DENMARK
NETHERLANDS
BELGIUM
BELARUS
LUXEMBOURG
UKRAINE
GERMANY
MOLDOVA
CZECH REPUBLIC
PORTUGAL
SPAIN
FRANCE
HUNGARY
ROMANIA
SWITZERLAND
ITALY
AUSTRIA
SERBIA
BULGARIA
SLOVENIA
MACEDONIA
SLOVAKIA
GREECE
CROATIA
CYPRUS
BOSNIA AND HERZEGOVINA
MONTENEGRO
ALBANIA

TUNISIA
DJIBOUTI
ERITREA
MOROCCO
LIBYA
MAURITANIA
ALGERIA
NIGER
EGYPT
2.5 million
51.8%
BURKINA FASO
MALI
SENEGAL
CABO VERDE
GAMBIA
CHAD
GUINEA
GUINEA-BISSAU
GHANA
NIGERIA
7.1 million
2.0%
SUDAN
ETHIOPIA
SIERRA LEONE
LIBERIA
TOGO BENIN
SOUTH SUDAN
CÔTE D'IVOIRE
(IVORY COAST)
CENTRAL AFRICAN REPUBLIC
SOMALIA
CAMEROON
UGANDA
KENYA
EQUATORIAL GUINEA
GABON
DEM. REP. OF THE CONGO
RWANDA
SAO TOME AND PRINCIPE
CONGO
BURUNDI
TANZANIA
ANGOLA
ZAMBIA
MALAWI
NAMIBIA
COMOROS
BOTSWANA
MADAGASCAR
ZIMBABWE
SOUTH AFRICA
MOZAMBIQUE
SWAZILAND
LESOTHO
MAURITIUS

What these circles and colors mean

Size indicates each country's total number of births annually.
Color indicates the rate of babies delivered by C-section.

Percentage of births by cesarean section

| 0 | 20 | 30 | 40 | 50 | 60 | No data |

10%
The World Health Organization associates a C-section rate of 10% with preventing the deaths of mothers and newborns.

BRAZIL
The country with one of the highest C-section rates (55.6%) launched a public health campaign in 2015 to promote natural births.

FINLAND
The lowest rate among developed countries (14.7%) is likely a product of midwife-led deliveries and strict clinical protocols.

EGYPT
Its rate (51.8%) is growing fast, as more women ask for C-sections and doctors try to avoid medical and legal complications.

AFRICAN NATIONS
Less than 1.6% of babies in Niger, Chad, and Ethiopia are delivered via C-section, largely owing to a shortage of care facilities.

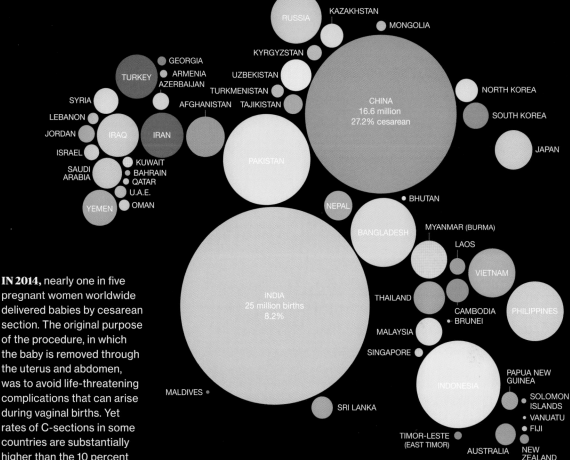

IN 2014, nearly one in five pregnant women worldwide delivered babies by cesarean section. The original purpose of the procedure, in which the baby is removed through the uterus and abdomen, was to avoid life-threatening complications that can arise during vaginal births. Yet rates of C-sections in some countries are substantially higher than the 10 percent rate the World Health Organization associates with preventing the deaths of mothers and newborns.

Why do some countries see so many C-sections? According to the WHO, factors favoring the procedure include families' and doctors' expectations of achieving safer outcomes and avoiding long or painful labors. High rates, such as those seen in Brazil, also can reflect a desire to time births more predictably, while low rates can indicate reduced access to medical care.

As doctors and expectant mothers evaluate the benefits of delivering through the birth canal, C-section rates could decline.

THE TERM "CESAREAN SECTION" HAS NOTHING TO DO WITH JULIUS CAESAR. MORE LIKELY IT COMES FROM THE LATIN WORD *CAEDARE*, MEANING "TO CUT."

UNDERSTANDING
GENDER

NO LONGER SIMPLY MALE OR FEMALE

Our society is in the midst of a conversation about gender issues, with evolving notions about what it means to be a woman or a man. At the same time, scientists are uncovering new complexities in the biological understanding of sex. Whereas genital differentiation takes place in the first two months of fetal development, sexual differentiation of the brain comes months later.

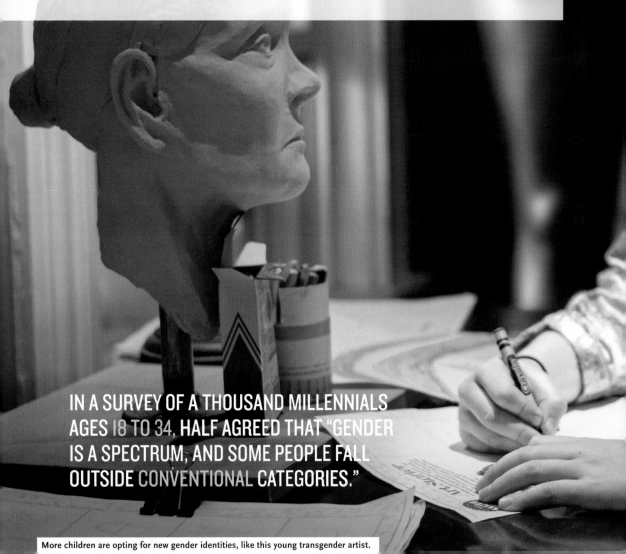

IN A SURVEY OF A THOUSAND MILLENNIALS AGES 18 TO 34, HALF AGREED THAT "GENDER IS A SPECTRUM, AND SOME PEOPLE FALL OUTSIDE CONVENTIONAL CATEGORIES."

More children are opting for new gender identities, like this young transgender artist.

Glossary of Terms for
GENDER

CISGENDER A term describing one whose gender identity matches the biological sex assigned at birth.

GENDER BINARY The idea that gender is strictly either male/man/masculine or female/woman/feminine based on sex assigned at birth, rather than a continuum or spectrum of gender identities and expressions.

GENDER CONFORMING One whose gender expression is consistent with cultural norms expected for that gender.

GENDER DYSPHORIA The medical diagnosis for being transgender. It is controversial because it implies that being transgender is a mental illness, rather than a valid identity.

GENDER EXPRESSION One's outward gender presentation: clothing, hairstyle, makeup, vocal inflection, body language.

GENDERFLUID One whose gender identity or expression shifts between man/masculine and woman/feminine or falls somewhere along this spectrum.

GENDER IDENTITY One's deep-seated, internal sense of who one is as a gendered being; the gender with which one identifies.

INTERSEX Any mix of male and female chromosomes, testicular and ovarian tissue, genitals, or other sexual characteristics.

NONBINARY A spectrum of gender identities and expressions. Terms include genderqueer, genderfluid, and pangender.

QUEER An umbrella term for a range of people who are not heterosexual and/or cisgender. Some consider the term derogatory.

TRANSGENDER: An adjective describing one whose gender identity does not match the biological sex assigned at birth. Sometimes abbreviated as trans.

CHINESE
TRADITIONS

TREATMENT EXTREMES

Wasp nests for itching skin and rashes, earthworms for asthma and convulsions: Traditional Chinese healers have turned to many items, not just plants, as remedies. Even scales from the pangolin, an African anteater, have been claimed to be a cancer treatment —a notion driving this rare animal to extinction.

BAIKAL SKULLCAP

CITRUS PE

CUTTLEFISH BONE

CITRON DAYLILY

CHINESE DATE

EPIMEDIU
LEAF

PANGOLIN SCALE

SWEET WORMWOOD

LICORICE ROOT

ROSEBUD

PAPER WASP NEST

MOLTED CICADA SHELL

TUCKAHOE

NIGHT-BLOOMING CEREUS

FRANKINCENSE

TRICHOSANTHES FRUIT

CHINESE FOXGLOVE ROOT

MONK FRUIT

EARTHWORM

JENNIFER DOUDNA
BIOCHEMIST

STARTING A REVOLUTION

Crispr-Cas9, the gene-editing technique that biochemist Jennifer Doudna has pioneered, is one that organisms already use on their own. The thrilling discovery is that we can employ it strategically—in specific places in the genome to achieve certain ends. "We uncovered the workings of an incredible molecular machine that could slice apart viral DNA with exquisite precision," Doudna says.

Jennifer Doudna in her lab at the Li Ka Shing Center, University of California, Berkeley

Doudna first heard about Crispr (clustered regularly interspaced short palindromic repeats) in 2006 when discussing immunological adaptations made by bacteria with geomicrobiologist Jill Banfield. When bacteria battle a virus, they place an excerpt of the virus's DNA into their own genome.

In 2011, Doudna, microbiologist Emmanuelle Charpentier, and their team used the Cas9 enzyme from common *Streptococcus* bacteria—and discovered what has been celebrated as "the cheapest, simplest, most effective way of manipulating DNA." With Crispr-Cas9, scientists can dispatch a synthetic replacement part to any location in a genome made of billions of nucleotides. After the enzyme snips out the unwanted DNA sequence, the cell inserts the chain of nucleotides delivered in the Crispr package.

THE PROMISE AND PERIL OF CRISPR

Crispr has transformed biology. For example, one could edit genes of crops to resist pests, eliminating the need for pesticides. Crispr could even be used to find and treat mutations that lead to cancer.

No scientific discovery of the past century holds more promise—or raises more ethical questions. If Crispr were used to edit a human embryo's germ line, the change would be passed on in perpetuity. "Application of the technology with the intention to establish a pregnancy or birth should not occur," says Doudna, "until we fully understand the scientific risks and ethical issues surrounding such profound use."

> **" AT ITS CORE, THE CRISPR GENE-EDITING TECHNOLOGY IS NOW GIVING HUMAN BEINGS THE OPPORTUNITY TO CHANGE THE COURSE OF EVOLUTION."**

Crispr techniques allow deliberate reconfiguration of bits of DNA's double helix.

KEY DATES

Doudna's Crispr
ACHIEVEMENTS

■ **2012**
Co-authors an article announcing the Crispr-Cas9 technique

■ **2015**
Calls for a moratorium on human genome editing

■ **2015**
Receives Breakthrough Prize in life sciences, awarded by Silicon Valley notables

■ **2017**
Publishes *A Crack in Creation: Gene Editing and the Unthinkable Power to Control Evolution* with co-author Samuel H. Sternberg

■ **2018**
Receives patents for Crispr-Cas9 compositions

MEDICINE
TIME LINE

6500 to 1 BC	AD 1 to 1500	1500 to 1850	1850 to 1900

ca 6500 BC
The first known surgery is completed.

ca 3000 BC
The Ayurveda, a Hindu medical treatise, establishes a holistic medical system still in use today.

ca 2500 BC
Chinese doctors use acupuncture to heal ailments.

ca 2000 BC
In Syria and Babylon, medicine becomes an important practice; recipes for ointments and poultices are recorded on clay tablets.

ca 1550 BC
Egyptians have about 700 drugs and medications in use.

440 BC
The Hippocratic Corpus, a collection of medical treatises from ancient Greece, is compiled.

ca 30
Roman doctors use splints and bandages stiffened with starch to set broken bones.

77
Pedanius Dioscorides writes a guide to medicinal herbs and drugs that remains authoritative until the 15th century.

1012
Persian physician Ibn Sina publishes an influential medical text, *The Canon of Medicine*.

ca 1286
Eyeglasses are invented in Italy.

1347–1351
The Black Death spreads across Europe and Asia in one of the most devastating pandemics in history.

1628
English physician William Harvey explains the circulation of blood in the body.

1796
English physician Edward Jenner introduces the smallpox vaccination in Europe.

1805
Japanese physician Hanaoka Seishu performs the first surgery on a patient using general anesthesia.

1824
Louis Braille invents the Braille alphabet to aid blind people in reading and writing.

1840
Jakob Henle proposes the germ theory of disease.

1854
English physician John Snow connects cholera and contaminated water.

1863
Louis Pasteur invents a sterilization process now known as pasteurization.

1867
Joseph Lister publishes a paper on the use of antiseptic surgical methods.

1885
Sigmund Freud begins developing his theories of psychoanalysis.

1893
Surgeon Daniel Hale Williams performs the first heart surgery.

1895
German physicist Wilhelm Röntgen takes the first x-ray.

| 1900 to 1930 | 1930 to 1970 | 1970 to 1985 | 1985 to PRESENT |

1900 to 1930

■ **1917**
Margaret Sanger opens a birth control clinic in the United States.

■ **1921**
Psychiatrist Hermann Rorschach introduces his inkblot test for studying personality.

■ **1922**
Vitamins D and E are first discovered.

■ **1925**
Biologist Ernest Just demonstrates that UV radiation can cause cancer.

■ **1928**
Scottish bacteriologist Alexander Fleming discovers penicillin.

1930 to 1970

■ **1937**
Italian scientist Daniel Bovet identifies the first antihistamine effective in treating allergies.

■ **1948**
The World Health Organization is founded.

■ **1950**
Link between smoking and lung cancer is shown.

■ **1952**
Jonas Salk develops the first polio vaccine.

■ **1953**
Francis Crick, James Watson, and Rosalind Franklin determine the double-helix structure of DNA.

■ **1967**
South African surgeon Christiaan Barnard performs the first successful heart transplant.

1970 to 1985

■ **1973**
American and English physicians begin to develop magnetic resonance imaging (MRI) scanning.

■ **1976**
The Ebola virus is first identified after outbreaks in Africa.

■ **1978**
The first "test tube" baby is born in England.

■ **1982**
The first genetically engineered insulin is produced.

■ **1983**
Luc Montagnier and Robert Gallo discover the human immuno-deficiency virus (HIV).

1985 to PRESENT

■ **1998**
Researchers at Johns Hopkins University successfully grow human stem cells in a lab.

■ **2001**
American researchers successfully clone a human embryo.

■ **2007**
Geneticist J. Craig Venter publishes his entire genetic sequence—the first genome published of a single person.

■ **2010**
World's first all-robotic surgery takes place in Canada.

■ **2013**
Researchers develop a 3-D printed prosthetic hand that can be produced at a low cost.

EYES ON THE
PRIZE

SEEING THE WAY TO NEW PATHS IN MEDICINE

Brows, lids, lashes; whites, iris, pupil: Each part of the eye has a role to play in the essential sense of seeing.

LOOKING DEEPER INTO OUR EYES

The eyes are windows to the soul, lamp of the body— literature is full of such metaphors, which are today taking on new meaning. Yet roughly one in every 200 people on Earth—39 million of us—can't see. Another 246 million have low vision to degrees that impose moderate or severe limits. These burdens alone justify the search for new treatments. Yet the eye is also getting increased attention because it provides a safe, accessible spot to test treatments that might also be used elsewhere in the body.

To start with, researchers can look directly into the eye to see what's wrong and whether a treatment is working. Likewise, the eye's owner can see out of it (or not), providing a quick, vital measure of function. The eye is also tough, so doctors can more safely try a remedy in the eye, such as gene therapy, that might wreak havoc elsewhere. The eye is becoming a window not just to the soul, but also to the possibilities— and limits—of therapeutic approaches on which medicine is betting its future.

Eyes Under Threat

Multiple diseases can afflict the same eye. Three common and treatable diseases occur in the front of the eye. There currently is no cure for age-related macular degeneration, which occurs in the back of the eye near the retina.

Normal vision

GLAUCOMA

Glaucoma is caused by fluid buildup in the eye, resulting in pressure that can damage the optic nerve. If it's caught early enough, surgery and medication may slow its advance.

CATARACTS

The world's leading cause of blindness, cataracts are caused when proteins in the lens clump together, blocking and distorting light to the retina. Surgery can restore sight.

Anterior chamber

Ciliary body

Retina

Choroid

Macula

VITREOUS CAVITY

Optic nerve

Cornea

Lens

Deteriorating cells

Iris

Zonules

Atrophic photoreceptors

Accumulated deposit of debris

REFRACTIVE ERRORS

Nearsightedness, farsightedness, and astigmatism are types of refractive errors, flaws that keep the eye from focusing light sharply on the retina. They're the most common causes of impairment yet easily corrected with lenses or surgery.

AGE-RELATED MACULAR DEGENERATION

Caused by an alteration of the underlying layers of the retina's macular area, AMD affects photoreceptors that process images. There is no cure.

Antibiotic Resistance

THE POULTRY CASE STUDY

Americans today eat three times as much poultry as they did in 1960. Since most U.S. chickens are raised in large, crowded facilities, farmers feed them antibiotics to prevent disease as well as speed their growth.

Decades of Antibiotics

Since the 1950s, farmers have fed antibiotic growth promoters (AGPs) to livestock. Overusing these substances can create superbugs, pathogens that are resistant to multiple drugs and could be passed along to humans. Mindful of that, companies such as Perdue Farms have stopped using the drugs to make chickens gain weight faster. Since Denmark banned AGPs in the 1990s, the major pork exporter says it's producing more pigs—and the animals get fewer diseases. Says Centers for Disease Control and Prevention epidemiologist Tom Chiller, "Antibiotics are miracle drugs that should only be used to treat diseases."

MEAT CONSUMPTION IN THE U.S.

100 pounds per person per year

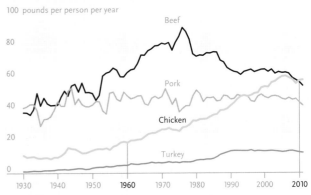

Beef
Pork
Chicken
Turkey

80
60
40
20
0

1930   1940   1950   1960   1970   1980   1990   2000   2010

Antibiotics as Growth Promoters

They help chickens grow bigger faster, making the meat . . .

. . . cheaper for the consumer.

In 1960 it took 63 days to grow a 3.4-pound broiler.

$3.24*
a pound

In 2011 it took 47 days to grow a 5.4-pound one.

$1.29
a pound

* 2011 dollars, adjusted for inflation

IN 2015, ANTIBIOTICS GIVEN TO MEAT ANIMALS AROUND THE WORLD TOTALED 126 MILLION POUNDS.

How Resistance Develops and Spreads

1.

Antibiotics can be given to livestock in their feed or sprayed on them, to be ingested when the animals groom themselves.

2.

The bacteria causing an infection are usually not resistant to drugs.

But some of them can be naturally drug resistant.

When antibiotics kill the nonresistant bacteria . . .

. . . the resistant ones, the superbugs, can flourish.

53%

of grocery store chicken sampled in a 2013 study had resistant *E. coli*.

3.

Superbugs can be passed to humans in many ways.

Farmworkers often have direct contact with animals.

Drug-resistant bacteria can linger on improperly cooked meat.

Fertilizer or water containing animal feces can spread superbugs to food crops.

FUTURE PROSTHETICS

TECHNOLOGY THAT CAN MAKE US MORE HUMAN

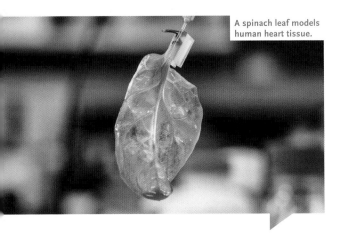

A spinach leaf models human heart tissue.

GROWING A HEART

POPEYE WAS RIGHT

One of the defining traits of a leaf is the branching network of thin veins that delivers water and nutrients to its cells. Now, scientists have used plant veins to replicate the way blood moves through human tissue.

Plant cells were removed from a spinach leaf, leaving behind a frame of cellulose. The remaining plant frame was bathed in live human cells, so that the human tissue grew on the spinach scaffolding and surrounded the tiny veins. Then the team sent fluids and microbeads through its veins to show that blood cells can flow through this system. The goal is to eventually be able to replace damaged tissue in patients who have had heart attacks or who have suffered other cardiac issues.

FEELINGS

SENSATIONAL

Scientists have made great strides toward making prosthetics that are part of the patients themselves, not just tools. One team in Europe wired pressure sensors in the fingers of an artificial hand to sensory nerves in an amputee's upper arm, allowing him to feel textures, pressure, and vibrations. In Chicago, a group of researchers created a thought-controlled leg that can climb stairs and go from sitting to standing in response to signals from nerves in a patient's stump. Another group, also in Chicago, developed pattern recognition, in which the prosthetic limbs interpret nerve signals from patients in real time, responding directly to intentions.

A boy tries on a 3-D–printed hand.

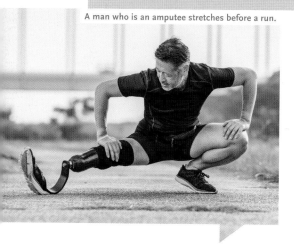

A man who is an amputee stretches before a run.

USING 3-D PRINTERS, POLYMER SCAFFOLDING, AND HUMAN CELLS AS INK, RESEARCHERS ARE ON THE VERGE OF CREATING LIVING LIMBS AND ORGANS.

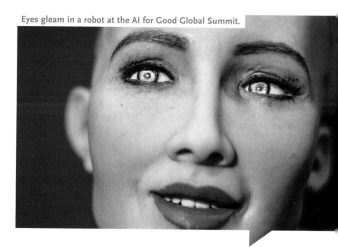

Eyes gleam in a robot at the AI for Good Global Summit.

ACCESSIBILITY

MAKERS MAKING A DIFFERENCE

Traditional prosthetics can cost thousands of dollars and need to be replaced as children grow. But over the last few years, with the help of an organization called e-NABLE, volunteers across the globe have been using open-source technology and 3-D printers to provide free prosthetic hands and below-elbow devices for children and adults who need them. These simple, mechanical prosthetics—which have no motors, sensors, or batteries—are individualized to meet each individual's physical needs.

Often made in bold colors with visible working parts, these prosthetics have a different appeal from those intended to resemble missing limbs. The attention the devices draw is not necessarily unwelcome, especially when it gives children wearing them a chance to talk to their peers about how they work.

Organizers estimate that volunteers, which number in the tens of thousands and span more than 100 countries, have designed and created over 5,000 devices. E-NABLE, which sees itself as part of a "connected humanitarianism" movement, is looking to help volunteers create additional 3-D printed devices and assistive technologies.

ROBOTICS

MUSCULAR ROBOTS

Researchers in Tokyo have developed a new method for using living rat muscle tissue in robotics. The "biohybrid" design simulates the look and movements of a human finger. The research group modeled their work on living muscle tissue. To grow their robot's muscles, they layered hydrogel sheets filled with myoblasts—rat muscle cells—on a robotic skeleton. The grown muscle is then stimulated with an electric current that forces it to contract.

The research team thinks that future versions of muscle-driven robots could help engineers create more nimble prosthetics. The human-like muscle system could also one day help scientists test drugs and toxins, reducing the need for animal testing.

PSYCHOBIOME

THE BRAIN-GUT CONNECTION

The human body contains as many microbes as it does cells—nearly 30 trillion of them. Several ecosystems are found on our skin: Your forearm has the richest community, with an average of 44 species. The human gut teems with bacteria, which help us digest food, absorb nutrients, and protect our intestinal walls. The more we learn about our microbes, the more we realize their profound effect on mental health, attitudes, and emotions—which is why many now call that population inside us our "psychobiome."

OUR LANGUAGE ALREADY HINTS AT HOW THE MICROBIOME INFLUENCES OUR FEELINGS, WHEN WE TALK ABOUT GUT FEELINGS, GUT INSTINCTS, GUTSY MOVES.

An illustration colorized to emphasize the variety of microbes in the human microbiome

Five Ways the Gut Affects
WELL-BEING

INFECTIONS AND DEPRESSION In 2000, following a contamination of the water supply, an infection spread among 5,000 residents of a single town, Walkerton, Ohio. In addition to causing gastrointestinal illness, the related inflammation resulted in widespread depression and anxiety.

STRESS AND INFLAMMATION Stress hormones are part of our fight-or-flight response. But they also quiet the immune system, allowing gut pathogens such as *Salmonella* and *E. coli* to flourish, which means people who are stressed become more susceptible to infection and inflammation.

TEENAGE HABITS AND DECISION-MAKING The sheathing of the brain's nerve fibers (myelination), a process governed by the microbiome, spreads to the frontal lobes in our teen years. This means executive function and thought processes are shaped in part by youthful eating habits and stressors.

FERMENTED FOODS AND MEMORY The psychobiotic *Lactobacillus plantarum*, found in foods such as kimchi and sauerkraut, has anti-inflammatory properties. Evidence from animal studies indicates that it improves memory even in cases of memory loss related to aging.

JUNK FOOD AND ANXIETY Foods with added sugars boost harmful bacteria in the gut and have been shown to bring on depression. In a study involving 23,000 mothers and children, junk food in a mother's diet while pregnant or in a child's own diet was a predictor of psychological problems in the children.

HERBS & SPICES
FOR HEALTH

BASIL
Fragrant annual
native to India

BAY
Aromatic shrub leaf
flavors soups.

CHERVIL
Delicate relative
of parsley

CHIVES
Tender stalks
in onion family

CILANTRO
Leaves of plant whose
seeds are coriander

DILL
Ancient cure
for indigestion

FENNEL
Seeds, leaves, stalks,
bulbs all tasty

LEMONGRASS
Southeast Asian native,
citrus flavor

MARJORAM
Sweet herb, makes
a calming tea

OREGANO
Classic herb in
Mediterranean cuisines

PARSLEY
Edible garnish high
in antioxidants

PEPPERMINT
Tea is a favorite
stomach soother.

ROSEMARY
Research affirms
tradition as pain reliever.

SAGE
Honeybees love
sage flowers.

TARRAGON
Fragile flavor best captured
in vinegar

THYME
Good in cooking;
tea also calms a cough.

ALLSPICE
Ground from dried berries, Caribbean native

BLACK PEPPER
Native to India, spurred spice trade in 1600s

CARDAMOM
Ancient Egyptians chewed it for clean breath.

CAYENNE
Powdered hot peppers, rich in vitamins and minerals

CINNAMON
Inner bark of tropical tree, lowers blood sugar

CLOVES
Ground tree buds, antioxidant and mildly anesthetic

CORIANDER
Seed of cilantro plant, often used in curries

CUMIN
Aromatic seed essential to Mexican and Indian cuisines

GINGER
Ground root, traditional remedy for seasickness

MACE
Outer covering of nutmeg; both appetite stimulants

PAPRIKA
Bright red, made of dried peppers, typical in Hungary

TURMERIC
Related to ginger, provides many health benefits

ANCIENT WISDOM

Herbs and spices add flavor, aroma, color, texture, and nutrients to food—and many improve health as well. Herbs are leaves or stems of plants from temperate zones, used fresh or dried. Spices come from many parts of tropical plants—dried seeds, flowers, fruit, bark, or roots—and are used either whole or ground fine. Most of these provide vitamins and minerals, and many have healing properties.

A WORD FROM

Passing on Knowledge Interviewing people is a standard method in ethnobotanical research. Through individual interviews with several people in the community who self-medicate with "bush medicines," I am hoping to develop a database of locally useful plants and to understand the myriad of ways in which these plants are used . . . The ultimate goal is to give back that information to the community, so that these precious oral traditions do not disappear.

—INA VANDEBROEK, *ethnobotanist*

MINDFULNESS

THE SCIENCE OF PAYING ATTENTION

Even just one generation ago, traits like compassion and focus were thought to be inherent and predetermined. But scientists have come to understand that mental patterns are malleable: Through practice and repetition, the brain's circuitry can be rerouted, and one's reactions and habits can be intentionally redirected. This is known as neuroplasticity.

Meditation is a deliberate approach to mindfulness in which one remains present and reflects on internal thoughts, physical responses, and external stimuli. Practitioners have been found to have better control of their attention and emotions. Meditation also appears to slow loss of the brain's gray matter and age-related cognitive decline.

A woman sits mindfully at the edge of the Trolltunga rock formation in Norway.

> ## " THE BEST WAY TO CAPTURE MOMENTS IS TO PAY ATTENTION. THIS IS HOW WE CULTIVATE MINDFULNESS. "
>
> **—JON KABAT-ZINN, AUTHOR AND MINDFULNESS TEACHER**

10 Principles of Living
MINDFULLY

These interconnected principles both facilitate and are the fruit of mindful meditation.

ACCEPTANCE By choosing to not force change, you are in a better position to release what needs to be let go of.

CALM Calm is a steadiness and freedom that prevails in distressing or disruptive situations, regardless of the emotions involved.

CLARITY Consistent habits of observation and openness yield deep wisdom and the ability to see yourself rightly.

COMPASSION When you're able to identify suffering and to have empathy with those in pain—whether yourself or others—you can act compassionately to bring relief.

CONNECTEDNESS We are connected to everything around us. Consider and celebrate the ways we need one another and the natural world.

CONSCIOUSNESS Practice being aware of what is immediately present and of what you're experiencing in the moment. Do not need to judge it as right or wrong. Just name it.

GRATEFULNESS Acknowledge the world's goodness and beauty and be receptive to these gifts. By cultivating gratitude, you reap great connection and joy.

IMPERMANENCE Being present in each moment is key in a changing, temporary world, where grasping at what is passing brings only grief and regret.

JOY Deep-seated bliss transcends the situations in which we find ourselves and guides us toward truth and health.

NEWCOMER'S EYES Observe yourself and what's around you with curiosity, wonder, and openness, as if seeing it for the first time—setting aside presumptions and previous experiences.

FURTHER

PERPETUATING THE SPECIES

These babies, born in 2010, will grow up to see a world populated by more than 10 billion. Earth's population reached 7 billion in 2011, more than doubling since 1960, and it has already jumped beyond 7.7 billion today, with people living longer and healthier lives in many regions of the world. Countries in the Middle East and Africa show the fastest rate of population increase; Europe and the United States show generally declining fertility.

Nurses cluster swaddled newborns for a group portrait at Winnie Palmer Hospital in Orlando, Florida.

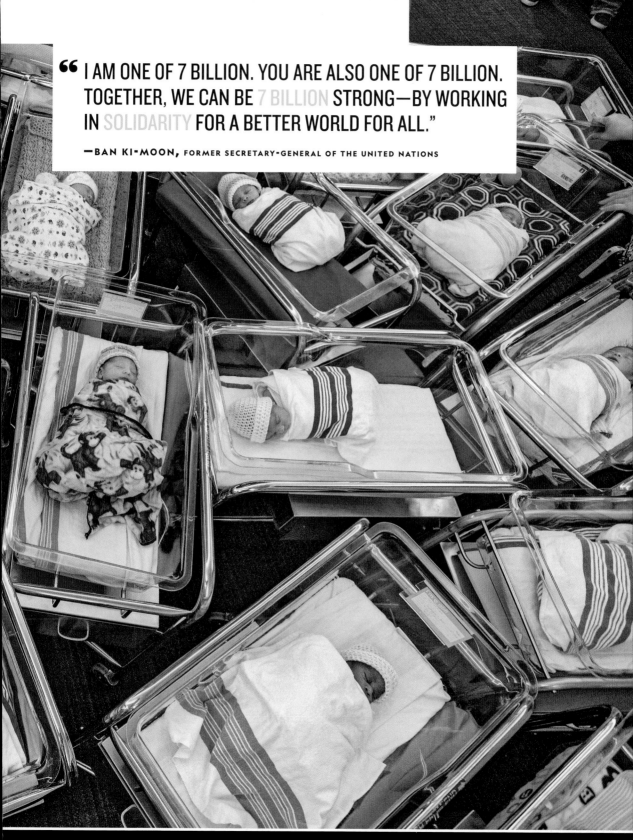

> " I AM ONE OF 7 BILLION. YOU ARE ALSO ONE OF 7 BILLION. TOGETHER, WE CAN BE 7 BILLION STRONG—BY WORKING IN SOLIDARITY FOR A BETTER WORLD FOR ALL."
>
> —BAN KI-MOON, FORMER SECRETARY-GENERAL OF THE UNITED NATIONS

YESTERDAY TO TOMORROW

WORLD HISTORY | U.K. HISTORY

Built some 4,500 years ago, the Giza Pyramids hold clues to life—and the afterlife—in Egypt's Old Kingdom.

QUIZ MASTER

p288

IN WHAT YEAR WAS THE CITY OF ROME FOUNDED?

p 286

WHICH GERMAN BROTHERS COLLECTED VOLUMES OF FOLKTALES IN THE 19TH CENTURY?

p291

HOW OLD WAS KING TUT WHEN HE BECAME PHARAOH?

p302

IN WHAT YEAR DID THE PANAMA CANAL OPEN?

IN WHAT YEAR DID THE INTERNATIONAL SPACE STATION BEGIN OPERATING WITH A CREW?

p305

p290

ON WHAT CONTINENT DID THE ASANTE KINGDOM RULE IN THE 18TH CENTURY?

WHAT IRISH CITY IS EUROPE'S 2020 CAPITAL OF CULTURE?

p314

WHAT CHARTER, ENACTED IN 1215, ENSURED INDIVIDUAL RIGHTS AND JUSTICE TO CITIZENS OF ENGLAND?

p294

IN WHAT CENTURY DID QUEEN SEMIRAMIS RULE THE ANCIENT KINGDOM OF BABYLON?

p292

p304

WHAT CITY, LOCATED IN MODERN-DAY TURKEY, WAS THE FIRST TO HAVE A SYSTEM OF STREET LIGHTING?

WHICH U.S. STATE FEATURES A UNION JACK ON ITS FLAG?

p319

WHO WAS THE U.K.'S LONGEST-SERVING PRIME MINISTER?

p313

p305

WHO SENT THE FIRST TELEGRAPH MESSAGE IN THE U.S.?

WHEN DID THE LONDON UNDERGROUND FIRST OPEN: 1863, 1913, OR 1953?

p309

PREHISTORY TO 1600
TIME LINE

PREHISTORY	3000 to 1000 BC	1000 to 500 BC	500 to 1 BC

ca 100,000 ya*
Early humans migrate from Africa to other continents.

ca 80,000 ya
Neanderthals and modern humans live alongside each other in Europe.

ca 14,500 ya
Human populations are present in North and South America.

ca 10,000 ya
Agriculture develops in the Yellow River Valley and other places in China.

ca 3200 BC
Sumer, the first known civilization, emerges in modern-day Iraq.

* years ago

ca 2575 BC
Ancient Egypt's Old Kingdom begins.

ca 2500–1900 BC
The Indus civilization thrives in modern-day Pakistan and northwest India.

ca 1766–1122 BC
The Shang dynasty rules in ancient China.

ca 1500 BC
Olmec culture develops in modern-day Mexico.

ca 1200 BC
Proto-Celtic people of Indo-European origin settle in central Europe.

753 BC
Rome is founded by Romulus and Remus, according to legend.

ca 700 BC
Athens and other Greek city-states become centers of learning and maritime trade.

ca 560 BC
Siddhartha Gautama is born in the Himalayan foothills; he is later known as the Buddha.

509 BC
The Roman Republic is established.

ca 500 BC
Iron tool technology spreads across Africa.

334 BC
Alexander the Great invades Persia and carves out an empire stretching from Greece to northwestern India.

ca 100 BC
Buddhism spreads into Central Asia along the Silk Road.

27 BC
Augustus becomes the first emperor of Rome.

| AD 1 to 500 | 500 to 1090 | 1090 to 1400 | 1400 to 1600 |

79
Mount Vesuvius erupts, destroying Pompeii and Herculaneum.

ca 300
Maya in South America develop a script and a calendar.

312
Constantine I becomes the emperor of Rome and expands legal rights for religions.

441
Attila the Hun launches a massive attack on the Eastern Roman Empire.

ca 500
The empire of Ghana gains prominence in West Africa.

570
Muhammad, the Prophet and future messenger of Islam, is born in Mecca.

800
Charlemagne is crowned the Holy Roman Emperor.

960
The Song dynasty reunifies China and ushers in economic, social, and cultural change.

ca 1000
Leif Eriksson sails to North America.

1054
The schism between the Roman and Eastern Christian churches becomes permanent.

1095
The First Crusade begins, inaugurating a series of religious wars that would last for hundreds of years.

1206
Genghis Khan becomes leader of the Mongol confederation.

1337
The Hundred Years' War begins between England and France.

1368
Zhu Yuanzhang founds the Ming dynasty in China.

1440
Moctezuma I becomes ruler of the Aztec.

1478
The Spanish Inquisition begins.

1517
Martin Luther instigates the Protestant Reformation.

1519–1521
Spain conquers the Aztec Empire, beginning a century-long colonial period.

1560s
The transatlantic slave trade grows in West Africa.

1577–1580
English explorer Sir Francis Drake circumnavigates the globe.

TALES OLDER
THAN THE HILLS

A BOY STEALS THE OGRE'S TREASURE
4,500 years old
A boy trespasses into a giant's house to steal his treasure. When the giant comes home, the boy hides and then manages to evade the giant's pursuit. Finally the boy kills the giant and takes his treasure.

THE SMITH AND THE DEVIL
6,000 years old
A blacksmith trades his soul to the devil for the power to weld any materials together. With his wish granted, the man traps the devil, sticking him to the ground until the evil spirit releases him from the bargain.

THE ANIMAL BRIDEGROOM
3,000 years old
Picking a rose lands a father in debt to a beast. In exchange for his freedom, his daughter is taken prisoner. After falling in love with the beast, she must overcome a curse to transform him into a prince.

FAIRY TALES—OLDER THAN YOU MIGHT THINK

As Wilhelm and Jacob Grimm collected Germanic folktales in the 19th century, they realized that many were similar to stories told in distant parts of the world. The brothers wondered whether similarities indicated a shared ancestry thousands of years old.

To test the Grimms' theory, anthropologist Jamie Tehrani and literary scholar Sara Graça da Silva traced 76 basic plots back to their oldest linguistic ancestor. If a similar tale was told in German and Hindi, the researchers concluded its roots lay in the languages' last common ancestor. "The Smith and the Devil," a story about a man who trades his soul for blacksmith skills, was first told some 6,000 years ago in Proto-Indo-European. In the United States, we tell a similar tale about blues guitarist Robert Johnson.

FRIENDS IN LIFE AND DEATH
2,000 years old
A man invites his dead friend to his wedding. When the groom accompanies his friend to the underworld, 400 years pass and he misses his own nuptials.

THE SUPERNATURAL HELPER
2,500 years old
A peasant falsely tells the king his daughter can spin gold out of straw. An elfin creature appears, offering the real skill in exchange for her firstborn child. The only way out is to guess his name—which she does.

MODERN TAKES

FRIENDS IN LIFE AND DEATH
A dead man accepts Don Juan's invitation to a banquet in exchange for Don Juan's attendance at another event—in the underworld.

THE ANIMAL BRIDEGROOM
In Disney's *Beauty and the Beast*, a witch's curse traps the prince in a beast's body until Belle's love breaks the spell.

THE SMITH AND THE DEVIL
Fictional scholar Faust and blues guitarist Robert Johnson are among the modern figures said to have sold their souls to the devil for knowledge.

A BOY STEALS THE OGRE'S TREASURE
Magic beans grow to great heights in "Jack and the Beanstalk," allowing Jack to climb up into a giant's lair and steal his treasures.

THE SUPERNATURAL HELPER
Trapped in an agreement to give Rumpelstiltskin her first child, a young queen overhears him chanting his name and gets out of the deal.

FOLKTALES
ARE PASSED DOWN ORALLY, OBSCURING THEIR AGE AND ORIGIN.

1600 TO RECENT PAST
TIME LINE

1600 to 1700	1700 to 1800	1800 to 1860	1860 to 1900

1600 to 1700

■ 1600s
European powers expand their colonization around the world.

■ ca 1600
Algonquin tribes unite to form the Powhatan Confederacy in North America.

■ 1633
For his theory that Earth circles the sun, Galileo goes on trial for heresy.

■ 1649
Civil war in England results in the execution of King Charles I.

■ 1661
Swedish banknotes become the first paper currency in use in Europe.

1700 to 1800

■ 1701
The Asante kingdom expands in West Africa under the reign of Osei Tutu.

■ 1762
Catherine II proclaims herself empress of Russia.

■ 1770
Aboard the *Endeavour*, James Cook claims Australia for Britain.

■ 1776
Americans post their Declaration of Independence.

■ 1789
A mob storms the Bastille, marking the beginning of the French Revolution.

1800 to 1860

■ 1801
A slave rebellion succeeds, leading to Haiti's independence from France three years later.

■ 1815
Simón Bolívar writes his "Letter From Jamaica," outlining his vision of South America freed of colonial rule.

■ 1833
Slavery is abolished throughout the British Empire.

■ 1837
Queen Victoria begins her 63-year reign.

■ 1845–1851
Irish potato famine causes poverty and mass starvation; millions emigrate to North America.

1860 to 1900

■ 1861
Tsar Alexander II frees serfs in Russia.

■ 1863
Abraham Lincoln issues the Emancipation Proclamation, freeing slaves in 10 states.

FREEDOM TO SLAVES!

■ 1867
Provinces in Canada unite into a single country.

■ 1884–1885
The Berlin Conference divides Africa among various European powers.

■ 1897
First Zionist Congress convenes in Basel, Switzerland.

1900 to 1925	1925 to 1950	1950 to 1975	1975 to 2000

1900 to 1925

■ 1914
The Panama Canal opens, enabling faster transoceanic shipping.

■ 1914
Assassination of Archduke Ferdinand sparks years-long World War I.

■ 1917
Lenin and the Bolsheviks overthrow the tsar in Russian Revolution.

■ 1920
Mohandas Gandhi becomes India's leader in its struggle for independence.

1925 to 1950

■ 1929
Wall Street stock market crashes, beginning the Great Depression.

■ 1933
Adolf Hitler is appointed chancellor of Germany.

■ 1939–1945
In World War II, Allied powers (including U.K., U.S., Soviet Union, France, and China) battle Axis powers (Germany, Italy, and Japan).

■ 1945
United Nations is founded.

■ 1949
Marxist leader Mao Zedong transforms China into Communist People's Republic of China.

1950 to 1975

■ 1955
Rosa Parks's arrest in Alabama sets the American civil rights movement in motion.

■ 1957
European Economic Community, precursor to the European Union, is established.

■ 1959
Fidel Castro takes over Cuba after leading a Marxist revolution.

■ 1973
Organization of Petroleum-Exporting Countries (OPEC) embargoes oil supplies, causing a worldwide energy crisis.

1975 to 2000

■ 1979
Muslim cleric Ayatollah Ruhollah Khomeini seizes power in Iran.

■ 1986
Disastrous accident at Chernobyl nuclear power plant in Ukraine forces massive resettlement.

■ 1989
Thousands of students occupy Beijing's Tian'anmen Square, advocating democracy in China.

■ 1989
Built in 1961 to encircle Germany's West Berlin, the Berlin Wall falls, a sign of the end of the Cold War.

■ 1990
Nelson Mandela is released after 27 years in prison, signifying end of apartheid in South Africa.

SEMIRAMIS
QUEEN OF BABYLON

THE ASSYRIAN EMPIRE'S ONLY WOMAN RULER

In the Neo-Assyrian regime of the ninth century BC, one woman commanded an entire empire—stretching from Asia Minor to today's western Iran. She was Sammu-ramat, thought to mean "high heaven," and she inspired universal respect. Centuries after her brief five-year reign, Greeks wrote about Semiramis, as they called her, and her achievements. From there, the Assyrian queen passed into the realm of legend. What stands out is how both the woman and the myth were celebrated for things traditionally associated with male rulers: scoring military triumphs, building architectural wonders, and ruling with wisdom.

66 AS FOR SEMIRAMIS, APART FROM HER WORKS AT BABYLON, MANY OTHERS ARE ALSO TO BE SEEN THROUGHOUT ALMOST THE WHOLE OF THE CONTINENT OF ASIA."

—FROM *THE GEOGRAPHY OF STRABO,* WRITTEN AROUND 10 BC

Queen Sammu-ramat of history begat Queen Semiramis of legend, whose civic accomplishments are lauded on the same level as her beauty.

Semiramis's
LIFE AND LEGEND

■ MARRIAGE
According to artifacts, Queen Sammu-ramat was married to King Shamshi-Adad V, who reigned 823–811 BC, and was the mother of King Adad-nirari III.

■ INHERITING THE THRONE
When the king died, his son, Adad-nirari III, was too young to rule, leaving Queen Sammu-ramat to govern Assyria through her regency.

■ BATTLE
One monument mentions that the queen accompanied her son into battle, which indicates her actions were honored and respected.

■ EARNING RESPECT
Another monument bears this exceptional dedication: "Sammu-ramat, Queen of Shamshi-Adad, King of the Universe, King of Assyria; Mother of Adad-nirari, King of the Universe, King of Assyria."

■ A PLACE IN HISTORY
In the fifth century BC, the historian Herodotus perpetuated memory of Sammu-ramat using the Greek form of her name, Semiramis, by which she is best known today.

■ MYTHIC ORIGINS
In the account perpetuated by Diodorus Siculus in the first century BC, Semiramis was the child of a Syrian goddess and a young Syrian man.

■ ANCIENT WONDERS
Greek historians said the queen ordered a new city, with fabulous hanging gardens, to be built on the banks of the Euphrates— Babylon. No historical evidence supports their claims.

■ CIRCLES OF HELL
She inspired the Italian medieval poet Dante, who placed her in his *Inferno,* where she is punished for her "sensual vices."

■ A LASTING LEGACY
The French Enlightenment writer Voltaire wrote a tragedy about her, which was later made into Rossini's 1823 opera, *Semiramide.*

A HISTORY OF DEMOCRACY

THE QUEST FOR EQUAL RIGHTS

Raphael's "School of Athens"

ANCIENT HISTORY

FIRST GRANTING OF RIGHTS, CA 594 BC

Solon of Athens institutes economic and political reforms, including granting all citizens the right to participate in the ecclesia (general assembly), which has legislative and judicial powers.

REFORMING POWER STRUCTURE, 508 BC

Athenian statesman Cleisthenes encourages participation in government by extending the right to participate to all free adult men born in townships—and becomes the father of democracy.

COMMON GOOD, 4TH CENTURY BC

Aristotle describes a "polity" as government by consent and for the common good—which resembles what comes to be known as a constitutional democracy.

EARLY TIMES

OLDEST PARLIAMENT, 930

During the Viking era and predating Iceland's written language, the first parliament, Althing, is established at Thingvellir, a place-name literally meaning "parliament plains." It has become the world's longest-running representative democracy.

LEVELS OF REPRESENTATION, CA 11TH TO 15TH CENTURIES

The Igbo society in what is now Nigeria has representative bodies at the village level that seek consensus under the leadership of elders. This decentralized, chiefless system endures until colonialism.

INDIVIDUAL FREEDOM, 1215

The Magna Carta—"Great Charter"—is issued in Latin by England's King John in the context of power struggles between the pope and the king of England. Reaffirmed by John's successors, it ensures basic individual rights and guarantees justice and the right to a fair trial, thus granting protection to individuals from higher authorities.

SELF-GOVERNANCE, 1620

Most of the men arriving on the *Mayflower* sign a compact that will influence governance in the Plymouth colony. The Mayflower Compact has inclinations toward democratic values of self-government and common consent.

The U.S. Constitution

Tunisian demonstrators during election, 2011

REVOLUTIONARY ERA

ALL CREATED EQUAL, 1776

Colonists in the Americas draft the Declaration of Independence—asserting "that all men are created equal, that they are endowed by their Creator with certain unalienable Rights, that among these are Life, Liberty and the pursuit of Happiness." This becomes a globally recognized document of self-governance and the fundamental rights of human beings.

BALANCE OF POWER, 1787

The U.S. Constitution is presented to the states for ratification. It outlines the workings of a federal democratic government, including the balance of power in a tripartite government, individual rights versus the state, and the limits of centralized government versus the state sovereignty. Amendments known as the Bill of Rights are added in 1789.

RIGHTS OF THE CITIZEN, 1789

As the French Revolution begins, France's National Assembly adopts the Declaration of the Rights of Man and of the Citizen, which is later revised and incorporated into subsequent constitutions.

MODERN TIMES

END TO COLONIALISM, 1950

India becomes a democratic republic when its new constitution takes effect—the world's largest democracy.

CIVIL PROTEST, 1989

Hundreds of thousands occupy China's Tiananmen Square to demand democratic reform. After a tense few months, the government responds with violence, martial law, and criminal prosecutions.

BRINGING DOWN APARTHEID, 1996

Following centuries of occupation by the Dutch and British, including decades of apartheid, the government of South Africa transitions to majority rule.

ARAB SPRING, 2010

The first of several pro-democracy protests takes place in Tunisia, inspiring uprisings across North Africa and the Middle East. Some countries suppress the movement; others, like Morocco, implement reforms.

ADA LOVELACE
EARLY PROGRAMMER

THE ENCHANTRESS OF NUMBERS

Augusta Ada Byron, who later became the Countess of Lovelace, was born in Britain in 1815—not a time known for women scientists. Her father, Lord Byron, was one of the most popular poets in Europe, and she herself was a celebrity of sorts. Ada Lovelace, as she was known, became the world's first programmer a century before computers were invented.

The visionary Ada Lovelace was the daughter of Romantic poet Lord Byron and Annabelle Byron, who encouraged her education in mathematics.

E ducated in math and science—part of her mother's efforts to tamp down any dangerous creative tendencies she may have inherited from her infamous father—Lovelace followed her scientific and technological passions, much a scandal at the time. But as her collaborator, Charles Babbage, wrote, Lovelace's "taste for mathematics is so decided that it ought not to be checked."

SEEING COMPUTERS' POTENTIAL

In 1833, the teenage Lovelace began to work with Babbage, a mathematician and engineer. They collaborated on his Analytical Engine, a precursor to the modern computer that could calculate complex mathematical problems.

Lovelace wrote a series of notes about the device for publication and included an algorithm for using the Analytical Engine to calculate a sequence of numbers called Bernoulli numbers. Her algorithm—which told the Analytical Engine exactly which functions to calculate and in what order—was the first computer program. Her mastery of abstract ideas and the science of operations anticipated computers' being able to process any information represented by numbers. It was a full century later, in the 1940s, that Alan Turing built the first modern computer.

Today Lovelace is honored as a pioneer in computer science. The second Tuesday of October is Ada Lovelace Day. A programming language bears her name. A medal named after her is awarded by the British Computer Society. She stands as a model and inspiration for girls interested in engineering and science.

> **" THIS SCIENCE CONSTITUTES THE LANGUAGE THROUGH WHICH ALONE WE CAN ADEQUATELY EXPRESS THE GREAT FACTS OF THE NATURAL WORLD."**

A model of Lovelace and Babbage's proto-computer

KEY DATES

Imagining and Inventing
MODERN COMPUTERS

■ 1833
Meets Babbage and hears of his hand-cranked calculator, the Difference Engine

■ 1835
Marries, at age 19, William King, age 30, eighth Baron King and first Earl of Lovelace

■ 1843
Publishes her translation of a French paper on Babbage's Analytical Engine

■ 1852
Dies from cancer, age 36

■ 2009
Ada Lovelace Day celebrated internationally for the first time

BEST OF @NATGEO

TOP PHOTOS OF HISTORIC PLACES

@yamashitaphoto | MICHAEL YAMASHITA
A restored section of the Great Wall of China at Jinshanling s part of a fortification system whose construction began in he third century BC.

@salvarezphoto | STEPHEN ALVAREZ
A Bedouin man leads camels past an intricately carved mausoleum facade in Petra, an ancient city in what is now Jordan.

@simonnorfolkstudio | SIMON NORFOLK
.ights shine in the streets of Matera, a city built out from what thought to be one of the earliest human settlements in Italy.

@salvarezphoto | STEPHEN ALVAREZ
The massive moai statues of Easter Island, erected betweer 1250 and 1500 AD, can weigh up to 86 tons.

> **66 MAN IS A HISTORY-MAKING CREATURE WHO CAN NEITHER REPEAT HIS PAST NOR LEAVE IT BEHIND."**
>
> —W. H. AUDEN, POET

@dguttenfelder | **DAVID GUTTENFELDER**
Grass carpets the site of a Viking ring fortress in Trelleborg, Denmark. These structures are remarkable for their symmetry and uniformity.

@irablockphoto | **IRA BLOCK**
A sacred destination for Buddhists, the Golden Rock gleams at the top of Mount Kyaiktiyo in Myanmar.

@argonautphoto | **AARON HUEY**
A pilgrim embraces the outside of the shrine of the Sufi saint Shah Yusuf Gardezi in Multan, Pakistan.

@simonnorfolkstudio | **SIMON NORFOLK**
Peaking during the Maya Classic period, Tikal in Guatemala maintains its wondrous temples, palaces, and plazas.

TERRA-COTTA
WARRIORS

A LEGION FOR ETERNITY

Workers digging a well outside the city of Xi'an, China, in 1974 struck upon one of the greatest archaeological discoveries in the world: a life-size clay soldier poised for battle. Government archaeologists arrived to find not one but thousands of clay soldiers, each with unique facial expressions and positioned according to rank, in trenchlike underground corridors. In some of the corridors, clay horses are aligned four abreast; behind them are wooden chariots. The terra-cotta army, we now know, was part of an elaborate mausoleum created to accompany the first emperor of China, Qin Shi Huang Di, into the afterlife.

THE AVERAGE TERRA-COTTA SOLDIER STANDS ABOUT FIVE FEET, EIGHT INCHES TALL.

Ranks of life-size clay soldiers, buried with the first emperor of China more than 2,000 years ago, were rediscovered in 1974.

The Emperor's
ARMY FOR
THE AFTERLIFE

■ **FIRST EMPEROR**
Ying Zheng took the throne in 246 BC at
the age of 13. By 221 BC, he had unified a
collection of warring kingdoms and took
the name of Qin Shi Huang Di—the First
Emperor of Qin.

■ **LABOR**
Court historian Sima Qian of the following
Han dynasty claims that more than 700,000
laborers worked on the project, though
modern scholars doubt that figure.

■ **BURIAL GUARDS**
An estimated 8,000 statues of warriors were
buried in three pits less than a mile from the
emperor's tomb.

■ **TOMB**
The burial complex covers almost 38
square miles.

■ **BURIED ALONGSIDE**
Artisans, craftsmen, and laborers—likely
including shackled convicts—who died
during the 36 years it took to build this
complex were buried here.

■ **BURSTS OF COLOR**
Qin's army of soldiers and horses was
a supernatural display swathed in a riot
of bold colors: red and green, purple
and yellow.

■ **PRESERVING EARTH**
The original paint degrades on exposure but
adheres to dirt, so preservationists are now
trying to preserve the earth itself.

■ **OTHER CULTURES**
Terra-cotta acrobats and bronze figures of
ducks, swans, and cranes uncovered at the
grand funerary complex may show evidence
of Greek influence.

■ **EXCAVATION**
Archaeologists have no plans to unearth the
first emperor's tomb, waiting instead for
new conservation technologies.

GENOME CLUES IN EGYPT

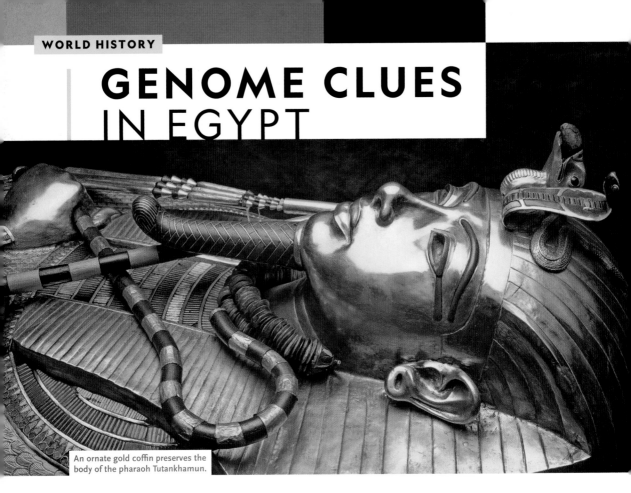

An ornate gold coffin preserves the body of the pharaoh Tutankhamun.

ANCIENT RIDDLES, MODERN SCIENCE

Tutankhamun was a pharaoh during ancient Egypt's New Kingdom era, about 3,300 years ago. He ascended to the throne at the age of nine but ruled for only 10 years before dying at 19, around 1324 BC. Despite his brief reign, King Tut is perhaps Egypt's best known pharaoh because of the treasures—including a solid gold death mask—found in his tomb in 1922.

Yet while King Tut may be seen as the golden boy of ancient Egypt today, he wasn't exactly a strapping sun god during his reign. Instead, a DNA study says, King Tut was a frail pharaoh, beset by malaria and a bone disorder—his health possibly compromised by his incestuous origins.

The study could be conducted on ancient Egyptian royal mummies because the embalming method the ancient Egyptians used seems to have protected DNA as well as flesh. Using DNA samples taken from the mummies' bones, scientists were able to create a five-generation family tree for the boy pharaoh.

One genealogical mystery lingers: Some Egyptologists have speculated that King Tut's mother was Akhenaten's chief wife, Queen Nefertiti, who was also Akhenaten's cousin. Others claim that DNA shows his mother was the daughter of Amenhotep III and Tiye and thus the sister of her husband, Akhenaten.

> ## " WE WERE ASTONISHED BY THE BEAUTY AND REFINEMENT OF THE ART DISPLAYED BY THE OBJECTS SURPASSING ALL WE COULD HAVE IMAGINED—THE IMPRESSION WAS OVERWHELMING. "

—HOWARD CARTER,
ARCHAEOLOGIST AND DISCOVERER OF TUT'S TOMB

LASTING LEGACIES

In addition to using DNA to identify royalty, scientists are evaluating the genetic makeup of mummies spanning 1,300 years. One surprising finding is that modern Egyptians have sub-Saharan ancestry not found in the ancient population, which was similar genetically to people from the Levant.

It had been thought that Egyptians acquired European and Middle Eastern ancestry over time, following conquests and contact with those populations. But scientists have determined that about 700 years ago, the amount of sub-Saharan DNA in Egyptians' makeup population increased. What facilitated this change is not clear. What is clear, however, is that Europeans are more closely related to ancient Egyptians than are modern Egyptians.

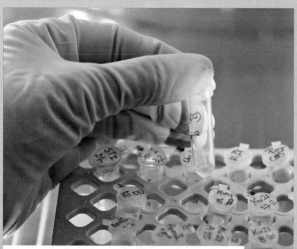

DNA samples from King Tut shed light on the royal lineage.

KEY FACTS

Ancient Egypt THEN AND NOW

■ **DUSTING FOR PRINTS**
To dust for prints at a crime scene, modern investigators use Egyptian blue, a pigment formulated some 5,250 years ago—in the time of the pharaohs.

■ **EMBALMING**
A decade-long investigation of prehistoric mummy wrappings roughly 6,600 years old established that Egyptians embalmed their dead thousands of years earlier than previously thought.

■ **FEMALE FIGURE**
Historians had speculated that Akhenaten's feminine features—such as wide hips, a potbelly, and female-like breasts—were caused by a genetic disorder, but none has been found. It is now believed that these features, evident in statues, were created for religious and political reasons.

■ **ANCIENT BEERS**
Archaeologists have excavated a tomb belonging to Khonso Im-Heb, who was head of granaries and beer brewing for the worship of the Egyptian mother goddess, Mut.

■ **METEORIC METAL**
Researchers have confirmed that the iron of a dagger placed on King Tutankhamun's mummified body has meteoric origins. This follows an earlier identification of 5,000-year-old Egyptian beads made of meteoric iron—the earliest known sign of metalwork.

■ **SATELLITE**
Using high-resolution satellite images near Lisht, at the edge of the Sahara, archaeologists identified looted pits that turned out to be an interlocking mortuary system housing at least 4,000 individuals in the afterlife.

INNOVATIONS
TIME LINE

6000 to 1500 BC	1500 to 1 BC	AD 1 to 1000	1000 to 1600

ca 6000 BC
The world's first known city, Çatalhöyük, is built in Anatolia.

ca 3500 BC
Wheeled vehicles are in use in the Middle East.

ca 3000 BC
Egyptians have developed a process for making paper from the papyrus plant.

ca 2500 BC
The Great Pyramids and the Sphinx are completed in Egypt.

ca 2500 BC
Peruvians use a canal system to irrigate crops.

ca 1525 BC
Stonehenge is completed in England.

---

ca 1400 BC
Iron weapons are in use by the Hittites of modern-day Turkey.

ca 500 BC
The abacus, earliest calculating tool, is in use in China.

ca 300 BC
The Maya begin constructing their monumental pyramids in Mexico and Central America.

214 BC
The main section of the Great Wall of China is completed.

ca 120 BC
Romans use concrete to create paved streets, aqueducts, and bridges.

---

ca 200
Porcelain is being produced in Han dynasty China.

350
Antioch, in today's Turkey, becomes the first city to have a system of street lighting.

ca 600
Chatrang, an early version of chess, is popular in parts of Central Asia.

607
Japan's Horyuji Temple, the world's oldest wooden building, is completed.

ca 800
Islamic scientists use the astrolabe for celestial observation.

---

ca 1000
Fireworks, made of a bamboo tube filled with gunpowder, are invented in China.

ca 1040
Chinese explorers use magnetic compasses to navigate.

ca 1286
In Italy, the first known eyeglasses are manufactured to correct vision.

ca 1450
The Inca construct a 20,000-mile-long roadway to unite their empire.

1455
Johannes Gutenberg prints the Bible on a movable type press.

| 1600 to 1800 | 1800 to 1900 | 1900 to 1950 | 1950 to PRESENT |

1609–1610
Galileo first observes Earth's moon and four moons of Jupiter with a telescope.

1626
St. Peter's Basilica is completed in Rome after 120 years of construction.

1716
The first lighthouse in North America is built, in Boston Harbor.

1752
After demonstrating the electrical nature of lightning, Benjamin Franklin invents the lightning rod.

1775
Inventor Alexander Cummings patents the first flushing toilet.

1843
Ada Lovelace and Charles Babbage collaborate on the world's first computer.

1844
Samuel Morse sends the first telegraph message in the United States.

1867
Alfred Nobel patents dynamite in Britain.

1876
Alexander Graham Bell invents the telephone and makes the first long-distance call.

1898
German chemist Hans von Pechmann synthesizes polyethylene, the world's first plastic.

1901
Italian scientist Guglielmo Marconi makes the first transatlantic radio broadcast.

1904
German engineer Christian Hülsmeyer patents the first radar system, used to prevent collisions among shipping vessels.

1931
The Empire State Building in New York City becomes the world's tallest building.

1943
Jacques Cousteau begins using the Aqua-Lung, which he designed with engineer Émile Gagnan, for underwater diving.

1945
Americans manufacture, test, and deploy the atom bomb.

1954
The first solar cells, converting sunlight to electricity, are developed.

1959
Unimate #001, the first industrial robot, is deployed in a General Motors engine plant.

1959
The microchip, key component of computers, is invented.

1989
The World Wide Web is initiated by British computer scientist Tim Berners-Lee.

2000
The International Space Station begins operating with a crew.

WAR IN OUR TIMES

THE EVOLUTION OF WEAPONS OF WAR

Strategies of war often pivot on newly available technologies, such as chemical weapons amid trenches in WWI and coordinated ground, naval, and air attacks in both theaters of WWII. By the late 20th century, the U.S. military was deploying surveillance drones (remotely piloted aerial systems). Unmanned weaponized drones soon followed and have been key in efforts against non-state actors such as al Qaeda and ISIS, which often embed militants among civilians in cities. Future conflicts will use multiple stealth vehicles, weapons systems, and cyberweapons.

SOME SOLDIERS NOW USE NANO-DRONES, MINIATURE CAMERA-EQUIPPED HELICOPTERS THAT WEIGH AN OUNCE OR TWO AND FIT INTO A POCKET.

The Global Hawk, an unmanned surveillance aircraft, images large areas from high altitudes for more than 30 hours at a time; one of many ways in which remotely piloted drones characterize military actions today.

KEEPING THE PEACE

Since its founding in 1948, the United Nations has operated 71 peacekeeping missions—almost two-thirds of those in the last 30 years. Today, over 110,000 peacekeepers are part of more than a dozen ongoing missions.

MAY 1948, MIDDLE EAST

The UN's first and longest-running peacekeeping mission continues to promote stability to the Middle East.

JANUARY 1949, INDIA AND PAKISTAN

This mission has been in place for decades to observe the cease-fire in the disputed region of Kashmir.

MARCH 1964, CYPRUS

With no political settlement between the Greek and Turkish communities, this mission maintains buffer zones, among other responsibilities.

MAY 1974, SYRIA

Originally in place to maintain the cease-fire between Israeli and Syrian forces, peacekeepers seek to de-escalate armed conflicts in the area.

MARCH 1978, LEBANON

Started to confirm Israel's withdrawal from Lebanon, the mission continues to monitor hostilities and ensure humanitarian access to civilians.

APRIL 1991, WESTERN SAHARA

This mission aims to help the people of Western Sahara choose independence or integration with Morocco.

JUNE 1999, KOSOVO

Having helped this republic (claimed by Serbia) gain autonomy, the mission now provides security and stability.

JULY 2007, DARFUR

Along with the African Union, this mission is in place to protect civilians, facilitate humanitarian aid, and help the political process.

U.S. armored vehicles approach the Syria-Turkey border, April 2017.

JULY 2010, DEMOCRATIC REPUBLIC OF THE CONGO

Armed peacekeepers are deployed to protect civilians under imminent threat of physical violence and to support stabilization efforts.

JUNE 2011, ABYEI

The armed mission in this volatile region, claimed by Sudan and South Sudan, monitors the border, facilitates delivery of aid, and protects civilians.

JULY 2011, SOUTH SUDAN

In South Sudan, the world's newest country, peacekeepers work to protect civilians, reduce hostilities, and deliver humanitarian assistance.

APRIL 2013, MALI

Alongside Mali's transitional authorities, this mission focuses on civilian security and the reestablishment of government after regional conflicts.

APRIL 2014, CENTRAL AFRICAN REPUBLIC

Created amid political crisis, this mission is tasked with protecting civilians and supporting transition processes.

OCTOBER 2017, HAITI

This nonmilitary mission, which follows successful elections, helps develop the National Police, strengthen justice institutions, and protect human rights.

UNITED KINGDOM
TIME LINE

| 250,000 to 1 BC | AD 1 to 1000 | 1000 to 1400 | 1400 to 1700 |

250,000 ya
The first weaponized hunters are active in Britain.

ca 6000 BC
The island of Britain becomes separated from the European mainland.

ca 3000 BC
Work begins on Stonehenge on the Salisbury Plain.

ca 2000 BC
The "Beaker folk" bury fine pottery vessels with their dead.

55–54 BC
Julius Caesar leads Roman forays into Britain.

ca 43
Londinium becomes the capital of the Roman province of Britannia.

122–128
Hadrian's Wall is built between the River Tyne and the Solway Firth, forming the northern boundary of the Roman Empire.

ca 400
The Roman legions leave Britain.

ca 410–800
The Saxons arrive and divide Britain into the kingdoms of Wessex, Kent, Mercia, East Anglia, and Northumbria.

ca 793–878
Vikings partake in a series of raids on Britain.

1066
The Normans defeat the Anglo-Saxons at the Battle of Hastings.

1066–1154
Norman rule in Britain brings Christian culture and cathedrals.

1086
Norman conqueror William I commissions the Domesday Book survey to quantify his newly won kingdom.

1215
The Magna Carta establishes basic individual liberties within the legal system.

1348–1349
The first outbreak of the Black Death ravages Britain.

1485
Victory for Henry Tudor ends the 32-year War of the Roses between the Houses of Lancaster and York.

1534
Henry VIII becomes the supreme head of the Church of England.

1558–1603
The reign of Elizabeth I brings a golden age: Britain breaks Spanish maritime might, and British colonies are established worldwide.

1564–1616
William Shakespeare writes 38 plays and scores of poems.

1653
After the execution of Charles I, Oliver Cromwell appoints himself Lord Protector.

1666
The Great Fire of London destroys much of the city.

| 1700 to 1830 | 1830 to 1900 | 1900 to 1950 | 1950 to PRESENT |

■ 1707
The Act of Union sees the Kingdom of England and the Kingdom of Scotland "United into One Kingdom by the Name of Great Britain."

■ 1760–1820
The reign of George III is marked by the rapid rise of factories and mills, attracting rural masses into Britain's cities.

■ 1776
The signing of the Declaration of Independence heralds the birth of the United States of America.

■ 1830
The steam age arrives with the opening of the Liverpool and Manchester Railway.

■ 1836–1870
Charles Dickens chronicles the epic changes sweeping Victorian Britain.

■ 1834
Slavery is abolished throughout the British Empire.

■ 1837
Queen Victoria inherits the throne and rules Britain through six decades of huge social and economic change.

■ 1851
London hosts the Great Exhibition, Prince Albert's celebration of British imperial and industrial power.

■ 1863
The London underground railway, the world's first, opens.

■ 1914–1918
World War I leaves over a million British dead and traumatizes a generation.

■ 1918
Women over 30 gain the right to vote.

■ 1936
Edward VIII succeeds his father, George V, and then abdicates the throne to marry American divorcée Wallis Simpson.

■ 1939–1945
Millions of Britons serve in World War II, defending the island nation from Hitler's Blitz and helping to liberate Western Europe.

■ 1940
Prime Minister Winston Churchill rallies the British for "their finest hour."

■ 1952
Queen Elizabeth II accedes to the throne. In 2015, she becomes Britain's longest-serving monarch.

■ 1966
England wins the World Cup, beating West Germany 4–2 in the final.

■ 1973
Britain joins the EEC, the forerunner of the European Union.

■ 1979
Margaret Thatcher becomes Britain's first female prime minister.

■ 2016
Britain votes to leave the European Union.

BRITAIN'S
ISLAND CULTURE

ATLANTIC OCEAN

Shetland Islands (Zetland)   Muckle Flugga

St. Magnus Bay   Fetlar   Yell

Mainland

The Deeps   NORTH SEA

Same Scale as Main Map

ATLANTIC OCEAN

Outer Hebrides

Inner Hebrides

Orkney Islands

HIGHLANDS
SCOTLAND   •Aberdeen

Grampian Mountains

G R E A T

Dundee•

Polyconic Projection

0   50   100
KILOMETERS

0   50   100
STATUTE MILES

•Edinburgh

Glasgow•

Southern Uplands

NORTH SEA

Newcastle•   •Sunderland

NORTHERN IRELAND

Belfast•   •Middlesbrough

U N I T E D   K I N G D O M

T H E   P E N N I N E S

ISLE OF MAN
Douglas•(ELLAN VANNIN)

B R I T I S H   I S L E S

York•
•Beverley

Blackpool•   Leeds•   *The Wolds*
•Kingston upon Hull

Liverpool•   •Manchester

I R E L A N D

Bolton•

Stoke on Trent•   •Sheffield

Dublin®
(Baile Átha Cliath)

IRISH SEA

Derby•   •Nottingham

IRELAND
(ÉIRE)

Cambrian Mountains

Wolverhampton•   •Norwich

E N G L A N D

•Leicester

WALES   BIRMINGHAM®   •Coventry

Cork
(Corcaigh)•

Worcester•   •Northampton   Cambridge•

Cheltenham•   Luton•   •Ipswich•Colchester

Cotswold Hills

Gloucester•   •Chelmsford

Swansea
(Abertawe)•   Newport•   Oxford•   •Southend-on-Sea

CELTIC SEA

Cardiff
(Caerdydd)•   Swindon•   ®LONDON

Reading•   *North Downs*

Bristol•   Basingstoke•

ENGLISH CHANNEL
(LA MANCHE)

Guernsey U.K.   FRANCE

CHANNEL ISLANDS   Jersey U.K.

Same Scale as Main Map

Southampton•   *South Downs*
•Brighton

Exeter•   Poole•   •Portsmouth
•Bournemouth

•Plymouth

E N G L I S H   C H A N N E L
(LA MANCHE)

FRANCE

THE SMALLER BRITISH ISLES

British Isles is a term that describes the main landmasses of the United Kingdom, but it also incorporates a vast scattering of small islands around coastlines and on rivers and lakes — with a wealth of subcultures, wildlife, and rare flora to explore.

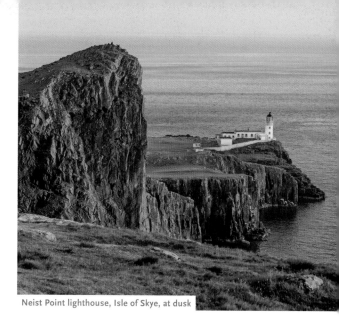

Neist Point lighthouse, Isle of Skye, at dusk

ISLE OF MAN

This island in the Irish Sea is known for having one of the world's oldest parliaments, the Tynwald Court, and for its generous low-tax economy with no stamp duty, capital gains, wealth, or inheritance taxes. Excellent roads vein its 221-square-mile area, well maintained for its annual TT Motorcycle Races in May and June.

GUERNSEY

This Channel Island has been occupied by Neolithic farmers, Roman legions, Normans, Dutch privateers, Victorian holidaymakers, and Nazis, who sent more than 1,000 of its residents to German work camps. That Guernsey has no corporation tax rate on most companies attracts potential residents.

JERSEY

Another tax haven, the Bailiwick of Jersey is a British crown dependency near the French coast. This small island is a self-governing parliamentary democracy under a constitutional monarchy, with its own financial, legal, and judicial systems. Jersey is not officially part of Britain, so it is not suffering the full economic pains of Brexit.

ISLE OF SKYE

Skye is the largest of the Inner Hebrides, and the most dramatic. Golden eagles circle the Cuillin's rocky peaks, red deer graze Skye's heather moorlands, and Atlantic salmon crowd its rivers. Dunvegan Castle, the seat of the MacLeod clan since the 13th century, is one of many such familial keeps on this Gaelic-speaking enclave.

LEWIS & HARRIS

The Isles of Lewis and Harris are the northernmost island of the Outer Hebrides chain, aka the Western Isles. The islands thrum with a creative force that puts the ancient Callanish Stones in historical perspective. The descendants of the people who constructed this Neolithic stone circle are now painters, photographers, candlemakers, potters, and weavers of wonderful Harris tweed.

ISLE OF WIGHT

Once a Norman kingdom, this island off Hampshire lies across the Solent strait from mainland Britain. It was here, in Osborne House, that Queen Victoria took her last breath in 1901. More recently, rock royalty has graced its music festival, including acts such as Jimi Hendrix, David Bowie, and the Rolling Stones.

HOLY ISLAND, ANGLESEY

Holy Island lies off the western side of the Isle of Anglesey in Wales. The unusual glut of burial chambers, standing stones, and religious sites gives this small island its name. Although little is known of its early settlers' beliefs, the jagged local coastline would test the faith of generations of sailors; the sea stacks and the cliffs of Anglesey were many a sailor's final sightings of this world.

CANVEY ISLAND

Canvey is a reclaimed island in the Thames estuary in Essex. Inhabited since the Roman invasion of Britain, it has since become the Netherlands of Britain. The island reaches just above sea level, and thus is prone to tidal flooding. Canvey's darkest hour came when the 1953 North Sea flood killed 59 islanders. The island is now protected by two miles of concrete seawalls.

ST. AGNES, ISLES OF SCILLY

St. Agnes is the southernmost point in England, being the farthest flung of the Isles of Scilly, the archipelago off the southwestern tip of Cornwall. The island's lighthouse was built in 1680, close to the treacherous Western Rocks, where tidal flows and currents caused many shipwrecks. The island's light thereafter became the first sign of Britain for returning seamen as the empire expanded.

GREAT WOMEN LEAD THE WAY

REWRITING THE RULES IN A WORLD RULED BY MEN

Britain has a long history of strong women, unafraid to challenge male orthodoxies. Queens and prime ministers, suffragettes and scientists—British women continue to take their place at the head of the table.

Hair cut short like a man's, O'Malley bowed but would not curtsy to the queen.

GRACE O'MALLEY

PIRATE MEETS QUEEN

Grace O'Malley (1530–1603) was Ireland's "Pirate Queen" as British rule advanced. O'Malley ruled the waves from Ireland's west coast, plundering ships as England divided up the Gaelic kingdoms of Ireland. Known locally as Gráinne Mhaol ("Bald Grace"), she cut her hair to pass as a man on her father's ships; she soon commanded armies of men to sail under her captaincy. When she sailed up the Thames to negotiate the release of her brothers, Queen Elizabeth received her at Greenwich Palace. There the two made their peace, O'Malley refusing to curtsy but bowing her head toward the English monarch whom she considered her equal.

EMMELINE PANKHURST

SUFFRAGE MAKES HEADLINES

Emmeline Pankhurst (1858–1928) probably did as much as anyone else to earn British women the right to vote. The pre–World War I activism of her Women's Social and Political Union, a militant wing of the women's movement, was the proving ground for universal suffrage in modern Britain. Their campaigns made headlines: Windows were smashed, fires set, demonstrations became violent, and hunger strikes led to force-feeding. One suffragette, Emily Davison, threw herself under the king's horse during the 1913 Epsom Derby. By 1918, British women (but only over the age of 30) had won the right to vote; by 2020, Britain has had two female prime ministers.

Despite arrests, Pankhurst persisted, leading British women in demanding equal rights.

Thatcher studied chemistry at Oxford, her tutor Nobel Prize winner Dorothy Hodgkin.

MARGARET THATCHER

FIRST AND LONGEST SERVING

Known as the Iron Lady, Margaret Thatcher (1925–2013) became Britain's first female prime minister in 1979. The longest-serving PM of the 20th century, she left a legacy of uncompromising leadership. In 1983, British forces recaptured the Falkland Islands from Argentine invaders; she broke the national miners' strike and privatized many of the industries that had fueled Britain's great industrial age; she survived an Irish Republican Army bombing that killed five of her colleagues at the 1984 Tory Conference in Brighton. Two years after leaving office in 1990, Margaret Thatcher went on to serve in the House of Lords as Baroness Thatcher.

POP!

FILMS ABOUT GREAT BRITISH LADIES

- Meryl Streep as Emmeline Pankhurst in *Suffragette* (Film: 2015)
- Meryl Streep as Margaret Thatcher in *The Iron Lady* (Film: 2011)
- Jenna Coleman as Queen Victoria in *Victoria* (TV drama: 2016–2017)
- Helen Mirren as Queen Elizabeth II in *The Queen* (Film: 2006)
- Claire Foy and Olivia Coleman as Queen Elizabeth II in *The Crown* (TV drama: 2016–present)

WOMEN GAINED THE RIGHT TO SERVE IN BRITAIN'S HOUSE OF COMMONS IN 1918 BUT NOT IN THE HOUSE OF LORDS UNTIL 1958.

Sturgeon represents Scottish independence as she speaks out against Brexit.

NICOLA STURGEON

VOCAL SCOTSWOMAN

Since 2014, Nicola Sturgeon (1970–) has been First Minister of Scotland and leader of the Scottish National Party (SNP). She is also Scotland's first woman leader since the establishment of the Scottish Parliament in 1999. Despite her deep opposition to Margaret Thatcher's conservative policies, Sturgeon was inspired by the success of Britain's first female prime minister. She joined the SNP in 1986 when she was 16 years old and became a member of Scottish Parliament in 1999. She has acted as SNP spokeswoman for health, education, and justice. Sturgeon has campaigned vigorously for Scottish independence and for Scotland's membership of the EU in the midst of Brexit.

GALWAY
MAKES WAVES

IRELAND'S CREATIVE WESTERN HUB

Named Europe's 2020 Capital of Culture, Galway is imbued with character that arises from centuries of synthesis. As a seaport and trading town, the city has long absorbed currents from outsiders—Normans, Spaniards, Sri Lankans, North Africans. The stony, windswept wilderness surrounding the city, County Galway and Connemara, has sent its sons and daughters abroad and welcomed them and their broadened worldviews back home again.

Closed to traffic, Shop Street—here decorated for Christmas—is Galway's spirited city center.

A Year of Celebrating Galway's
RICH HISTORY

■ SMALL TOWNS, BIG IDEAS

A flagship program celebrates Meitheal, the ancient Irish tradition of coming together for a common purpose, working together to ensure that all members of the community succeed and achieve a common goal.

■ GALWAY STORIES

2020: Doire Press presents a new collection of stories set in Galway city and county by 20 acclaimed writers who live, or have lived, in Galway, as well as maps, photographs, and background information on each neighborhood.

■ AN LUCHT SIÚIL

An Lucht Siúil (People on the Move) will take audiences on a fascinating journey, exploring the many different nomadic cultures in Europe and around the world and their history of constant movement over millennia.

■ FUN FUNAMBULISM

An international community-based project aimed at promoting physical and mental well-being, safe risktaking, and social inclusion through the art of high-wire walking (funambulism). Volunteers who have trained will walk across a high wire over the River Corrib.

■ GALWAY 20

Galway is a city that nurtures a strong, confident, bohemian vibe, a spirit that finds full expression each summer at the Galway Arts Festival. To celebrate the next generation of talent and creativity, Galway 20 offers young Galway artists a platform to talk about their city, their work, and their ideas for making new waves in 2020 and beyond.

> " GALWAY IS WHERE MY HEART IS AND WILL FOREVER BE."
>
> —MICHAEL D. HIGGINS,
> POET AND PRESIDENT OF IRELAND

ROYAL HOT SPOTS

PLACES AROUND THE GLOBE THAT RESONATE WITH THE ROYAL FAMILY

THE ENGLISH MARKET
Cork, Ireland
Queen Elizabeth made fast friends with a fishmonger here by the name of Pat O'Connell during a royal visit in 2011. The queen was so amused by Pat's quip about how the ugly monkfish was known as the "mother-in-law" fish that she invited him to visit Buckingham Palace three years later.

BALMORAL CASTLE
Aberdeenshire, Scotland
Balmoral has been a much loved hunting retreat for the royal family ever since Queen Victoria and Prince Albert found respite here. The castle was completed in 1856, an example of Scottish baronial architecture. Balmoral is a working estate, with grouse moors and managed herds of deer. The queen also keeps Highland cattle and her beloved horses here.

PORTLAND ISLAND
Canada
Princess Margaret was gifted the lovely Portland Island in Canada by the royal authorities of British Columbia in 1958 and held it until her death in 2002. The princess offered it back to the people on permanent loan in 1966, and the island and surrounding waters would eventually become known as Princess Margaret Marine Park.

SICILY, ITALY, AND CRETE, GREECE
During World War II, Prince Philip, Duke of Edinburgh, who was born in Greece, served the Royal Navy, the British Army, and the Royal Air Force during the Allied invasion of Sicily at the Battles of Crete and Cape Matapan.

NASSAU
New Providence, Bahamas
Princess Margaret and her then husband, Antony Armstrong-Jones, the Earl of Snowdon, spent their honeymoon aboard the royal yacht *Britannia* in 1960 on a six-week cruise of the Caribbean. The couple returned to Nassau, in the Bahamas, in 1967. The royal family has a long history in the region, with Prince Albert in particular championing the 19th-century push to abolish slavery.

INDIA
Prince Charles is known to love India, where his "honorary grandfather," Lord Mountbatten, was the last viceroy before independence was declared in 1948. He has made two official visits: in 1991 for the funeral of Indian Prime Minister Rajiv Gandhi and in 2010 to inaugurate Commonwealth Games in New Delhi.

BAY HOTEL
Cape Town, South Africa
Before he headed to the South Pole for his Walking With The Wounded fundraiser, Prince Harry stayed at this beachfront hotel, located on the upscale Camps Bay strip. On a visit in 1999, his grandmother, Queen Elizabeth, faced calls for Britain to apologize to the Afrikaner people for its treatment of their Boer ancestors during the Anglo-Boer War of 1899–1902.

NORTH AMERICA

SOUTH AMERICA

ATLANTIC OCEAN

HONG KONG

On July 1, 1997, after 156 years of British rule, the colony of Hong Kong was transferred to China. It encompassed Hong Kong Island and the Kowloon Peninsula, as well as the New Territories, which Britain had leased for 99 years. Prince Charles was on hand as the Union Jack was lowered on Britain's last substantial overseas territory.

WINDSOR CASTLE
Berkshire, England

Home, sweet home for the queen is probably Windsor Castle, just 22 miles (35 km) from Buckingham Palace. This is the family's country getaway, the biggest occupied castle in the world. Located on the grounds of this (originally) 11th-century Norman castle is St. George's Chapel, the site of the 2018 wedding of Prince Harry and Meghan Markle.

HELMAND, AFGHANISTAN

After officer training, Prince Harry, Duke of Sussex, was commissioned into the Blues and Royals. In 2007–08, he served briefly in Helmand, Afghanistan. He returned to Afghanistan for a 20-week deployment in 2012–13 with the Army Air Corps.

SINGAPORE

The modern royals are regular visitors to the island state of Singapore, which was once a British colony. The English statesman Stamford Raffles founded Singapore in 1819 as a trading post of the British East India Company. In 1858, the islands were ceded to the British raj as a crown colony. Singapore gained independence in 1963, and the royal family has been welcomed there ever since.

ROPE

A S I A

P A C I F I C

O C E A N

AUSTRALIA

Queen Elizabeth's many visits to Australia included her opening of the Sydney Opera House in 1973. Three years before, she toured extensively in celebration of the bicentenary of Captain James Cook's 1770 sail up the east coast. Her Majesty has now visited "down under" 16 times; she is the only reigning British monarch to have set foot on Australian soil.

F R I C A

I N D I A N

O C E A N

AUSTRALIA

TREETOPS HOTEL
Aberdare National Park, Kenya

Princess Elizabeth learned she would soon become Queen Elizabeth during a stay in Treetops Hotel. On February 7, 1952, in the foothills of Mount Kenya, Prince Philip broke the news that her father, George VI, had died. Some 58 years later, in 2010, the queen's grandson Prince William proposed to Kate Middleton while holidaying near Mount Kenya.

NEW ZEALAND

Queen Elizabeth and Prince Philip went to New Zealand a year after their first planned visit was postponed due to her father's death. The momentous Royal Visit of 1953–54 saw mass crowds greet the couple and was the first of her nine visits to the island nation. In 1963, the queen participated in the islands' Waitangi celebrations.

FLAGS FEATURING
THE UNION JACK

Since the height of the British Empire in Victorian times, many overseas territories, dependenc
and even Commonwealth countries have retained the Union Jack on their flags.

ANGUILLA
British overseas territory

The flag of Anguilla consists of a blue ensign with the British flag in the canton and the coat of arms of Anguilla in the fly. The three dolphins in the coat of arms represent endurance, unity, and strength.

ASCENSION ISLAND
British overseas territory

The flag of Ascension Island was adopted in 2013. The flag consists of a blue ensign with the coat of arms of Ascension Island in the fly.

AUSTRALIA
Commonwealth realm

The flag of Australia consists of a bl or a red field with the Union Jack in canton and a large white seven-poin star known as the Commonwealth S in the lower hoist quarter.

BERMUDA
British overseas territory

Adopted in 1910, the flag of Bermuda is a British red ensign with the Union Jack in the upper left corner and the coat of arms of Bermuda in the lower right.

BRITISH COLUMBIA
Province of Canada

British Columbia's flag is based on the shield of the provincial arms of British Columbia. At the top of the flag is the Union Jack, with a crown in its center; in the lower part of the flag is a setting sun, reflecting the province's location in western Canada.

BRITISH VIRGIN ISLANDS
British overseas territory

The flag of the British Virgin Island features a blue ensign with the Uni Jack in the canton and the coat of ar of the British Virgin Islands in the f

CAYMAN ISLANDS
British overseas territory

The flag of the Cayman Islands was adopted in 1958 when the colony was granted a coat of arms, which is shown in the fly against the blue background, with the Union Jack in the canton.

COOK ISLANDS
Realm of New Zealand

The flag of the Cook Islands is composed of a dark blue ensign, the Union Jack in the upper left, and 15 white five-pointed stars arranged in a circle in the fly.

FALKLAND ISLANDS
British overseas territory

The flag of the Falkland Islands wa adopted in 1999 and consists of a defaced blue ensign, the Union Jack the canton, and the Falkland Island coat of arms in the fly.

WHEN THE CANADIAN GOVERNMENT DECIDED TO INTRODUCE A NEW FLAG, DEBATE ABOUT WHETHER TO INCLUDE THE UNION JACK OR NOT DIVIDED THE COUNTRY. THE CURRENT MAPLE LEAF DESIGN WAS MADE OFFICIAL IN 1965.

FIJI
Independent republic

Adopted after gaining independence in 1970, the flag of Fiji consists of a pale blue ensign and the Union Jack in the upper left field. The national coat of arms is in the fly, showing a yellow lion holding a cocoa bean above the Cross of St. George.

HAWAII
U.S. state

The flag of Hawaii, designed at the request of King Kamehameha I in the early 19th century, includes eight stripes of red, white, and blue that represent the eight main islands. The Union Jack is positioned in the upper left corner signifying Hawaii's friendship with Britain.

MANITOBA
Province of Canada

The flag of Manitoba features a red ensign with the shield of the province's coat of arms in the fly, which includes the Cross of St. George. The flag was officially adopted in 1966.

MONTSERRAT
British overseas territory

The coat of arms on the flag of Montserrat dates from 1909 and shows a red-haired woman dressed in green, holding a Christian cross and harp. The harp and the woman honor the Irish immigrants who settled on the island in 1632.

NEW SOUTH WALES
State of Australia

The flag of New South Wales has a British blue ensign with the state badge. The badge depicts the Cross of St. George in red on a white disk, with four eight-pointed gold stars and a golden lion.

NEW ZEALAND
Commonwealth realm

The flag of New Zealand has a British blue ensign with the Union Jack in the canton and four red stars with white borders on the fly. The stellar pattern reflects the constellation of Crux, the Southern Cross.

NIUE
Realm of New Zealand

The flag of Niue was adopted in 1975 and has the Union Jack in the upper left corner showing a star in the middle and four stars forming a diamond around it.

ONTARIO
Province of Canada

Introduced in 1965, the provincial flag of Ontario consists of a red ensign with the Union Jack in the canton and the Ontario shield of arms in the fly.

PITCAIRN ISLANDS
British overseas territory

The flag of the Pitcairn Islands, with the Union Jack in the canton and the coat of arms in the fly, was approved by Queen Elizabeth II and adopted in 1984.

QUEENSLAND
State of Australia
The state flag of Queensland is a blue ensign with the state badge on a white disk in the fly. The badge is a light blue Maltese cross with an imperial crown at its center.

ROSS DEPENDENCY
Realm of New Zealand
The New Zealand flag is the basis for the flag of the Ross Dependency, but an interesting variation surfaced in 1994 when James Dignan's design concept showed an ice blue background representing the Ross Sea and a white horizontal bar at the base of the flag representing the Ross Ice Shelf.

ST. HELENA & DEPENDENCIES
British overseas territory
The flag of St. Helena has a blue field with the Union Jack in the upper left quadrant and the coat of arms of St. Helena on the fly.

SOUTH AUSTRALIA
State of Australia
The flag of South Australia was adopted in 1904 and has a blue ensign with the Union Jack in the upper left quadrant and the state badge on the fly, showing a piping shrike with outstretched wings.

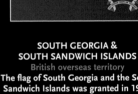

SOUTH GEORGIA &
SOUTH SANDWICH ISLANDS
British overseas territory
The flag of South Georgia and the South Sandwich Islands was granted in 1985. The coat of arms in the fly shows a fur seal and a macaroni penguin, along with the motto "*Leo Terram Propriam Protegat—* Let the lion protect its own land."

TASMANIA
State of Australia
The flag of Tasmania consists of a blue ensign with the state badge—a white disk with a red lion—in the fly.

TRISTAN DA CUNHA
British overseas territory
The flag of Tristan da Cunha was adopted in 2002 and consists of a blue ensign with the coat of arms of Tristan da Cunha, which has a Tristan longboat and a central shield decorated with yellow-nosed albatrosses and Tristan rock lobsters.

TURKS & CAICOS ISLANDS
British overseas territory
The flag of the Turks and Caicos Islands features a blue ensign with the Union Jack and the coat of arms of the Turks and Caicos Islands. The coat of arms consists of a yellow shield encompassing a conch shell, a lobster, and a *Melocactus* (a type of Caribbean cactus).

TUVALU
Commonwealth realm
The flag of Tuvalu is a sky blue ensign with the Union Jack shown in the upper left canton and stars arranged in the fly to accurately represent the geographical layout of Tuvalu's nine islands.

VICTORIA
State of Australia
The flag of Victoria is a blue ensign with the state badge depicted in the fly. The badge represents the Southern Cross topped by an imperial crown.

WESTERN AUSTRALIA
State of Australia
The state flag of Western Australia was adopted in 1953 and is a blue ensign with the state badge depicted in the fly. The badge consists of a golden disk in which a native black swan faces toward the hoist.

Britain's Four
DEPENDENCIES

■ GIBRALTAR

The flag of Gibraltar consists of an elongated banner of arms based on Gibraltar's coat of arms, granted by Royal Warrant from Queen Isabella I of Castile in 1502. The rocky outpost has long balanced both Spanish and English influences.

■ GUERNSEY

A relative newcomer on the international stage, the flag of Guernsey was adopted in 1985 to differentiate the island's sporting competitors from those of England, whose flag they previously used. The flag of Guernsey kept the red of England's Cross of St. George and added a gold Norman cross within it, in recognition of Normandy's historic and cultural contribution to the Channel Islands.

■ ISLE OF MAN

The flag of the Isle of Man is a triskelion, consisting of three armored legs with golden spurs on a red background. This was adopted as the island's official flag in 1929, supplanting the Union Jack. The flag is based on the Manx coat of arms, dating back to the 13th century. The small island has hosted many of Europe's wandering tribes, including the Celts, Saxons, and Vikings.

■ JERSEY

Reminiscent of the Cross of St. Patrick, the flag of Jersey is a red saltire on a white background. In the upper quadrant the badge of Jersey is topped with a yellow Plantagenet crown, commemorating the first universally acclaimed royal dynasty of England. The flag was adopted by Jersey in 1979, proclaimed by Queen Elizabeth II in 1980, and first officially hoisted in 1981.

FLAGS OF DEPENDENCIES & TERRITORIES

ome of the flags created for lesser-known, more remote territories
e among the world's most creative designs.

AUSTRALIA

CHRISTMAS ISLAND
Australian external territory
e colors of the Christmas Island flag
esent the land and sea. The Southern
onstellation appears in the bottom left.
golden bosun, a symbol of the island,
across the green. A map of the island
appears in the center of the flag.

COCOS ISLANDS
Australian external territory
Adopted in 2004, the flag of the Cocos
(Keeling) Islands has a green field with a
palm tree shown within a gold disk in
the canton, a gold crescent in the center,
and a gold Southern Cross in the fly.

NORFOLK ISLAND
Australian external territory
The flag depicts the Norfolk Island
(Araucaria heterophylla) in a white
between two green bands.

DENMARK

FAROE ISLANDS
Dependency of the
Kingdom of Denmark
The flag of the Faroe Islands consists
of an offset cross, which symbolizes
Christianity. The design incorporates
a red Nordic cross, offset to the left,
with azure trim on a background of white.

GREENLAND (KALAALLIT NUNAAT)
Dependency of the
Kingdom of Denmark
The flag of Greenland features two equal
horizontal stripes of white and red with
a large circle slightly to the pole side
of center. The top half of the disk is red;
the bottom half is white.

FRANCE

FRENCH POLYNESIA
French overseas territory
nch Polynesia's flag has a back-
d of traditional Polynesian colors,
ed and white, and features a
e under a golden sun. The crew
resents the five island groups:
Austral, Gambier, Marquesas,
Society, and Tuamotu.

NEW CALEDONIA
French overseas territory
Three stripes represent the ocean
and the sky (blue); the blood shed by
Kanaks (red); and the land (green).
To the pole side of the flag is a yellow
disk with a black flèche faîtière.

SAINT-PIERRE & MIQUELON
Unofficial flag of
French overseas territory
These French islands off the east co
Newfoundland and Labrador in Canada
an unofficial local flag. The ship is said
Grande Hermine. Three fields comme
the islanders' primary cultures: Bas
Bretons, and Normans.

ARUBA
Dependency of the
Kingdom of the Netherlands

...ed in 1976, Aruba's national flag
...s of a field of light blue—with two
...parallel horizontal yellow stripes in
...m half—and a four-pointed red star,
...ed in white, in the canton. The star
...ents the four cardinal directions,
...g to the many countries of origin
...e people of Aruba. The blue field
...nts the sky and the sea. The yellow
...ents the independence movement
...abundance of the Caribbean island.

CURAÇAO
Dependency of the Kingdom
of the Netherlands

...lag of Curaçao consists of a blue
...d with a horizontal yellow stripe
...below the midline and two white,
...inted stars in the canton. The blue
...esents the sea and sky divided by
...ow stroke representing the bright
...ean sun. The two stars symbolize
...Curaçao and Klein Curaçao.

SINT MAARTEN
Dependency of the
Kingdom of the Netherlands

...lag of Sint Maarten is a horizontal
...r of red and blue with the coat of
...ns of Sint Maarten on a white
...on. The red represents solidarity
...courage, the blue peace, and the
white purity and faith.

KEY FACTS

The New Kiwi Flag
THAT WASN'T

In 2015 and 2016, New Zealanders held referenda to update their flag, which has long featured the Union Jack and the pattern of stars representing the Southern Cross. Many felt it was time for change, particularly as the New Zealand flag closely resembles that of Australia. Others felt that the presence of the Union Jack represents a continuity and a nod to a proud history of military sacrifices made for Britain during two world wars. A preliminary vote eliminated several innovative designs, many featuring the island symbols of the ferns and the koru (the fern frond that also looks like a rolling wave). In a choice between the old flag and designer Kyle Lockwood's version of the silver fern flag, New Zealanders opted to stick with the flag they have flown since 1902.

FURTHER

ARS LONGA: ART LIVES ON TO TELL THE TALE

All history is a story, and artists tell the stories best. Here schoolchildren sit before Pablo Picasso's legendary "Guernica," painted in 1937 in response to the agonies of the Spanish Civil War. Some look down, some look away, some stare transfixed, but all come away from the experience with a deeper sense of connection with the people and events of the past.

Children visit the Reina Sofía Museum in Madrid, encouraged by their teacher to pause and take some time to understand Picasso's "Guernica."

“ THERE ARE TWO LANGUAGES . . . THESE ARE VERBAL—WHICH SEPARATES PEOPLE—[AND] VISUAL, WHICH IS UNDERSTOOD BY EVERYBODY.” —YAACOV AGAM, ARTIST

OUR WORLD

WORLD VIEWS | CONTINENTS & OCEANS

The moon and stars enhance a spectacular sunrise over New Mexico.

QUIZ MASTER

Geographical Wizard? Places to know and forces to understand—geography sits at the heart of all knowledge. Here are maps galore, but they can only hint at the diversity of features that make Earth such a fascinating place to study.

—**CARA SANTA MARIA**, *Our Favorite Nerd*

THE UNITED **NATIONS** BEGAN IN 1945 WITH HOW **MANY** MEMBER STATES?

P357
AT **63.8 MILLION** SQUARE MILES, WHAT IS THE **LARGEST** OCEAN ON THE PLANET?

WHAT PERCENT OF THE **EARTH'S** SURFACE IS COVERED WITH **LANDMASSES?**

p331

p372
p330
IN WHAT COUNTRY HAVE **THE WORLD'S OLDEST** ROCKS BEEN FOUND?

WHAT SPECIES OF BIRD CALLS **THE SALAR DE ATACAMA** IN CHILE HOME?

p361
WHAT IS THE **SMALLEST** OCEAN ON THE PLANET?

WHICH **BODY OF WATER** DOES THE MISSISSIPPI **RIVER** EMPTY INTO?

p340
p338

p332

FOR WHAT MINERAL DOES THE **CHILEAN GOVERNMENT CONTROL ABOUT 20 PERCENT OF THE WORLD'S RESERVES?**

p342

WHAT IS THE NAME **OF THE SMALL COUNTRY** LOCATED IN THE PYRENEES **MOUNTAINS BETWEEN FRANCE** AND SPAIN?

IN WHICH CANADIAN PROVINCE **CAN YOU FIND THE** GREAT BEAR RAINFOREST?

p338

ON WHICH CONTINENT IS TOURISM GROWING MOST RAPIDLY?

p333

WHAT IS THE OLDEST FRESHWATER LAKE ON EARTH, LOCATED IN **RUSSIA?**

p344

HOW MANY YEARS AGO DID THE TIBETAN PLATEAU FORM?

WHICH BODY OF WATER **CONTAINS THE MOST** OFFSHORE **DRILLING RIGS?**

OUR PHYSICAL
WORLD

CANADA
Oldest rocks
An area of exposed bed-rock discovered in north-ern Quebec is estimated to be as much as 2.28 billion years old. At more than 250 million years older than any rocks previously dated, the Nuvvuagittuq greenstone belt is one of the oldest pieces of the planet's crust known.

ANDES
Longest mountain system
Measuring about 4,700 miles, the Andes are the world's longest mountain system on land. The range stretches the full length of the continent, through seven countries. Its highest peak, at 22,841 feet, is Argentina's Aconcagua.

ABOUT 29.1%—57 MILLION SQUARE MILES—OF EARTH'S SURFACE IS NOT COVERED BY WATER.

RUSSIA
Expansive country
The world's largest country, Russia spans two continents (Europe and Asia), nine time zones, and all climates except tropical. European Russia, west of the Ural Mountains, features a broad plain with low hills and holds most of the population. Asian Russia is dominated by Siberia, which extends from the Urals to the Pacific, ranging from Arctic tundra to swamps and forested plateaus.

AUSTRALIA
The Outback
Australia is dominated by the outback, a vast region of remote desert and semi-arid lands in the interior of the continent. Not much grows in the outback, but cattle and sheep graze on the outskirts.

OUR POLITICAL
WORLD

UNITED STATES

Growing Cities

People are increasingly moving to urban areas, creating mega-cities—cities with populations of at least 10 million. The U.S. has two megacities: New York–Newark–Jersey City (20.3 million) and Los Angeles (13.4 million).

CHILE

National Copper Mines

In 1971, Chile nationalized the country's copper mines and later grouped them under a single company known as the National Copper Corporation of Chile (CODELCO). Today, Chile is the largest copper producer in the world, with about 20 percent of all copper reserves under its purview.

JAPAN
Aging Population

As the planet's human population continues to grow, some countries are seeing an aging population instead of a booming one. Japan's low birthrate has led to a population that is growing smaller and older over time. By 2065, it's projected that 38 percent of Japan's population will be over the age of 65.

TAIWAN
The People's Republic of China claims Taiwan as its 23rd province. Taiwan's government (Republic of China) maintains that there are two political entities.

Winkel Tripel Projection

0 miles 2000

0 kilometers 2000

NORTH AFRICA
Rising Tourism

The global tourism market is massive, with some 1.4 billion people traveling internationally every year. In recent years, African tourism—especially to northern countries such as Morocco and Tunisia—has grown at a faster rate than that in the rest of the world.

BEST OF @NATGEO

TOP PHOTOS OF LANDSCAPES

@franslanting | FRANS LANTING
A river winds through a golden-hued valley in Wrangell–St. Elias National Park & Preserve, Alaska.

@renan_ozturk | RENAN OZTURK
Climbers celebrate their ascent on a red rock peak in Bears Ears National Monument, Utah.

@GEOSTEINMETZ | GEORGE STEINMETZ
Summer rain pools amid white sand dunes at Lençóis Maranhenses National Park in Brazil.

@simonnorfolkstudio | SIMON NORFOLK
Socotra in the Arabian Sea is the only native habitat for dragon blood trees, named for their red resin.

"WILDNESS REMINDS US WHAT IT MEANS TO BE HUMAN, WHAT WE ARE CONNECTED TO RATHER THAN WHAT WE ARE SEPARATE FROM."

—TERRY TEMPEST WILLIAMS, AUTHOR AND CONSERVATIONIST

@ladzinski | **KEITH LADZINSKI**
Triple waterfalls plunge into a lagoon at the foot of Kirkjufell Mountain in Iceland.

@pedromcbride | **PETE MCBRIDE**
Lights accentuate architecture and activity in Manhattan, home to more than 1.6 million people.

@irablockphoto | **IRA BLOCK**
Daylight fades from the Diomede Islands, separated by the U.S.-Russian boundary in the Bering Strait.

@paleyphoto | **MATTHIEU PALEY**
Spring turns the hills around Song Köl lake a soft green in Kyrgyzstan in Central Asia.

THE CONTINENTS

LANDFORMS CHANGE SHAPE OVER MILLENNIA

With the unceasing movement of Earth's tectonic plates, continents "drift" over geologic time—breaking apart, reassembling, and again fragmenting to repeat the process. Three times during the past billion years, Earth's drifting landmasses have merged to form so-called supercontinents. Rodinia, the earliest known supercontinent, began breaking apart in the late Precambrian, about 750 million years ago (mya).

EURASIA

PANGAEA

NORTH AMERICA

PANTHALASSIC OCEAN

SOUTH AMERICA

AFRICA

ANTARCTICA

PANGAEA, 240 MILLION YEARS AGO

Even when most of Earth's landmass was a single continent, named Pangaea, surrounded by a single ocean, the Panthalassic (predecessor to the Pacific), configurations began taking shape that presaged the continents of today. The Tethys Ocean ultimately became the Mediterranean.

DINOSAURS ROAMED POLE TO POLE ON PANGAEA, BUT OVER TIME THE CONTINENTS SPLIT AND DISTINCT DINOSAUR SPECIES EVOLVED SEPARATELY IN DIFFERENT LOCATIONS.

China

TETHYS OCEAN

AUSTRALIA

KEY DATES

Stages in Earth's
EVOLUTION

■ **PRECAMBRIAN TIME
(4,500–542 MYA)**
Archaean eon (ca 3,800–2,500 mya)
First life-forms appear on Earth.

Proterozoic eon (2,500–542 mya)
In latter part of this eon, continental
fragments join into one: Pannotia.

■ **PHANEROZOIC EON
(542 MYA–PRESENT)**
Paleozoic era (542–251 mya)
Includes Cambrian, 500 mya: Multicellular
animals leave abundant fossil evidence.

Includes Devonian, 400 mya: Freshwater
fish migrate freely; plants colonize land.

Mesozoic era (251–65.5 mya)
Includes Triassic, 240 mya: Geologic
catastrophes caused massive extinctions;
surviving lizards evolved into dinosaurs.

Cenozoic era (65.5 mya–present)
Includes K-T extinction event, 65 mya:
Half the plant and animal species
become extinct.

Includes last great ice age, 18,000 ya:
North and south are locked in ice;
continents as we know them begin to
form, further defined by retreating glaciers.

NORTH AMERICA

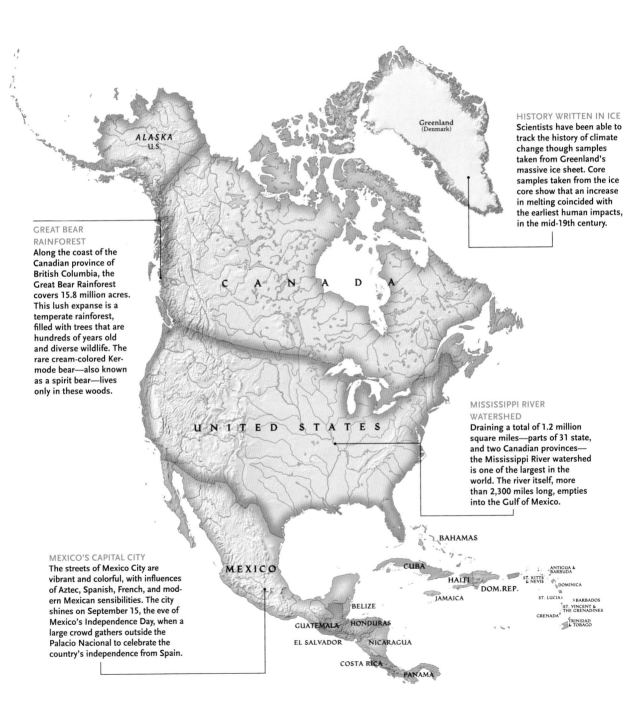

HISTORY WRITTEN IN ICE
Scientists have been able to track the history of climate change though samples taken from Greenland's massive ice sheet. Core samples taken from the ice core show that an increase in melting coincided with the earliest human impacts, in the mid-19th century.

GREAT BEAR RAINFOREST
Along the coast of the Canadian province of British Columbia, the Great Bear Rainforest covers 15.8 million acres. This lush expanse is a temperate rainforest, filled with trees that are hundreds of years old and diverse wildlife. The rare cream-colored Kermode bear—also known as a spirit bear—lives only in these woods.

MISSISSIPPI RIVER WATERSHED
Draining a total of 1.2 million square miles—parts of 31 state, and two Canadian provinces— the Mississippi River watershed is one of the largest in the world. The river itself, more than 2,300 miles long, empties into the Gulf of Mexico.

MEXICO'S CAPITAL CITY
The streets of Mexico City are vibrant and colorful, with influences of Aztec, Spanish, French, and modern Mexican sensibilities. The city shines on September 15, the eve of Mexico's Independence Day, when a large crowd gathers outside the Palacio Nacional to celebrate the country's independence from Spain.

Greenland
(Denmark)

ALASKA
U.S.

C A N A D A

UNITED STATES

MEXICO

BAHAMAS

CUBA

HAITI
DOM.REP.

JAMAICA

BELIZE

GUATEMALA   HONDURAS

EL SALVADOR   NICARAGUA

COSTA RICA

PANAMA

ANTIGUA &
BARBUDA
ST. KITTS
& NEVIS
DOMINICA
ST. LUCIA
BARBADOS
ST. VINCENT &
THE GRENADINES
GRENADA
TRINIDAD
& TOBAGO

North Rim of Arizona's Grand Canyon

Continental
FACTS

TOTAL NUMBER OF COUNTRIES
23

TOTAL AREA
9,449,000 square miles (24,474,000 sq km)

MOST POPULOUS COUNTRY
United States: 329,256,000

LEAST POPULOUS COUNTRY
Saint Kitts and Nevis: 53,000

LARGEST COUNTRY BY AREA
Canada: 3,855,101 square miles (9,984,670 sq km)

SMALLEST COUNTRY BY AREA
Saint Kitts and Nevis: 101 square miles (261 sq km)

HIGHEST ELEVATION
Denali (Mount McKinley),
United States: 20,310 feet (6,190 m)

LOWEST ELEVATION
Death Valley, United States: −282 feet (−86 m)

SOUTH AMERICA

BOGOTÁ, COLOMBIA
The capital city of Colombia is also the country's largest. It lies on a plateau of the Andes, and the nearby heights of Monserrate offer a bird's-eye view of Bogotá.

TRANS-AMAZONIAN HIGHWAY
Snaking through Brazil's Amazon—the world's largest and most diverse tropical rainforest—is a growing system of roads. Called the Trans-Amazonian highway, it is meant to ease transport for materials taken from the rainforest, such as timber, minerals, and farmed goods. But ongoing construction of this road poses even more risks to a vital ecosystem.

ATACAMA SALT FLATS
In the northeast region of Chile, surrounded by mountains, lies the Salar de Atacama, a massive salt flat that extends over nearly 1,200 square miles. In summer the rare Andean flamingos make their home in the flats, feeding off small organisms living in the salty pools spread throughout the landscape.

WILDLIFE OF PATAGONIA
At the southern end of the continent, Patagonia is a large region of steppe and desert climates poised at the meeting place of the Atlantic, Pacific, and Antarctic Oceans. Here you'll find most of the world's guanacos, a relative of the llama, and the black and white Commerson's dolphins swimming alongside boats.

Peru's Machu Picchu Inca ruins

Continental FACTS

TOTAL NUMBER OF COUNTRIES
12

TOTAL AREA
6,880,000 square miles (17,819,000 sq km)

MOST POPULOUS COUNTRY
Brazil: 208,847,000

LEAST POPULOUS COUNTRY
Suriname: 598,000

LARGEST COUNTRY BY AREA
Brazil: 3,287,596 square miles (8,515,770 sq km)

SMALLEST COUNTRY BY AREA
Suriname: 63,251 square miles (163,820 sq km)

HIGHEST ELEVATION
Cerro Aconcagua, Argentina: 22,834 feet (6,960 m)

LOWEST ELEVATION
Laguna del Carbón, Argentina: −344 feet (−105 m)

THE SAMI PEOPLE
The Sami are an indigenous people native to the far northern regions of Europe. Today, some 80,000 Sami live in Norway, Sweden, Finland, and Russia. Many Sami still maintain the tradition as reindeer herders, following the massive animals through the tundra as they seek good grazing.

CITY OF CANALS
Founded nearly 750 years ago, Amsterdam is a city filled with history. Known for its many canals, rich artistic legacy, and iconic architecture, the Dutch capital is a tourist destination for many travelers.

ANDORRA
One of the smallest nations in Europe, Andorra is located between France and Spain in the Pyrenees mountains. The population is just under 77,000, and most of its people live in the capital city of Andorra la Vella.

EUROPE'S HIGHEST PEAK
At 18,510 feet, Mount El'brus, located in the Caucasus Mountains in Russia, is the tallest peak in Europe. El'brus is a volcano with two domes, with the second at the shorter height of 18,442 feet. The taller summit was first climbed in 1874 by a team led by the guide Akhia Sottaiev.

ICELAND

(ÉIRE) IRELAND

UNITED KINGDOM

NORWAY

SWEDEN

FINLAND

ESTONIA

LATVIA

LITHUANIA

RUSSIA

R U S S I A

BELARUS

KAZAKHSTAN

DENMARK

NETH.

BELG.

LUX.

GERMANY

POLAND

UKRAINE

CZECHIA (CZECH REP.)

SLOVAKIA

LIECH.

SWITZ.

AUSTRIA

MOLD.

FRANCE

SLOV.

HUNGARY

ROMANIA

CROATIA

MONACO

SAN MARINO

BOSN. & HERZG.

SERBIA

ANDORRA

ITALY

MONTEN.

KOS.

BULGARIA

SPAIN

PORTUGAL

VATICAN CITY

NORTH MACED.

TURKEY

ALBANIA

GREECE

MALTA

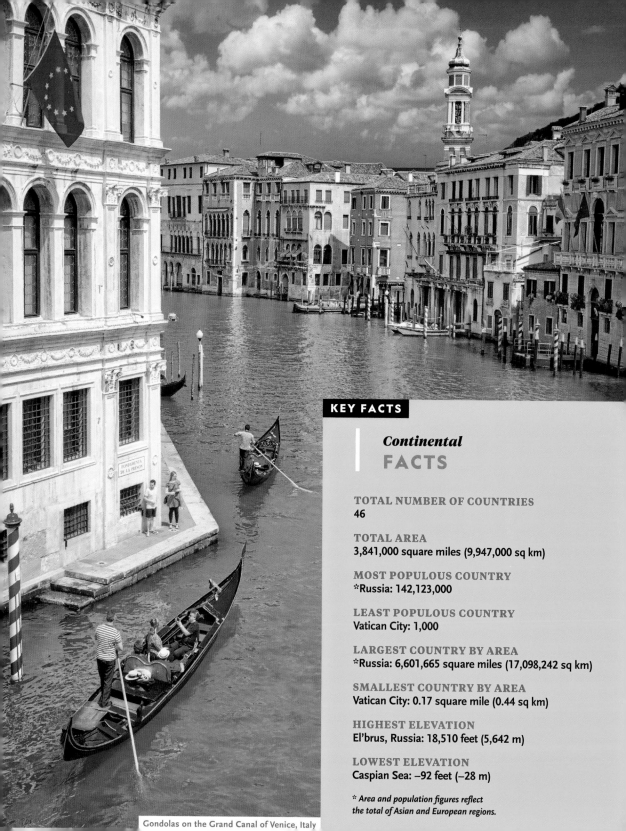

KEY FACTS

Continental FACTS

TOTAL NUMBER OF COUNTRIES
46

TOTAL AREA
3,841,000 square miles (9,947,000 sq km)

MOST POPULOUS COUNTRY
*Russia: 142,123,000

LEAST POPULOUS COUNTRY
Vatican City: 1,000

LARGEST COUNTRY BY AREA
*Russia: 6,601,665 square miles (17,098,242 sq km)

SMALLEST COUNTRY BY AREA
Vatican City: 0.17 square mile (0.44 sq km)

HIGHEST ELEVATION
El'brus, Russia: 18,510 feet (5,642 m)

LOWEST ELEVATION
Caspian Sea: −92 feet (−28 m)

* Area and population figures reflect the total of Asian and European regions.

Gondolas on the Grand Canal of Venice, Italy

CELESTIAL MOUNTAINS
Lying on the border of China
and Kyrgyzstan, the Tien Shan
mountain range extends about
1,500 miles across the plains of
central Asia. Dotted with glaciers, the melting water from
these mountains feeds many
rivers and supports forests on
the lower mountain slopes.

LAKE BAIKAL
The oldest and deepest
freshwater lake on Earth
Lake Baikal has been
around for some 25 mill
years. It contains nearly
20 percent of the planet'
fresh liquid water. Becau
of its isolation and its ag
many distinct species of
plants and animals have
emerged in and around
lake. Some call Lake Bai
the "Galápagos of Russi

RISING SEAS IN THE MALDIVES
This small country in the northern
Indian Ocean comprises about
1,200 small islands. The Maldives
is the lowest-lying country in the
world, and rising sea levels resulting from climate change pose a
significant threat to its people,
animals, and plants.

THE TIBETAN PLATEAU
The collision of two tectonic plates
50 million years ago resulted in the
creation of the Himalaya mountain
range and the Tibetan Plateau.
The largest and highest plateau
on Earth, the land lifted here in a
wide, flat expanse that is known
as the "roof of the world."

TURKEY
GEORGIA
CYPRUS
LEBANON
ARMENIA
ISRAEL
SYRIA
AZERBAIJAN
JORDAN
IRAQ
KUWAIT
SAUDI
ARABIA
BAHRAIN
QATAR
U.A.E.
YEMEN
OMAN
IRAN
TURKMENISTAN
UZBEKISTAN
KAZAKHSTAN
KYRGYZSTAN
TAJIKISTAN
AFGHANISTAN
PAKISTAN
NEPAL
BHUTAN
INDIA
BANGLADESH
MYANMAR
(BURMA)
SRI LANKA
MALDIVES
R U S S I A
MONGOLIA
NORTH
KOREA
SOUTH
KOREA
JAPAN
C H I N A
TAIWAN
LAOS
THAILAND
VIETNAM
CAMBODIA
PHILIPPINES
BRUNEI
M A L A Y S I A
SINGAPORE
I N D O N E S I A
TIMOR-LESTE
(EAST TIMOR)

Hong Kong skyline at twilight

Continental
FACTS

TOTAL NUMBER OF COUNTRIES
46

TOTAL AREA
17,209,000 square miles (44,570,000 sq km)

MOST POPULOUS COUNTRY
China: 1,384,689,000

LEAST POPULOUS COUNTRY
Maldives: 392,000

LARGEST COUNTRY BY AREA
*China: 3,705,405 square miles (9,596,960 sq km)

SMALLEST COUNTRY BY AREA
Maldives: 115 square miles (298 sq km)

HIGHEST ELEVATION
Mount Everest, China/Nepal: 29,035 feet (8,850 m)

LOWEST ELEVATION
Dead Sea, Israel/Jordan: –1,401 feet (–427 m)

*Russia straddles both Asia and
Europe and exceeds China in area.

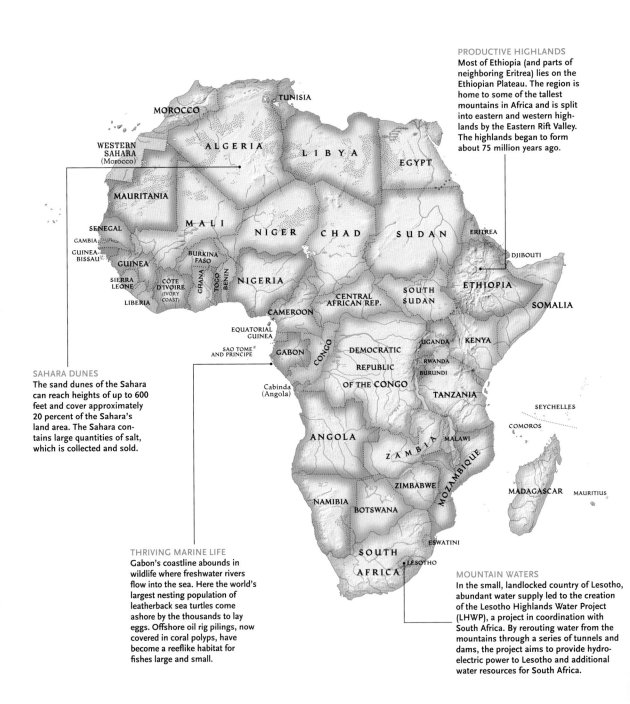

PRODUCTIVE HIGHLANDS
Most of Ethiopia (and parts of neighboring Eritrea) lies on the Ethiopian Plateau. The region is home to some of the tallest mountains in Africa and is split into eastern and western highlands by the Eastern Rift Valley. The highlands began to form about 75 million years ago.

SAHARA DUNES
The sand dunes of the Sahara can reach heights of up to 600 feet and cover approximately 20 percent of the Sahara's land area. The Sahara contains large quantities of salt, which is collected and sold.

THRIVING MARINE LIFE
Gabon's coastline abounds in wildlife where freshwater rivers flow into the sea. Here the world's largest nesting population of leatherback sea turtles come ashore by the thousands to lay eggs. Offshore oil rig pilings, now covered in coral polyps, have become a reeflike habitat for fishes large and small.

MOUNTAIN WATERS
In the small, landlocked country of Lesotho, abundant water supply led to the creation of the Lesotho Highlands Water Project (LHWP), a project in coordination with South Africa. By rerouting water from the mountains through a series of tunnels and dams, the project aims to provide hydro-electric power to Lesotho and additional water resources for South Africa.

MOROCCO
TUNISIA
WESTERN SAHARA (Morocco)
ALGERIA
LIBYA
EGYPT
MAURITANIA
MALI
NIGER
CHAD
SUDAN
ERITREA
SENEGAL
GAMBIA
GUINEA-BISSAU
GUINEA
BURKINA FASO
DJIBOUTI
SIERRA LEONE
CÔTE D'IVOIRE (IVORY COAST)
GHANA
TOGO
BENIN
NIGERIA
CENTRAL AFRICAN REP.
SOUTH SUDAN
ETHIOPIA
SOMALIA
LIBERIA
CAMEROON
EQUATORIAL GUINEA
SAO TOME AND PRINCIPE
GABON
CONGO
DEMOCRATIC REPUBLIC OF THE CONGO
UGANDA
KENYA
RWANDA
BURUNDI
Cabinda (Angola)
TANZANIA
SEYCHELLES
COMOROS
ANGOLA
ZAMBIA
MALAWI
MOZAMBIQUE
MADAGASCAR
MAURITIUS
ZIMBABWE
NAMIBIA
BOTSWANA
ESWATINI
SOUTH AFRICA
LESOTHO

Giraffes in a Kalahari Desert game reserve, Botswana

Continental
FACTS

TOTAL NUMBER OF COUNTRIES
54

TOTAL AREA
11,608,000 square miles (30,065,000 sq km)

MOST POPULOUS COUNTRY
Nigeria: 203,453,000

LEAST POPULOUS COUNTRY
Seychelles: 95,000

LARGEST COUNTRY BY AREA
Algeria: 919,590 square miles (2,381,741 sq km)

SMALLEST COUNTRY BY AREA
Seychelles: 176 square miles (455 sq km)

HIGHEST ELEVATION
Kilimanjaro, Tanzania: 19,340 feet (5,895 m)

LOWEST ELEVATION
Lake Assal, Djibouti: −509 feet (−155 m)

AUSTRALIA & OCEANIA

HUNDREDS OF LANGUAGES
More than 8 million people live in Papua New Guinea, many of them belonging to the 700 or so tribes that call the nation home. Each of these tribes has its own language. The country lists 3 official languages but nearly 850 unofficial ones.

MARSHALL ISLANDS

PALAU

FEDERATED STATES OF MICRONESIA

K I R I B A T I

NAURU

SACRED ROCKS
In Australia's Northern Territory, a dome-shaped rock known as Uluru rises 2,831 feet from the sandy red plains. Uluru, along with a smaller rock formation known as Kata Tjuta, is sacred to the Anangu people indigenous to this area of the continent.

PAPUA NEW GUINEA

SOLOMON ISLANDS

TUVALU

SA

VANUATU

FIJI

AUSTRALIA

TONGA

MONOTREMES
One of the most uncommon groups of animals in the world can be found only in Australia and New Guinea. Monotremes, including platypuses and echidnas, are mammals that lay eggs. Only five species of monotremes are known to exist in the world.

GLACIAL SYSTEMS
Both the North and South Islands contain glaciers, part of the diverse geological landscape of New Zealand. The Southern Alps, on the South Island, are a 300-mile-long mountain system that is home to hundreds of glaciers. Largest among them is Tasman Glacier, which measures 16.8 miles long and nearly 2 miles wide at some points.

NEW ZEALAND

Continental
FACTS

TOTAL NUMBER OF COUNTRIES
14

TOTAL AREA
3,286,000 square miles (8,510,700 sq km)

MOST POPULOUS COUNTRY
Australia: 23,470,000

LEAST POPULOUS COUNTRY
Nauru: 10,000

LARGEST COUNTRY BY AREA
Australia: 2,988,901 square miles (7,741,220 sq km)

SMALLEST COUNTRY BY AREA
Nauru: 8 square miles (21 sq km)

HIGHEST ELEVATION
Mount Wilhelm, Papua New Guinea: 14,793 feet
(4,509 m)

LOWEST ELEVATION
Lake Eyre, Australia: −52 feet (−16 m)

Australia's Sydney Opera House

ANTARCTICA

HYDROPONICS
Though Antarctica is a vast, cold desert, new plant life is starting to emerge. Scientists in subzero Antarctic research stations have successfully grown small crops of vegetables through a hydroponic system that relies on careful use of water, nutrients, light, and carbon dioxide.

ANTARCTIC PENINSULA

RITSCHER UPLAND

Riiser-Larsen Peninsula

COATS LAND

QUEEN MAUD LAND

ENDERBY LAND

MAWSON COAST

VALKYRIE DOME

MAC. ROBERTSON LAND

AMERICAN HIGHLAND

POLAR PLATEAU

DOME ARGUS

EAST ANTARCTICA

TRANSANTARCTIC MOUNTAINS

ELLSWORTH LAND

WEST ANTARCTICA

TITAN DOME

HOLLICK–KENYON PLATEAU

MARIE BYRD LAND

WILKES LAND

LAW DOME

VICTORIA LAND

TALOS DOME

USARP MTS.

VOLCANIC ACTIVITY
There are a number of mountains throughout Antarctica, and the western region of the continent is home to many volcanoes. Mount Erebus, located on Ross Island, is the south-ernmost active volcano on the planet, and its peak stands at 12,448 feet above sea level.

ICE SHEET
The continent of Antarctica is covered with ice—the largest single piece of ice on Earth. Measuring more than 5 million square miles, the area of the Antarctic Ice Sheet is equivalent to that of the Lower 48 United States and Mexico combined.

An iceberg arch off the Antarctic Peninsula

OCEANS
OF THE WORLD

A BLUE PLANET

Earth's predominant physical feature is the vast, continuous body of water that accounts for more than two-thirds of its surface, totaling some 139 million square miles. The global ocean is a dominant climate factor, with currents carrying heat from the Equator toward the poles, and a vital resource providing food to much of the world's population and serving as a key transportation route between continents.

NORTH

PACIFIC

OCEAN

TROPIC OF CANCER

EQUATOR

INDIAN
OCEAN

TROPIC OF CAPRICORN

SOUTH

PACIFIC

OCEAN

ANTARCTIC CIRCLE

WHEREVER TWO CURRENTS MEET . . . THERE ARE ZONES OF GREAT TURBULENCE AND UNREST . . . AT SUCH PLACES THE RICHNESS AND ABUNDANCE OF MARINE LIFE REVEALS ITSELF MOST STRIKINGLY.

—RACHEL CARSON, IN *THE SEA AROUND US*

ARCTIC CIRCLE

NORTH ATLANTIC OCEAN

TROPIC OF CANCER

EQUATOR

SOUTH ATLANTIC OCEAN

INDIAN OCEAN

TROPIC OF CAPRICORN

Warm current
Cold current

Rivers in the Ocean
Great surface currents circle the major
ocean basins, ferrying the heat of the tropical
sun north to warm and expand the temperate zones.

ANTARCTIC CIRCLE

ATLANTIC OCEAN

OCEAN TRENDS

Oceans are living things, with environments and processes that affect us all. They play huge roles in our lives as highways for travel and sources of food. Their vitality shapes the future of life on this planet. Here are a few indicators of ocean well-being today.

Chlorophyll

Tiny phytoplankton are crucial to life inside and outside the oceans, and their blooming is tracked through the observation of chlorophyll concentrations. Nutrient-deficient areas are known as "deserts." Fluctuations and storms such as El Niño and Atlantic hurricanes can shift these patterns, causing some "deserts" to occasionally bloom.

Chlorophyll concentration (mg/m³), July 2002–Aug. 2013 average
>.01
1
20
■ No data

Fishing Activity

Roughly one billion people depend on fish as their main protein source. As demand for fish has risen, the global fishing industry has grown. Unfortunately, fishing is often practiced unsustainably, and current overfishing threatens ocean ecosystems. Crude fishing techniques can result in unintentional bycatch, which accounts for more than 40 percent of all marine catch globally.

Marine Catch, 2014
■ Top 10 countries

Average annual marine catch metric tons per sq km/year
10
3
0.25

Sea Surface Temperatures

Sea surface temperature drives many of the oceans' most crucial systems. Destructive tropical storms are generated and sustained only in areas with high surface temperatures. So with ocean temperatures rising across the globe, the threat of more frequent and more destructive storms is increasing as well.

Sea surface temperature, July 2002–Aug. 2013 average
High
Low

KEY FACTS

About the ATLANTIC

TOTAL AREA
35,400,000 square miles (91,700,000 sq km)

AVERAGE DEPTH
10,925 feet (3,300 m)

DEEPEST POINT
Puerto Rico Trench: −28,232 feet (−8,605 m)

LARGEST ISLAND
Greenland

THE DEEPEST POINT IN THE ATLANTIC OCEAN IS THE BOTTOM OF THE PUERTO RICO TRENCH, 28,232 FEET DOWN.

CONTINENTAL SHELF

GREENLAND

ICELAND PLATEAU

ARCTIC CIRCLE

REYKJANES RIDGE

ROCKALL PLATEAU

BATTLE OF THE ATLANTIC
Running from 1939 to 1945, the Battle of the Atlantic was the longest continuous military campaign of World War II. German U-boats clashed with Allied ships, and underwater wreckage from the years-long battle can still be found.

Flemish Cap

CELTIC SHELF

N O R T H

A T L A N T I C

O C E A N

MID-ATLANTIC RIDGE

TROPIC OF CANCER

PUERTO RICO TRENCH

VIKING CROSSINGS
Evidence of Viking settlements in Canada shows that Christopher Columbus wasn't the first European to set foot on North America. Indeed, Vikings were crossing the Atlantic Ocean nearly five centuries before the *Niña*, the *Pinta*, and the *Santa María* set sail.

M I D - A T L A N T I C

STRAIT OF GIBRALTAR
Measuring 36 miles long and eight miles wide at its most narrow point, the Strait of Gibraltar has played an important role in Atlantic trade for hundreds of years. This channel connects the Atlantic Ocean to the Mediterranean Sea, allowing ships to traverse the two important bodies of water.

S O U T H

A T L A N T I C

WALVIS RIDGE

TROPIC OF CAPRICORN

O C E A N

RIO GRANDE RISE

Agulhas Bank

SOUTH PACIFIC OCEAN

MID-ATLANTIC RIDGE

UMVOTO RISE

PATAGONIAN SHELF

FALKLAND PLATEAU

NORTH SCOTIA RIDGE

SOUTH SANDWICH TRENCH

ATLANTIC-INDIAN RIDGE

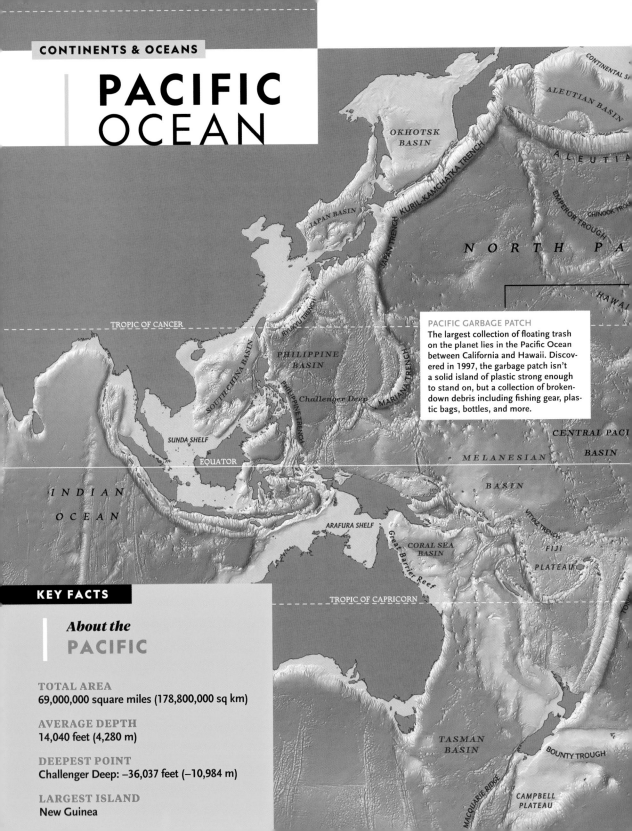

PACIFIC
OCEAN

OKHOTSK
BASIN

CONTINENTAL SH

ALEUTIAN BASIN

ALEUTIA

CHINOOK TRO

EMPEROR TROUGH

N O R T H   P A

HAWAI

JAPAN BASIN

KURIL-KAMCHATKA TRENCH

JAPAN TRENCH

TROPIC OF CANCER

RYUKYU TRENCH

PHILIPPINE
BASIN

SOUTH CHINA BASIN

PHILIPPINE TRENCH

Challenger Deep

MARIANA TRENCH

PACIFIC GARBAGE PATCH

The largest collection of floating trash
on the planet lies in the Pacific Ocean
between California and Hawaii. Discovered in 1997, the garbage patch isn't
a solid island of plastic strong enough
to stand on, but a collection of broken-
down debris including fishing gear, plastic bags, bottles, and more.

CENTRAL PACI

MELANESIAN

BASIN

BASIN

SUNDA SHELF

EQUATOR

VITIAZ TRENCH

FIJI

PLATEAU

I N D I A N

O C E A N

ARAFURA SHELF

Great Barrier Reef

CORAL SEA
BASIN

TONG

TROPIC OF CAPRICORN

TASMAN
BASIN

BOUNTY TROUGH

MACQUARIE RIDGE

CAMPBELL
PLATEAU

KEY FACTS

About the
PACIFIC

TOTAL AREA
69,000,000 square miles (178,800,000 sq km)

AVERAGE DEPTH
14,040 feet (4,280 m)

DEEPEST POINT
Challenger Deep: −36,037 feet (−10,984 m)

LARGEST ISLAND
New Guinea

THE PACIFIC OCEAN IS THE WORLD'S LARGEST OCEAN BY FAR, COVERING ABOUT ONE-THIRD OF THE PLANET'S SURFACE—APPROXIMATELY 69 MILLION SQUARE MILES.

ALASKA PLAIN

RENCH

TUFTS PLAIN

NORTHEAST PACIFIC OCEAN

FIC OCEAN

PACIFIC BASIN

Kingman Reef

Christmas Ridge

GE

NIHIKI TEAU

Society Ridge

Tuamotu Ridge

TIKI BASIN

SOUTH PACIFIC OCEAN

UTHWEST PACIFIC BASIN

VILLE

Georges Bank

NORTH ATLANTIC OCEAN

TROPIC OF CANCER

MIDDLE AMERICA TRENCH

GUATEMALA BASIN

COCOS RIDGE

PANAMA BASIN

EQUATOR

PERU BASIN

PERU CHILE TRENCH

NASCA RIDGE

CHILE BASIN

TROPIC OF CAPRICORN

SALAS Y GÓMEZ RIDGE

CHILE TRENCH

HUMBOLDT PLAIN

GIANT KELP FORESTS
On the Pacific coast of North America, growths of giant kelp form a canopy that could compare to any rainforest. The kelp thrives in cool, shallow oceans where the water is rich in nutrients rising up from the deep sea. A diverse array of animals thrives in the kelp forests, from snails to sea otters.

SEAFARING HERITAGE
Starting in about 1500 BC, Indigenous cultures in the South Pacific were taking to the water. With their large, double-hulled outrigger vessels, these early seafarers traversed large swaths of the ocean, settling new islands and developing culture centered around the ocean that continues to this day.

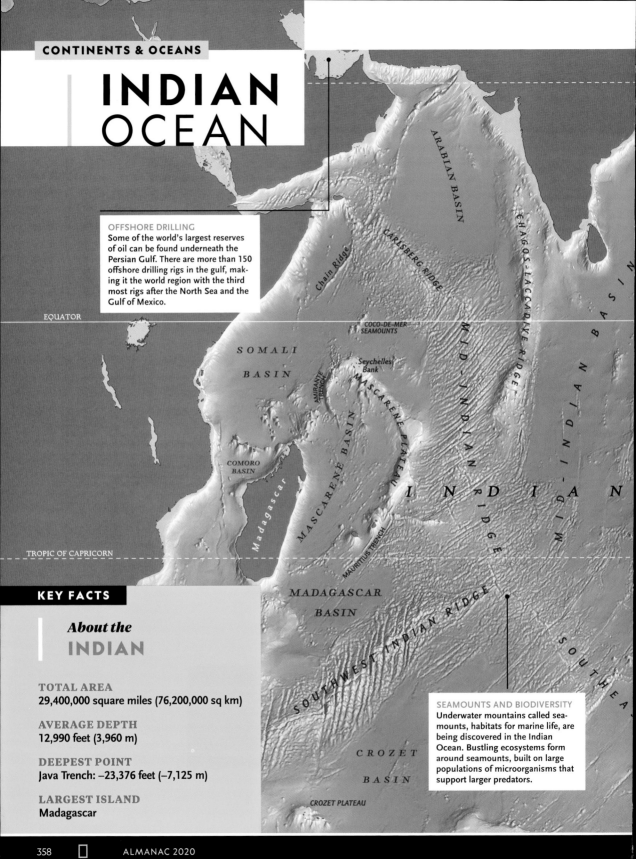

INDIAN OCEAN

OFFSHORE DRILLING
Some of the world's largest reserves of oil can be found underneath the Persian Gulf. There are more than 150 offshore drilling rigs in the gulf, making it the world region with the third most rigs after the North Sea and the Gulf of Mexico.

EQUATOR

ARABIAN BASIN

CHAGOS-LACCADIVE RIDGE

CARLSBERG RIDGE

Chain Ridge

COCO-DE-MER SEAMOUNTS

MID-INDIAN BASIN

SOMALI BASIN

Seychelles Bank

MASCARENE PLATEAU

AMIRANTE TRENCH

MASCARENE BASIN

COMORO BASIN

Madagascar

I N D I A N

MID-INDIAN RIDGE

MAURITIUS TRENCH

TROPIC OF CAPRICORN

MADAGASCAR BASIN

SOUTHWEST INDIAN RIDGE

SOUTHEA

CROZET BASIN

CROZET PLATEAU

KEY FACTS

About the INDIAN

TOTAL AREA
29,400,000 square miles (76,200,000 sq km)

AVERAGE DEPTH
12,990 feet (3,960 m)

DEEPEST POINT
Java Trench: –23,376 feet (–7,125 m)

LARGEST ISLAND
Madagascar

SEAMOUNTS AND BIODIVERSITY
Underwater mountains called seamounts, habitats for marine life, are being discovered in the Indian Ocean. Bustling ecosystems form around seamounts, built on large populations of microorganisms that support larger predators.

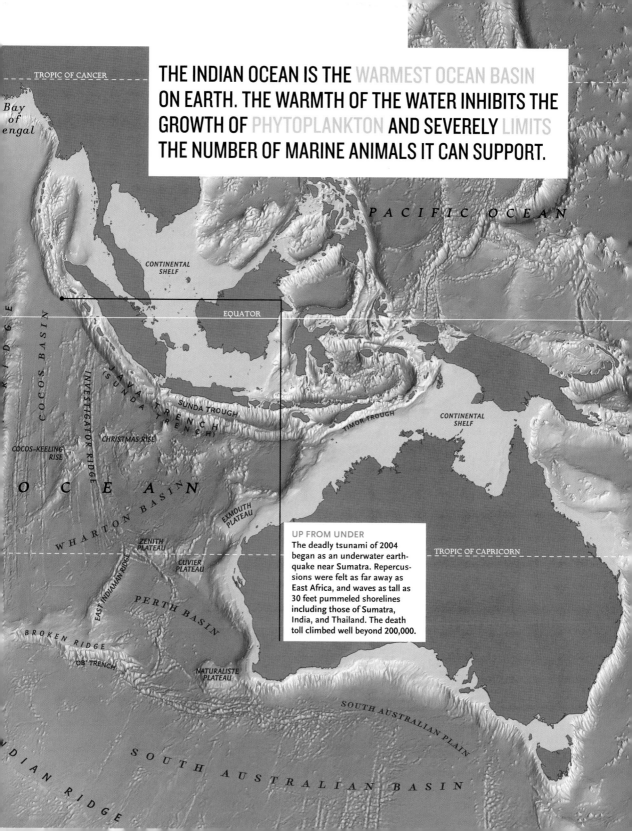

THE INDIAN OCEAN IS THE WARMEST OCEAN BASIN ON EARTH. THE WARMTH OF THE WATER INHIBITS THE GROWTH OF PHYTOPLANKTON AND SEVERELY LIMITS THE NUMBER OF MARINE ANIMALS IT CAN SUPPORT.

TROPIC OF CANCER

Bay of engal

PACIFIC OCEAN

CONTINENTAL SHELF

EQUATOR

RIDGE

COCOS BASIN

INVESTIGATOR RIDGE

JAVA (SUNDA) TRENCH

SUNDA TRENCH

CHRISTMAS RISE

COCOS-KEELING RISE

TIMOR TROUGH

CONTINENTAL SHELF

O C E A N

WHARTON BASIN

EXMOUTH PLATEAU

ZENITH PLATEAU

CUVIER PLATEAU

TROPIC OF CAPRICORN

EAST INDIAMAN RIDGE

PERTH BASIN

BROKEN RIDGE

OB' TRENCH

NATURALISTE PLATEAU

SOUTH AUSTRALIAN PLAIN

NDIAN RIDGE

SOUTH AUSTRALIAN BASIN

UP FROM UNDER
The deadly tsunami of 2004 began as an underwater earthquake near Sumatra. Repercussions were felt as far away as East Africa, and waves as tall as 30 feet pummeled shorelines including those of Sumatra, India, and Thailand. The death toll climbed well beyond 200,000.

ARCTIC
OCEAN

ARCTIC CIRCLE

POLAR VORTEX
Above the Arctic, a spinning mass of cold air called the polar vortex grows and shrinks with the changing seasons. Constantly spinning counterclockwise around the North Pole, it stays at a higher latitude in summer and a lower one in winter. Sometimes the intensely cold air at its bottom edge escapes the spin and heads south, causing extreme winter weather farther south.

NAN...
NAKKE
EURASI
AMUNDSE
LOMONOSOV

CONTINENTAL SHELF

MAKAROV BASIN

MENDELEYEV RIDGE

SARGO PLATEAU

A R

NAUTILUS BASIN

CHUKCHI PLATEAU

ALPHA RIDGE

NORTHWIND RIDGE

STEFANSSON BASIN

CANADA
AMERASIAN BASIN

KEY FACTS

About the
ARCTIC

TOTAL AREA
5,600,000 square miles (14,700,000 sq km)

AVERAGE DEPTH
3,240 feet (987 m)

DEEPEST POINT
Molloy Deep: −18,599 feet (−5,669 m)

LARGEST ISLAND
Greenland

WARMING WATERS
As summer sea ice in the Arctic disappears, the diversity of life that relies on its presence will disappear as well. Since the 1980s, more than a million square miles of Arctic sea ice have been lost, and polar bears, walruses, seabirds, fish, even algae, and more have struggled to keep up with the changing environment.

THE ARCTIC OCEAN IS THE PLANET'S SMALLEST OCEAN, COVERING JUST 5.6 MILLION SQUARE MILES.

CENTRAL BASIN

SVYATAYA ANNA TROUGH

BARENTS TROUGH

FRANTS-VIKTORIYA TROUGH

OLGA BASIN

BASIN

BASIN

YERMAK PLATEAU

Molloy Deep

KNIPOVICH RIDGE

MOHN'S RIDGE

LOFOTEN BASIN

VORING PLATEAU

NORWEGIAN BASIN

MERIDIAN OF GREENWICH (LONDON)

LENA TROUGH

BOREAS BASIN

TIC OCEAN

GREENLAND BASIN

CONTINENTAL SHELF

JAN MAYEN RIDGE

ICELAND PLATEAU

KOLBEINSEY RIDGE

AEGIR RIDGE

ICELAND-FAROE RISE

RIDGE

GREENLAND

ICELAND BASIN

ARCTIC CIRCLE

REYKJANES RIDGE

ATLANTIC OCEAN

IRMINGER BASIN

ELLESMERE ISLAND
Canada's Ellesmere Island is the northernmost piece of land in the Arctic archipelago. A polar desert, it receives very little rainfall and supports a small but unique collection of plants and animals.

BAFFIN BASIN

OCEAN AROUND
ANTARCTICA

INDIA

KERGUELEN PLATEAU

PRINCESS ELIZ
TROUG'

B A S I N   T H E

S O U T H E

ANTARCTIC CONVERGENCE
There is no land boundary between
the waters that comprise the Antarctic Ocean and the Pacific, Atlantic,
and Indian Oceans. Instead, the
boundary is an uneven line where the
cold Antarctic waters flow north to
meet the warmer waters of the
world's other oceans.

ATLANTIC-INDIAN RIDGE

ATLANTIC-INDIAN

MERIDIAN OF GREENWICH (LONDON)

AMERICA-ANTARCTICA RIDGE
(NORTH-WEDDELL RIDGE)

ATLANTIC

ANTARCTIC CIRCLE

A T L A N T I C   O C E A N   R I D G E

CONTINENTAL SHELF

M I D - A T L A N T I C

SOUTH SANDWICH TRENCH

GEORGIA BASIN

FALKLAND RIDGE

South Shetland
Trough
DRAKE
PASSAGE

O

TROPIC OF CAPRICORN

ICEBERGS
Most of the Earth's icebergs are found in
Antarctica and the Arctic, where cold waters
prevent large chunks that have broken off
glaciers or ice sheets from melting. Scientists follow icebergs because they can offer
insight into ocean currents, circulation, and
the way that ice shelves break up over time.

NORTH SCOTIA RIDGE

FALKLAND TROUGH

FALKLAND PLATEAU

CHILE TRENCH

THE WATERS AROUND ANTARCTICA MAY PLUNGE DOWN MORE THAN 16,000 FEET AT THEIR DEEPEST POINT. AN EXPEDITION CURRENTLY UNDER WAY IS CONFIRMING THAT MEASUREMENT.

HUMPBACK WHALES

In the chilly waters around Antarctica, humpback whales are a common sight. They feed on krill—small, shrimp-like creatures that are also prey for many seabirds and other marine mammals. Humpback whales have one of the longest animal migrations, traveling from their breeding grounds in warm tropical areas to feed in the colder waters near the poles.

BEST OF @NATGEO

TOP PHOTOS OF OCEANSCAPES

@geosteinmetz | GEORGE STEINMETZ
Tourists riding camels cast shadows on the white sand of Cable Beach, a popular travel destination in Broome, Australia.

@jenniferhayesig | JENNIFER HAYES
Southern stingrays float in the North Sound of Grand Cayman, where sandbars and shallow waters are ideal habitat.

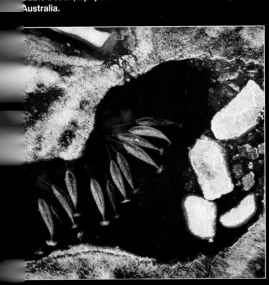

@paulnicklen | PAUL NICKLEN
A pod of narwhals surfaces in Arctic waters. The distinctive ivory tusk seen on males is actually a tooth growing through the lip.

@thomaspeschak | THOMAS PESCHAK
A school of bigeye jacks moves through the Cabo Pulmo Marine Reserve, a protected area of reefs off the Baja California peninsula.

@jimmychin | JIMMY CHIN
The Ilulissat Icefjord is a gateway for icebergs calving from an active glacier to enter Disko Bay on Greenland's west coast.

@thomaspeschak | THOMAS PESCHAK
A double rainbow arcs from blue water between D'Arros Island and St. Joseph Atoll in the Seychelles.

@ladzinski | KEITH LADZINSKI
Sunset tints the sky above Keyhole Arch at Pfeiffer Beach, a secluded stretch of Big Sur coastline.

@daviddoubilet | DAVID DOUBILET
Brown boobies perch on coral in Tubbataha Reefs Natural Park, reachable only by boat in the Sulu Sea in the Philippines.

FLAGS OF THE WORLD

EACH OF TODAY'S 195 COUNTRIES FLIES AN HONORED AND SYMBOLIC FLAG

AFGHANISTAN

AREA 251,827 sq mi
(652,230 sq km)
POPULATION 34,941,000
CAPITAL Kabul

ALBANIA

AREA 11,100 sq mi
(28,748 sq km)
POPULATION 3,057,000
CAPITAL Tirana

ALGERIA

AREA 919,590 sq mi
(2,381,741 sq km)
POPULATION 41,657,000
CAPITAL Algiers

ANDORRA

AREA 181 sq mi
(468 sq km)
POPULATION 86,000
CAPITAL Andorra la Vella

ANGOLA

AREA 481,351 sq mi
(1,246,700 sq km)
POPULATION 30,356,000
CAPITAL Luanda

ANTIGUA AND BARBUDA
AREA 171 sq mi
(443 sq km)
POPULATION 96,000
CAPITAL St. John's

ARGENTINA

AREA 1,073,518 sq mi
(2,780,400 sq km)
POPULATION 44,694,000
CAPITAL Buenos Aires

ARMENIA
AREA 11,484 sq mi
(29,743 sq km)
POPULATION 3,038,000
CAPITAL Yerevan

AUSTRALIA
AAREA 2,988,901 sq mi
(7,741,220 sq km)
POPULATION 23,470,000
CAPITAL Canberra

AUSTRIA

AREA 32,383 sq mi
(83,871 sq km)
POPULATION 8,793,000
CAPITAL Vienna

AZERBAIJAN

AREA 33,436 sq mi
(86,600 sq km)
POPULATION 10,047,000
CAPITAL Baku

BAHAMAS, THE

AREA 5,359 sq mi
(13,880 sq km)
POPULATION 330,000
CAPITAL Nassau

BAHRAIN

AREA 293 sq mi
(760 sq km)
POPULATION 1,443,000
CAPITAL Manama

BANGLADESH

AREA 57,321 sq mi
(148,460 sq km)
POPULATION 159,453,000
CAPITAL Dhaka

BARBADOS

AREA 166 sq mi
(430 sq km)
POPULATION 293,000
CAPITAL Bridgetown

BELARUS

AREA 80,155 sq mi
(207,600 sq km)
POPULATION 9,528,000
CAPITAL Minsk

BELGIUM

AREA 11,787 sq mi
(30,528 sq km)
POPULATION 11,571,000
CAPITAL Brussels

BELIZE
AREA 8,867 sq mi
(22,966 sq km)
POPULATION 386,000
CAPITAL Belmopan

BENIN

AREA 43,484 sq mi
(112,622 sq km)
POPULATION 11,341,000
CAPITALS Porto-Novo (official capital),
Cotonou (administrative)

BHUTAN

AREA 14,824 sq mi
(38,394 sq km)
POPULATION 766,000
CAPITAL Thimphu

BOLIVIA

AREA 424,164 sq mi
(1,098,581 sq km)
POPULATION 11,138,000
CAPITALS La Paz (administrative),
Sucre (constitutional)

BOSNIA AND HERZEGOVINA
AREA 19,767 sq mi
(51,197 sq km)
POPULATION 3,850,000
CAPITAL Sarajevo

BOTSWANA

AREA 224,607 sq mi
(581,730 sq km)
POPULATION 2,215,000
CAPITAL Gaborone

BRAZIL
AREA 3,287,956 sq mi
(8,515,770 sq km)
POPULATION 208,847,000
CAPITAL Brasília

BRUNEI
AREA 2,226 sq mi
(5,765 sq km)
POPULATION 451,000
CAPITAL Bandar Seri Begawan

" PRIDE AND INDUSTRY."

—NATIONAL MOTTO OF BARBADOS

BULGARIA

AREA 42,811 sq mi
(110,879 sq km)
POPULATION 7,058,000
CAPITAL Sofia

BURKINA FASO

AREA 105,869 sq mi
(274,200 sq km)
POPULATION 19,743,000
CAPITAL Ouagadougou

BURUNDI

AREA 10,745 sq mi
(27,830 sq km)
POPULATION 11,845,000
CAPITAL Gitega

CABO VERDE

AREA 1,557 sq mi
(4,033 sq km)
POPULATION 568,000
CAPITAL Praia

CAMBODIA

AREA 69,898 sq mi
(181,035 sq km)
POPULATION 16,450,000
CAPITAL Phnom Penh

CAMEROON

AREA 183,568 sq mi
(475,440 sq km)
POPULATION 25,641,000
CAPITAL Yaoundé

CANADA

AREA 3,855,101 sq mi
(9,984,670 sq km)
POPULATION 35,882,000
CAPITAL Ottawa

CENTRAL AFRICAN REPUBLIC

AREA 240,535 sq mi
(622,984 sq km)
POPULATION 5,745,000
CAPITAL Bangui

CHAD

AREA 495,755 sq mi
(1,284,000 sq km)
POPULATION 15,833
CAPITAL N'Djamena

CHILE

AREA 291,932 sq mi
(756,102 sq km)
POPULATION 17,925,000
CAPITAL Santiago

CHINA

AREA 3,705,407 sq mi
(9,596,960 sq km)
POPULATION 1,384,689,000
CAPITAL Beijing

COLOMBIA

AREA 439,735 sq mi
(1,138,910 sq km)
POPULATION 48,169,000
CAPITAL Bogotá

COMOROS

AREA 863 sq mi
(2,235 sq km)
POPULATION 821,000
CAPITAL Moroni

CONGO

AREA 132,047 sq mi
(342,000 sq km)
POPULATION 5,062,000
CAPITAL Brazzaville

CONGO, DEMOCRATIC REPUBLIC OF THE

AREA 905,354 sq mi
(2,344,858 sq km)
POPULATION 85,281,000
CAPITAL Kinshasa

COSTA RICA

AREA 19,730 sq mi
(51,100 sq km)
POPULATION 4,987,000
CAPITAL San José

CÔTE D'IVOIRE

AREA 124,504 sq mi
(322,463 sq km)
POPULATION 26,261,000
CAPITALS Abidjan (administrative),
Yamoussoukro (legislative)

CROATIA

AREA 21,851 sq mi
(56,594 sq km)
POPULATION 4,270,000
CAPITAL Zagreb

CUBA

AREA 42,803 sq mi
(110,860 sq km)
POPULATION 11,116,000
CAPITAL Havana

CYPRUS

AREA 3,572 sq mi
(9,251 sq km)
POPULATION 1,237,000
CAPITAL Nicosia

CZECHIA (CZECH REPUBLIC)

AREA 30,451 sq mi
(78,867 sq km)
POPULATION 10,686,000
CAPITAL Prague

DENMARK

AREA 16,639 sq mi
(43,094 sq km)
POPULATION 5,810,000
CAPITAL Copenhagen

DJIBOUTI

AREA 8,958 sq mi
(23,200 sq km)
POPULATION 884,000
CAPITAL Djibouti

DOMINICA

AREA 290 sq mi
(751 sq km)
POPULATION 74,000
CAPITAL Roseau

DOMINICAN REPUBLIC

AREA 18,792 sq mi
(48,670 sq km)
POPULATION 10,299,000
CAPITAL Santo Domingo

ECUADOR

AREA 109,483 sq mi
(283,561 sq km)
POPULATION 16,499,000
CAPITAL Quito

EGYPT

AREA 386,662 sq mi
(1,001,450 sq km)
POPULATION 99,413,000
CAPITAL Cairo

EL SALVADOR

AREA 8,124 sq mi
(21,041 sq km)
POPULATION 6,187,000
CAPITAL San Salvador

EQUATORIAL GUINEA

AREA 10,831 sq mi
(28,051 sq km)
POPULATION 797,000
CAPITAL Malabo

ERITREA
AREA 45,406 sq mi
(117,600 sq km)
POPULATION 5,971,000
CAPITAL Asmara

ESTONIA
AREA 17,463 sq mi
(45,228 sq km)
POPULATION 1,244,000
CAPITAL Tallinn

ESWATINI
AREA 6,704 sq mi
(17,364 sq km)
POPULATION 1,087,000
CAPITALS Mbabane (administrative),
Lobamba (legislative and royal)

ETHIOPIA
AREA 426,372 sq mi
(1,104,300 sq km)
POPULATION 108,386,000
CAPITAL Addis Ababa

FIJI
AREA 7,056 sq mi
(18,274 sq km)
POPULATION 926,000
CAPITAL Suva

FINLAND
AREA 130,558 sq mi
(338,145 sq km)
POPULATION 5,537,000
CAPITAL Helsinki

FRANCE
AREA 248,573 sq mi
(643,801 sq km)
POPULATION 67,364,000
CAPITAL Paris

GABON
AREA 103,347 sq mi
(267,667 sq km)
POPULATION 2,119,000
CAPITAL Libreville

GAMBIA, THE
AREA 4,363 sq mi
(11,300 sq km)
POPULATION 2,093,000
CAPITAL Banjul

GEORGIA
AREA 26,911 sq mi
(69,700 sq km)
POPULATION 4,926,000
CAPITAL Tbilisi

GERMANY
AREA 137,847 sq mi
(357,022 sq km)
POPULATION 80,458,000
CAPITAL Berlin

GHANA
AREA 92,098 sq mi
(238,533 sq km)
POPULATION 28,102,000
CAPITAL Accra

GREECE
AREA 50,949 sq mi
(131,957 sq km)
POPULATION 10,762,000
CAPITAL Athens

GRENADA
AREA 133 sq mi
(344 sq km)
POPULATION 112,000
CAPITAL St. George's

GUATEMALA
AREA 42,042 sq mi
(108,889 sq km)
POPULATION 16,581,000
CAPITAL Guatemala City

GUINEA
AREA 94,926 sq mi
(245,857 sq km)
POPULATION 11,855,000
CAPITAL Conakry

GUINEA-BISSAU
AREA 13,948 sq mi
(36,125 sq km)
POPULATION 1,833,000
CAPITAL Bissau

GUYANA
AREA 83,000 sq mi
(214,969 sq km)
POPULATION 741,000
CAPITAL Georgetown

HAITI
AREA 10,714 sq mi
(27,750 sq km)
POPULATION 10,788,000
CAPITAL Port-au-Prince

HONDURAS
AREA 43,278 sq mi
(112,090 sq km)
POPULATION 9,183,000
CAPITAL Tegucigalpa

HUNGARY
AREA 35,918 sq mi
(93,028 sq km)
POPULATION 9,826,000
CAPITAL Budapest

ICELAND
AREA 39,769 sq mi
(103,000 sq km)
POPULATION 344,000
CAPITAL Reykjavík

INDIA
AREA 1,269,219 sq mi
(3,287,263 sq km)
POPULATION 1,296,834,000
CAPITAL New Delhi

INDONESIA
AREA 735,358 sq mi
(1,904,569 sq km)
POPULATION 262,787,000
CAPITAL Jakarta

IRAN
AREA 636,371 sq mi
(1,648,195 sq km)
POPULATION 83,025,000
CAPITAL Tehran

IRAQ
AREA 169,235 sq mi
(438,317 sq km)
POPULATION 40,194,000
CAPITAL Baghdad
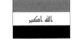

IRELAND
AREA 27,133 sq mi
(70,273 sq km)
POPULATION 5,068,000
CAPITAL Dublin

ISRAEL
AREA 8,019 sq mi
(20,770 sq km)
POPULATION 8,425,000
CAPITAL Jerusalem

ITALY
AREA 116,348 sq mi
(301,340 sq km)
POPULATION 62,247,000
CAPITAL Rome

JAMAICA
AREA 4,244 sq mi
(10,991 sq km)
POPULATION 2,812,000
CAPITAL Kingston

JAPAN
AREA 145,914 sq mi
(377,915 sq km)
POPULATION 126,168,000
CAPITAL Tokyo

JORDAN
AREA 34,495 sq mi
(89,342 sq km)
POPULATION 10,458,000
CAPITAL Amman

KAZAKHSTAN
AREA 1,052,089 sq mi
(2,724,900 sq km)
POPULATION 18,745,000
CAPITAL Nur-Sultan (Astana)

KENYA

AREA 224,081 sq mi
(580,367 sq km)
POPULATION 48,398,000
CAPITAL Nairobi

KIRIBATI

AREA 313 sq mi
(811 sq km)
POPULATION 109,000
CAPITAL Tarawa

KOSOVO

AREA 4,203 sq mi
(10,887 sq km)
POPULATION 1,908,000
CAPITAL Prishtina

KUWAIT

AREA 6,880 sq mi
(17,818 sq km)
POPULATION 4,622,000
CAPITAL Kuwait City

KYRGYZSTAN

AREA 77,201 sq mi
(199,951 sq km)
POPULATION 5,849,000
CAPITAL Bishkek

LAOS

AREA 91,429 sq mi
(236,800 sq km)
POPULATION 7,234,000
CAPITAL Vientiane

LATVIA

AREA 24,938 sq mi
(64,589 sq km)
POPULATION 1,924,000
CAPITAL Riga

LEBANON

AREA 4,015 sq mi
(10,400 sq km)
POPULATION 6,100,000
CAPITAL Beirut

LESOTHO

AREA 11,720 sq mi
(30,355 sq km)
POPULATION 1,962,000
CAPITAL Maseru

LIBERIA

AREA 43,000 sq mi
(111,369 sq km)
POPULATION 4,810,000
CAPITAL Monrovia

LIBYA

AREA 679,362 sq mi
(1,759,540 sq km)
POPULATION 6,755,000
CAPITAL Tripoli

LIECHTENSTEIN

AREA 62 sq mi
(160 sq km)
POPULATION 39,000
CAPITAL Vaduz

LITHUANIA

AREA 25,212 sq mi
(65,300 sq km)
POPULATION 2,793,000
CAPITAL Vilnius

LUXEMBOURG

AREA 998 sq mi
(2,586 sq km)
POPULATION 606,000
CAPITAL Luxembourg

MADAGASCAR

AREA 226,658 sq mi
(587,041 sq km)
POPULATION 25,684,000
CAPITAL Antananarivo

MALAWI

AREA 45,747 sq mi
(118,484 sq km)
POPULATION 19,843,000
CAPITAL Lilongwe

MALAYSIA

AREA 127,355 sq mi
(329,847 sq km)
POPULATION 31,810,000
CAPITAL Kuala Lumpur

MALDIVES

AREA 115 sq mi
(298 sq km)
POPULATION 392,000
CAPITAL Male

MALI

AREA 478,841 sq mi
(1,240,192 sq km)
POPULATION 18,430,000
CAPITAL Bamako

MALTA

AREA 122 sq mi
(316 sq km)
POPULATION 449,000
CAPITAL Valletta

MARSHALL ISLANDS

AREA 70 sq mi
(181 sq km)
POPULATION 76,000
CAPITAL Majuro

MAURITANIA

AREA 397,955 sq mi
(1,030,700 sq km)
POPULATION 3,840,000
CAPITAL Nouakchott

MAURITIUS

AREA 788 sq mi
(2,040 sq km)
POPULATION 1,364,000
CAPITAL Port Louis

MEXICO

AREA 758,449 sq mi
(1,964,375 sq km)
POPULATION 125,959,000
CAPITAL Mexico City

MICRONESIA

AREA 271 sq mi
(702 sq km)
POPULATION 104,000
CAPITAL Palikir

MOLDOVA

AREA 13,070 sq mi
(33,851 sq km)
POPULATION 3,438,000
CAPITAL Chisinau

MONACO

AREA 1 sq mi
(2.0 sq km)
POPULATION 38,000
CAPITAL Monaco

MONGOLIA

AREA 603,908 sq mi
(1,564,116 sq km)
POPULATION 3,103,000
CAPITAL Ulaanbaatar

MONTENEGRO

AREA 5,333 sq mi
(13,812 sq km)
POPULATION 614,000
CAPITAL Podgorica

MOROCCO

AREA 172,414 sq mi
(446,550 sq km)
POPULATION 34,314,000
CAPITAL Rabat

MOZAMBIQUE

AREA 308,642 sq mi
(799,380 sq km)
POPULATION 27,234,000
CAPITAL Maputo

MYANMAR (BURMA)

AREA 261,228 sq mi
(676,578 sq km)
POPULATION 55,623,000
CAPITAL Nay Pyi Taw

NAMIBIA

AREA 318,261 sq mi
(824,292 sq km)
POPULATION 2,533,000
CAPITAL Windhoek

NAURU

AREA 8 sq mi
(21 sq km)
POPULATION 10,000
CAPITAL No official capital; government offices in Yaren District

NEPAL

AREA 56,827 sq mi
(147,181 sq km)
POPULATION 29,718,000
CAPITAL Kathmandu

NETHERLANDS

AREA 16,040 sq mi
(41,543 sq km)
POPULATION 17,151,000
CAPITAL Amsterdam

NEW ZEALAND

AREA 103,799 sq mi
(268,838 sq km)
POPULATION 4,546,000
CAPITAL Wellington

NICARAGUA

AREA 50,336 sq mi
(130,370 sq km)
POPULATION 6,085,000
CAPITAL Managua

NIGER

AREA 489,191 sq mi
(1,267,000 sq km)
POPULATION 19,866,000
CAPITAL Niamey

NIGERIA

AREA 356,669 sq mi
(923,768 sq km)
POPULATION 203,453,000
CAPITAL Abuja

NORTH KOREA

AREA 46,540 sq mi
(120,538 sq km)
POPULATION 25,381,000
CAPITAL Pyongyang

NORTH MACEDONIA

AREA 9,928 sq mi
(25,713 sq km)
POPULATION 2,119,000
CAPITAL Skopje

NORWAY

AREA 125,021 sq mi
(323,802 sq km)
POPULATION 5,372,000
CAPITAL Oslo

OMAN

AREA 119,499 sq mi
(309,500 sq km)
POPULATION 3,494,000
CAPITAL Muscat

PAKISTAN

AREA 307,374 sq mi
(796,095 sq km)
POPULATION 207,863,000
CAPITAL Islamabad

PALAU

AREA 177 sq mi
(459 sq km)
POPULATION 22,000
CAPITAL Melekeok (on Babelthuap)

PANAMA

AREA 29,120 sq mi
(75,420 sq km)
POPULATION 3,801,000
CAPITAL Panama City

PAPUA NEW GUINEA

AREA 178,703 sq mi
(462,840 sq km)
POPULATION 7,027,000
CAPITAL Port Moresby

PARAGUAY

AREA 157,048 sq mi
(406,752 sq km)
POPULATION 7,026,000
CAPITAL Asunción

PERU

AREA 496,224 sq mi
(1,285,216 sq km)
POPULATION 31,331,000
CAPITAL Lima

PHILIPPINES

AREA 115,831 sq mi
(300,000 sq km)
POPULATION 105,893,000
CAPITAL Manila

POLAND

AREA 120,728 sq mi
(312,685 sq km)
POPULATION 38,421,000
CAPITAL Warsaw

PORTUGAL

AREA 35,556 sq mi
(92,090 sq km)
POPULATION 10,355,000
CAPITAL Lisbon

QATAR

AREA 4,473 sq mi
(11,586 sq km)
POPULATION 2,364,000
CAPITAL Doha

ROMANIA

AREA 92,043 sq mi
(238,391 sq km)
POPULATION 21,457,000
CAPITAL Bucharest

RUSSIA

AREA 6,601,665 sq mi
(17,098,242 sq km)
POPULATION 142,123,000
CAPITAL Moscow

RWANDA

AREA 10,169 sq mi
(26,338 sq km)
POPULATION 12,187,000
CAPITAL Kigali

SAINT KITTS AND NEVIS

AREA 101 sq mi
(261 sq km)
POPULATION 53,000
CAPITAL Basseterre

SAINT LUCIA

AREA 238 sq mi
(616 sq km)
POPULATION 166,000
CAPITAL Castries

SAINT VINCENT AND GRENADINES

AREA 150 sq mi
(389 sq km)
POPULATION 102,000
CAPITAL Kingstown

SAMOA

AREA 1,093 sq mi
(2,831 sq km)
POPULATION 201,000
CAPITAL Apia

SAN MARINO

AREA 24 sq mi
(61 sq km)
POPULATION 34,000
CAPITAL San Marino

SÃO TOMÉ AND PRINCIPE

AREA 372 sq mi
(964 sq km)
POPULATION 204,000
CAPITAL São Tomé

SAUDI ARABIA

AREA 830,000 sq mi
(2,149,690 sq km)
POPULATION 33,091,000
CAPITAL Riyadh

SENEGAL

AREA 75,955 sq mi
(196,722 sq km)
POPULATION 15,021,000
CAPITAL Dakar

SERBIA

AREA 29,913 sq mi
(77,474 sq km)
POPULATION 7,078,000
CAPITAL Belgrade

SEYCHELLES

AREA 176 sq mi
(455 sq km)
POPULATION 95,000
CAPITAL Victoria

SIERRA LEONE

AREA 27,699 sq mi
(71,740 sq km)
POPULATION 6,312,000
CAPITAL Freetown

SINGAPORE

AREA 269 sq mi
(697 sq km)
POPULATION 5,996,000
CAPITAL Singapore

SLOVAKIA

AREA 18,933 sq mi
(49,035 sq km)
POPULATION 5,445,000
CAPITAL Bratislava

SLOVENIA

AREA 7,827 sq mi
(20,273 sq km)
POPULATION 2,102,000
CAPITAL Ljubljana

SOLOMON ISLANDS

AREA 11,157 sq mi
(28,896 sq km)
POPULATION 660,000
CAPITAL Honiara

SOMALIA

AREA 246,201 sq mi
(637,657 sq km)
POPULATION 11,259,000
CAPITAL Mogadishu

SOUTH AFRICA

AREA 470,693 sq mi
(1,219,090 sq km)
POPULATION 55,380,000
CAPITALS Pretoria (Tshwane) (administrative),
Cape Town (legislative), Bloemfontein
(judicial)

SOUTH KOREA

AREA 38,502 sq mi
(99,720 sq km)
POPULATION 51,418,000
CAPITAL Seoul

SOUTH SUDAN

AREA 248,777 sq mi
(644,329 sq km)
POPULATION 10,205,000
CAPITAL Juba

SPAIN

AREA 195,124 sq mi
(505,370 sq km)

POPULATION 49,331,000
CAPITAL Madrid

SRI LANKA

AREA 25,332 sq mi
(65,610 sq km)
POPULATION 22,577,000
CAPITALS Colombo (administrative),
Sri Jayewardenepura Kotte (legislative)

SUDAN

AREA 718,723 sq mi
(1,861,484 sq km)
POPULATION 43,121,000
CAPITAL Khartoum

SURINAME

AREA 63,251 sq mi
(163,820 sq km)
POPULATION 598,000
CAPITAL Paramaribo

SWEDEN

AREA 173,860 sq mi
(450,295 sq km)
POPULATION 10,041,000
CAPITAL Stockholm

SWITZERLAND

AREA 15,937 sq mi
(41,277 sq km)
POPULATION 8,293,000
CAPITAL Bern

SYRIA

AREA 71,498 sq mi
(185,180 sq km)
POPULATION 19,454,000
CAPITAL Damascus

TAJIKISTAN

AREA 55,637 sq mi
(144,100 sq km)
POPULATION 8,605,000
CAPITAL Dushanbe

TANZANIA

AREA 365,754 sq mi
(947,300 sq km)
POPULATION 55,451,000
CAPITAL Dar es Salaam (administrative);
Dodoma (official)

THAILAND

AREA 198,117 sq mi
(513,120 sq km)
POPULATION 68,616,000
CAPITAL Bangkok

TIMOR-LESTE (EAST TIMOR)

AREA 5,743 sq mi
(14,874 sq km)

POPULATION 1,322,000
CAPITAL Díli

TOGO

AREA 21,925 sq mi
(56,785 sq km)
POPULATION 8,176,000
CAPITAL Lomé

TONGA

AREA 288 sq mi
(747 sq km)
POPULATION 106,000
CAPITAL Nuku'alofa

TRINIDAD AND TOBAGO

AREA 1,980 sq mi
(5,128 sq km)
POPULATION 1,216,000
CAPITAL Port of Spain

TUNISIA

AREA 63,170 sq mi
(163,610 sq km)
POPULATION 11,516,000
CAPITAL Tunis

TURKEY

AREA 302,535 sq mi
(783,562 sq km)
POPULATION 81,257,000
CAPITAL Ankara

TURKMENISTAN

AREA 188,456 sq mi
(488,100 sq km)
POPULATION 5,411,000
CAPITAL Ashgabat

TUVALU

AREA 10 sq mi
(26 sq km)
POPULATION 11,000
CAPITAL Funafuti

UGANDA

AREA 93,065 sq mi
(241,038 sq km)
POPULATION 40,854,000
CAPITAL Kampala

UKRAINE

AREA 233,032 sq mi
(603,550 sq km)
POPULATION 43,952,000
CAPITAL Kiev

UNITED ARAB EMIRATES

AREA 32,278 sq mi
(83,600 sq km)
POPULATION 9,701,000
CAPITAL Abu Dhabi

UNITED KINGDOM

AREA 94,058 sq mi
(243,610 sq km)
POPULATION 65,105,000
CAPITAL London

UNITED STATES

AREA 3,796,741 sq mi
(9,833,517 sq km)
POPULATION 329,256,000
CAPITAL Washington, D.C.

URUGUAY

AREA 68,037 sq mi
(176,215 sq km)
POPULATION 3,369,000
CAPITAL Montevideo

UZBEKISTAN

AREA 172,742 sq mi
(447,400 sq km)
POPULATION 30,024,000
CAPITAL Tashkent

VANUATU

AREA 4,706 sq mi
(12,189 sq km)
POPULATION 288,000
CAPITAL Port-Vila

VATICAN CITY (HOLY SEE)

AREA 0.17 sq mi
(0.44 sq km)
POPULATION 1,000
CAPITAL Vatican City

VENEZUELA

AREA 352,144 sq mi
(912,050 sq km)
POPULATION 31,689,000
CAPITAL Caracas

VIETNAM

AREA 127,881 sq mi
(331,210 sq km)
POPULATION 97,040,000
CAPITAL Hanoi

YEMEN

AREA 203,850 sq mi
(527,968 sq km)
POPULATION 28,667,000
CAPITAL Sanaa

ZAMBIA

AREA 290,587 sq mi
(752,618 sq km)
POPULATION 16,445,000
CAPITAL Lusaka

ZIMBABWE

AREA 150,872 sq mi
(390,757 sq km)
POPULATION 14,030,000
CAPITAL Harare

UNITED NATIONS

IN SEARCH OF A PEACEFUL WORLD

The UN works to maintain international peace, develop friendly relations among nations, and achieve international cooperation in solving world problems.

In 1945, the 51 original Member States represented more than 80 percent of the world's population.

MORE OF THE
WORLD

BEYOND COUNTRY STATUS

There are 195 countries, 36 dependencies, and five other political units that make up the world today.

FIVE OTHER POLITICAL ENTITIES EXIST TODAY: GAZA STRIP, NORTHERN CYPRUS, TAIWAN, WEST BANK, AND WESTERN SAHARA.

THE WORLD

Dependencies Listed by SOVEREIGNTY

AUSTRALIA
Christmas Island, Cocos (Keeling) Islands, Norfolk Island

DENMARK
Faroe Islands, Greenland (Kalaallit Nunaat)

FRANCE
French Polynesia, New Caledonia, Saint-Barthélemy, Saint Martin, Saint-Pierre and Miquelon, Wallis and Futuna

NETHERLANDS
Aruba, Curaçao, Sint Maarten

NEW ZEALAND
Cook Islands, Niue, Tokelau

UNITED KINGDOM
Anguilla, Bermuda, British Virgin Islands, Cayman Islands, Falkland Islands, Gibraltar, Guernsey, Isle of Man, Jersey, Montserrat, Pitcairn Islands, Saint Helena and Dependencies, Turks and Caicos Islands

Atoll islands surround Bora Bora, part of French Polynesia.

FUTURE
OF THE PLANET

TAKING EARTH'S TEMPERATURE

Temperatures are increasing at different rates around the planet, and regions will feel the consequences of climate change differently. This map—created based on analysis of more than 40 social, economic, and environmental factors, including poverty, population growth, infrastructure, and areas of flooding and drought—represents patterns of vulnerability over the next 30 years.

Urban Vulnerability

Large Cities With High or Severe Risk
(by projected population in 2035)

▽ 18 million people or more

▽ 12–17.9 million

▿ 6–11.9 million

Large Cities With Low Risk
(by projected population in 2035)

◯ 18 million people or more

◯ 12–17.9 million

◦ 6–11.9 million

Cities not shown have a projected population less than 6 million or are at medium risk from climate change.

SAU PAULO, BRAZIL, IS AMONG THE PLACES AT LOWEST RISK AS A RESULT OF CLIMATE CHANGE. THE CITY HAS BEEN IMPLEMENTING A MUNICIPAL CLIMATE LAW, INCLUDING LOWERING GREENHOUSE GAS EMISSIONS, SINCE 2009.

ASIA

Kabul
Baghdad
andria
Lahore
Riyadh
Karachi
Ahmadabad
Poona
Chittagong
Mumbai
Rangoon
hartoum
Hyderabad
Bangkok
Manila
Addis Ababa
Bangalore
Chennai
Ho Chi
Minh City
Kampala
Kuala Lumpur
Nairobi
Singapore
Dar es Salaam
Jakarta

Antananarivo

Johannesburg

AUSTRALIA

**Climate Change
Vulnerability**
Severe   Low
No data

FUTURE OF
THE WILD ON EARTH

WHERE NATURE STILL PREVAILS

Every continent on Earth contains landscapes that are still relatively untouched by the impact of human developments. Of the 14 biomes, or types of plant and animal community, those least affected by human development are deserts, tropical forests, and northern forests.

Low Impact Areas by Biome

- Montane grasslands & shrublands
- Temperate grasslands, savannas, & shrublands
- Desert & xeric shrublands
- Mediterranean forests, woodlands, & scrub
- Tropical & subtropical grasslands, savannas, & shrublands
- Temperate coniferous forests
- Tropical & subtropical coniferous forests
- Tropical & subtropical dry broadleaf forests
- Temperate broadleaf & mixed forests
- Tropical & subtropical moist broadleaf forests
- Flooded grasslands & savannas
- Boreal forests/taiga
- Tundra
- Mangroves
- Ice and rock

  Human-impacted area

MORE THAN 70% OF THE PLANET'S REMAINING
WILDERNESS LIES WITHIN THE BORDERS
OF FIVE COUNTRIES: AUSTRALIA, BRAZIL, CANADA,
RUSSIA, AND THE UNITED STATES.

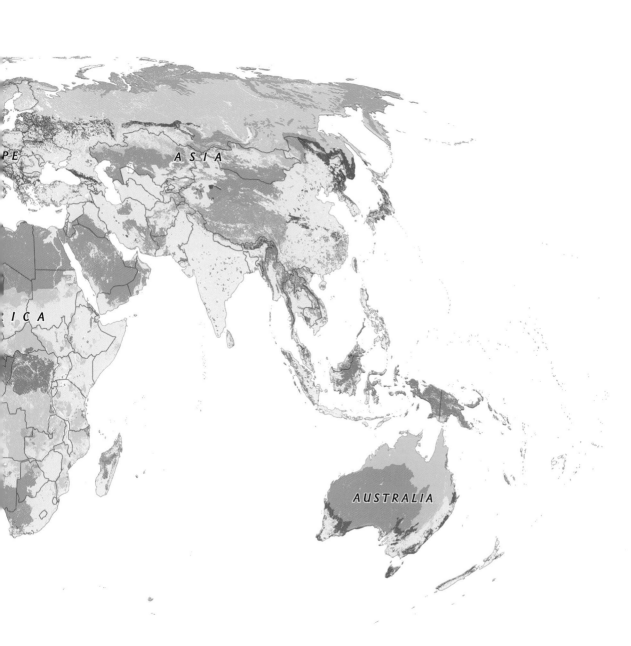

FUTURE OF
HUMANS ON EARTH

ARE THINGS GETTING BETTER?

Health, wealth, education, nutrition, housing, safety, connections—
many factors contribute to quality of life. But improvements in lifestyle
are not felt equally throughout the world. This map provides a picture of
human development, or how well the average person is flourishing.
Where data is available, the map looks beyond the national level to
regional differences.

Human Develpment, 2017

- Very High
- High
- Medium
- Low
- No data

IN GHANA, TOGO, BENIN, AND NIGERIA, OIL DEVELOPMENT AND TRADE HAVE HELPED TO INCREASE WEALTH WHILE BRINGING NEW CHALLENGES, SUCH AS POLLUTION.

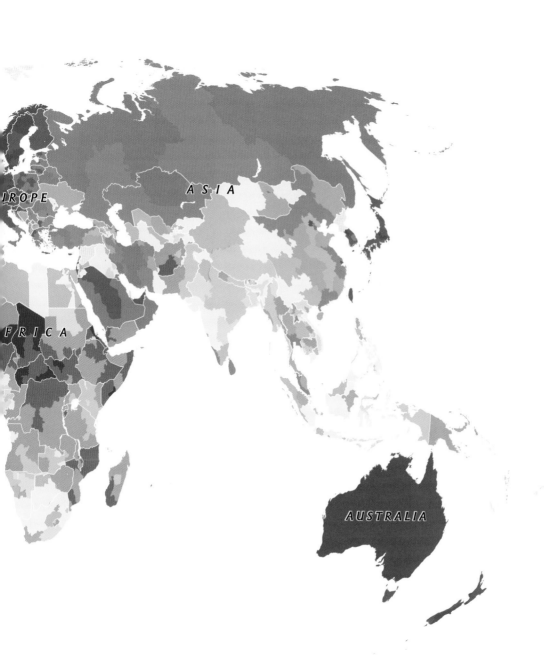

FURTHER

THE BEAT GOES ON

The Unisphere stood 140 feet tall at the heart of the 1964 New York World's Fair. Showing the Earth as one, with three rings representing the earliest orbiting space missions, the massive stainless-steel structure symbolized the fair's theme, "Peace Through Understanding." Thanks to persistent community effort and public investment, it still stands in Queens, New York, today. Its nearby fountain system took a beating from superstorm Sandy but, now renovated, the fountains offer refreshing cool to summer visitors.

A long-exposure shot turns visitors and fountains ghostly at the base of the Unisphere in New York City's Flushing Meadows–Corona Park.

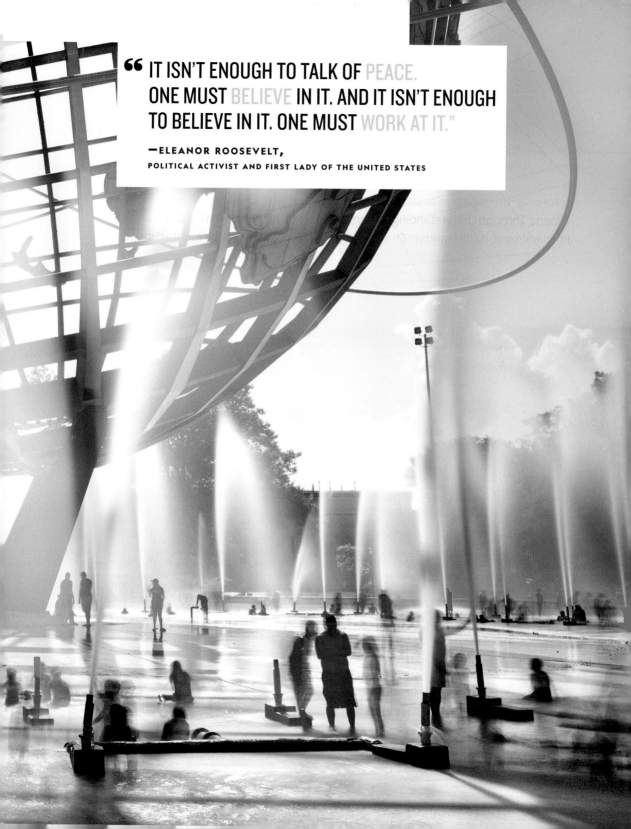

> **" IT ISN'T ENOUGH TO TALK OF PEACE. ONE MUST BELIEVE IN IT. AND IT ISN'T ENOUGH TO BELIEVE IN IT. ONE MUST WORK AT IT."**
>
> **—ELEANOR ROOSEVELT,**
> **POLITICAL ACTIVIST AND FIRST LADY OF THE UNITED STATES**

CREDITS

dani3315/Shutterstock; 284 (CTR RT), Jose Ignacio Soto/Shutterstock; 284 (LO), Nicolae Gjebic/Shutterstock; 285 (TOP), Stefan Ataman/Shutterstock; 285 (UP LE), Semiramis, designed 1872, carved 1873 (marble), Story, William Wetmore (1819–1895) Dallas Museum of Art, Texas, USA/gift of Morynne and Robert E. Motley in memory of Robert Earl Motley, Jr., 1942–1998/Bridgeman Images; 285 (UP RT), Henner Damke/Shutterstock; 285 (CTR), Chiffanna/Shutterstock; 285 (LO), Smithsonian Institution/Science Source; 286 (UP LE), Joe McNally; 286 (UP CTR), Seal depicting a mythological animal and pictographic symbols, from Mohenjo-Daro, Indus Valley, Pakistan, 3000–1500 b.c. (stone), Harappan/National Museum of Karachi, Karachi, Pakistan/Bridgeman Images; 286 (UP RT), Aranami/Shutterstock; 286 (CTR LE), anyaivanova/Shutterstock; 286 (CTR RT), Greece: Marble bust of Alexander the Great at the British Museum, London/Pictures from History/Bridgeman Images; 286 (LO LE), Weeding, The Rice Culture in China (color woodblock print), Chinese School (19th century)/Private Collection/Archives Charmet/Bridgeman Images; 286 (LO CTR LE), DEA/G. Dagli Orti/De Agostini/Getty Images; 286 (LO CTR RT), Rodolfo Parulan, Jr./Getty Images; 286 (LO RT), Photos.com/Getty Images; 286-7, Leeuwtje/Getty Images; 287 (UP LE), Boris Vetshev/Shutterstock; 287 (UP CTR LE), Fine Art Images/Heritage Images/Getty Images; 287 (UP CTR RT), Ms FR 22495 f.265v Battle of Damietta in Egypt in 1218–19, during the fifth crusade (1217–1221) from Historia by Guillaume de Tyr, 1337 (vellum), French School (14th century)/Bibliotheque Nationale, Paris, France/Tallandier/Bridgeman Images; 287 (UP RT), KHM-Museumsverband, Weltmuseum Vienna; 287 (CTR), Luther as Professor, 1529 (oil on panel), Cranach, Lucas, the Elder (1472–1553)/Schlossmuseum, Weimar, Germany/Bridgeman Images; 287 (LO LE), clu/Getty Images; 287 (LO CTR), rimglow/Getty Images; 287 (LO RT), Pilgrim's "Blue and White" Gourd With Floral Decorations, ca 1403–1424 (ceramic), Chinese School (15th century)/Musee Guimet, Paris, France/Bridgeman Images; 288-9, Jason Treat, NGM Staff. Art: Sam Falconer. Sources: Sara Graça da Silva, Institute for the Study of Literature and Tradition (IELT), New University of Lisbon, Portugal; Jamie Tehrani, Durham University; 290 (UP LE), Asante funerary mask, from Ghana (ceramic), African School/Private Collection/Photo © Boltin Picture Library/Bridgeman Images; 290 (UP RT), Universal History Archive/Getty Images; 290 (CTR LE), Powhatan, Father of Pocahontas, Engraving/Private Collection/J. T. Vintage/Bridgeman Images; 290 (CTR LE CTR), Portrait of Grand Duchess Catherine Alekseevna, future Empress Catherine II the Great, ca 1760 (oil on canvas), Antropov, Alexei Petrovich (1716–1795)/Radishchev State Art Museum, Saratov, Russia/Bridgeman Image; 290 (CTR RT CTR), Portrait of Simon Bolívar; Retrato de Simon Bolivar, ca 1925 (oil on canvas), Colombian School (19th century)/Private Collection/Photo © Christie's Images/Bridgeman Images; 290 (CTR RT), Photo Researchers/Getty Images; 290 (LO LE), Portrait of King Charles I (1600–1649) (oil on canvas), Dyck, Anthony van (1599–1641) (workshop of)/Private Collection/Photo © Philip Mould Ltd, London/Bridgeman Images; 290 (LO CTR), Cross-section of H.M.S. Endeavour, Captain Cook's ship from his first voyage (1768–1771) (color litho), Adams, Dennis (1914–2001)/Alecto Historical Editions, London, UK/Bridgeman Images; 290 (LO RT), Queen Victoria, 1877 (oil on panel), Angeli, Heinrich von (1840–1925)/Private Collection/Photo © Christie's Images/Bridgeman Images; 290-91, ArtisticPhoto/Shutterstock; 291 (UP), Keystone/Getty Images; 291 (UP CTR LE), Soviet poster featuring Lenin (color litho), Russian School (20th century)/Private Collection/Peter Newark Historical Pictures/Bridgeman Images; 291 (CTR), Hulton Archive/Getty Images; 291 (CTR RT), David Hume Kennerly/Getty Images; 291 (LO LE), Dinodia Photos/Getty Images; 291 (LO CTR LE), swim ink 2/Corbis via Getty Images; 291 (LO CTR RT), Catalina M/Shutterstock; 291 (LO RT), Chris Jackson/Getty Images; 292-3, Fine Art Images/Heritage Image Partnership Ltd/Alamy Stock Photo; 294 (UP), Pascal Deloche/Getty Images; 294 (LO), Departure of the Pilgrim Fathers for America (gouache on paper), Embleton, Ron (1930–1988)/Private Collection/© Look and Learn/Bridgeman Images; 295 (LE), Todd Gipstein/National Geographic Image Collection; 295 (RT), Franck Prevel/Getty Images; 296-7, Universal Images Group/Getty Images; 297, De Agostini Picture Library/Getty Images; 298 (UP LE), Michael Yamashita/National Geographic Image Collection; 298 (UP RT), Stephen Alvarez; 298 (LO LE), Simon Norfolk; 298 (LO RT), Stephen Alvarez; 299 (UP LE), David Guttenfelder; 299 (UP RT), Ira Block; 299 (LO LE), Aaron Huey/National

Geographic Image Collection; 299 (LO RT), Simon Norfolk; 300-301, Tom Till/Getty Images; 302 and 303, Kenneth Garrett/National Geographic Image Collection; 304 (UP LE), Paul Paladin/Shutterstock; 304 (UP CTR LE), asharkyu/Shutterstock; 304 (UP CTR RT), Seated Mastiff, ca 100 (earthenware), Chinese School, Eastern Han dynasty (25–220)/Indianapolis Museum of Art at Newfields, USA/Eleanor Evans Stout and Margaret Stout Gibbs Memorial Fund/in memory of Wilbur D. Peat/Bridgeman Images; 304 (UP RT), fotohunter/Shutterstock; 304 (CTR), Agnieszka Skalska/Shutterstock.com; 304 (LO LE), Pecold/Shutterstock; 304 (LO CTR), Marques/Shutterstock; 304 (LO RT), Jan Schneckenhaus/Shutterstock; 304-305, Luis Castaneda Inc./Getty Images; 305 (UP LE), De Agostini Picture Library/Getty Images; 305 (UP CTR LE), SSPL/Getty Images; 305 (UP CTR RT), ullstein bild/ullstein bild via Getty Images; 305 (UP RT), SSPL/Getty Images; 305 (LO LE), Portrait of Benjamin Franklin (Boston, 1706–Philadelphia, 1790), American scientist and politician/De Agostini Picture Library/M. Seemuller/Bridgeman Images; 305 (LO CTR), New York Public Library/Science Source; 305 (LO RT), Nerthuz/Shutterstock; 306, George Rolhmaller/U.S. Air Force/Getty Images; 307, Delil Souleiman/AFP/Getty Images; 308 (UP LE), Cavemen during the Ice Age, after a sketch by Professor Klaatsch, late 19th century (color litho), Kranz, Wilhelm (b.1853)/Bibliotheque des Arts Decoratifs, Paris, France/Archives Charmet/Bridgeman Images; 308 (UP CTR LE), michelangeloop/Shutterstock; 308 (UP CTR RT), Tony Baggett/Shutterstock; 308 (UP RT), Andy Lidstone/Shutterstock.com; 308 (LO LE), Beaker Folk: Late Neolithic/Early Bronze Age ca 4000 b.c. from temperate European zones. Distinctive bell-shaped beaker with stamped geometric decoration. British Museum, London/Universal History Archive/UIG/Bridgeman Images; 308 (LO CT), Combatcamerauk/Shutterstock.com; 308 (LO RT), Venetian Doctor during the time of the plague (pen & ink and w/c on paper), Grevenbroeck, Jan van (1731–1807)/Museo Correr, Venice, Italy/Bridgeman Images; 308-309, fotoVoyager/Getty Images; 309 (UP LE), pryzmat/Shutterstock; 309 (UP CT), Fototeca Storica Nazionale/Getty Images; 309 (UP RT), Popperfoto/Getty Images; 309 (CTR LE), York Street Mill, Belfast, Northern Ireland, ca 1880 (engraving), English School (19th century)/Private Collection/Photo © Ken Welsh/Bridgeman Images; 309 (CT RT), Everett – Art/Shutterstock; 309 (LO LE), Soundsnaps/Shutterstock; 309 (LO CTR), Winston Churchill, English prime minister, making the victory gesture in front of 10 Downing Street in June 1943, colorized document/Bridgeman Images; 309 (LO RT), Tim Graham/Getty Images; 310, NG Maps; 311, Maurizio Rellini/SIME/eStock Photo; 312 (UP), Grana Uile introduced to Queen Elizabeth, illustration from Anthologia Hibernica vol. II, print made by Clayton, published 1794 (engraving), Beauford, William (1735–1819)/Private Collection/Bridgeman Images; 312 (LO), Edward Gooch Collection/Getty Images; 313 (LE), David Montgomery/Getty Images; 313 (RT), Jeff J. Mitchell/Getty Images; 314-15, Gareth McCormack/Getty Images; 324-5, Paolo Woods and Gabriele Galimberti. Artwork © 2019 Estate of Pablo Picasso/Artists Rights Society (ARS), New York; 326-7, va103/Getty Images; 328 (LE), NPeter/Shutterstock; 328 (RT), TommoT/Shutterstock; 328 (LO), Daniel J. Cox/Getty Images; 329 (UP), Dmitrijs Kaminskis/Shutterstock; 329 (CTR LE), Paul Nicklen/National Geographic Image Collection; 329 (CTR RT), Tetiana Yurchenko/Shutterstock; 329 (LO), Sergii Nagornyi/Shutterstock; 330-33, NG Maps; 334 (UP LE), Frans Lanting/lanting.com; 334 (UP RT), Renan Ozturk; 334 (LO LE), George Steinmetz; 334 (LO RT), Simon Norfolk; 335 (UP LE), Keith Ladzinski; 335 (UP RT), Pete McBride; 335 (LO LE), Ira Block; 335 (LO RT), Matthieu Paley; 336-7 and 338, NG Maps; 339, Michele Falzone/Getty Images; 340, NG Maps; 341, emicristea/Getty Images; 342, NG Maps; 343, Werner Bertsch/Huber Images/eStock Photo; 344, NG Maps; 345, travellinglight/Getty Images; 346, NG Maps; 347, Westend61/Getty Images; 348, NG Maps; 349, Richard Taylor/SIME/eStock Photo; 350, NG Maps; 351, Robin Galloway/Getty Images; 352-63, NG Maps; 364 (UP LE), George Steinmetz/National Geographic Image Collection; 364 (UP RT), Jennifer Hayes; 364 (LO LE), Paul Nicklen/National Geographic Image Collection; 364 (LO RT), Thomas Peschak/National Geographic Image Collection; 365 (UP LE), Jimmy Chin; 365 (UP RT), Thomas P. Peschak/National Geographic Image Collection; 365 (LO LE), Keith Ladzinski; 365 (LO RT), David Doubilet/National Geographic Image Collection; 372, Osugi/Shutterstock.com; 373, Mint Images/Frans Lanting/Getty Images; 372-79, NG Maps; 380-81, Matthew Pillsbury.

INDEX

Since 1888, the National Geographic Society has funded more than 13,000 research, exploration, and preservation projects around the world. National Geographic Partners distributes a portion of the funds it receives from your purchase to National Geographic Society to support programs including the conservation of animals and their habitats.

National Geographic Partners
1145 17th Street NW
Washington, DC 20036-4688 USA

Get closer to National Geographic explorers and photographers, and connect with our global community. Join us today at nationalgeographic.com/join

For information about special discounts for bulk purchases, please contact National Geographic Books Special Sales: specialsales@natgeo.com

For rights or permissions inquiries, please contact National Geographic Books Subsidiary Rights: bookrights@natgeo.com

ISBN: 978-1-4262-2052-4
ISBN: 978-1-4262-2053-1 (U.K. edition)

Printed in the United States of America

19/WOR/1

THE BIGGEST • THE BEST

National Geographic's flagship *Atlas of the World*, now in its 11th edition, provides authoritative maps of every country, ocean, and region of the world, as well as thematic maps and accompanying graphics showing important population, environmental, and economic patterns.
A must for all global citizens.

NATIONAL GEOGRAPHIC
ATLAS
OF THE
WORLD
ELEVENTH EDITION